DESIGN FOR RESIDENTIAL CONSTRUCTION

A PROJECT-ORIENTED APPROACH

FREDA CRUNDEN   *MAURICE COSYN*

McGraw-Hill Ryerson Limited

Toronto Montreal New York Auckland Bogotá Caracas
Hamburg Lisbon London Madrid Mexico Milan New Delhi
Paris San Juan São Paulo Singapore Sydney Tokyo

ISBN 0-07-549850-2

SPONSORING EDITOR: Fred Di Gasparro
DEVELOPMENTAL EDITOR: Nancy Leaver
COPY EDITOR: Wendy Thomas
DESIGN: Brant Cowie/ArtPlus Limited
TECHNICAL ILLUSTRATIONS: Donna Guilfoyle, Cathy Campion/ ArtPlus Limited
PAGE MAKE-UP: Heather Brunton/ArtPlus Limited
TYPE OUTPUT: TypeLine Express Limited
PHOTO EDITOR: Jacqueline Russell
PRODUCTION: Rebecca Lane

Printed and bound in Canada

1 2 3 4 5 6 7 8 9 0   D   0 9 8 7 6 5 4 3 2 1

Canadian Cataloguing in Publication Data

Crunden, Freda
    Design for residential construction
ISBN 0-07-549850-2

1. Architecture, Domestic — Designs and plans.
2. Architectural drawing.   I. Cosyn, Maurice.
II. Title.

NA7115.C78 1991   728   C90-095599-6

Care has been taken to trace the ownership of copyright material contained in this text. The publishers will gladly take any information that will enable them to rectify any reference or credit in subsequent editions.

Acknowledgements

The authors would like to express their gratitude to the following individuals and organizations for their support in the production of this text:

Roy Goostrey, a contributing editor who wrote Chapter 2, Introduction to Computer-Aided Drafting (CAD), and gave a great deal of helpful advice and encouragement.

Katherine Crunden-Conte, for diligent hours at the computer and assisting with the format.

Isobel Cosyn, for typing, proofreading, and encouragement.

Ken Crunden, for preliminary editing and proof-reading.

Herbert Kirkby, for his photographic work.

Jack Homer of Boehmers Limited, for his professional advice.

All the CASS drafting students over the years, especially Rebecca Shellington, Jason Giroux, Jason Gale, and Peter Gallagher.

The reviewers, for their discerning and encouraging comments.

Jennifer Joiner, former editor at McGraw-Hill Ryerson, for undertaking this project; Janice Matthews, for preliminary editing; Nancy Leaver, for developmental editing on the text; Jacqueline Russell, for obtaining photographs and permissions; Wendy Thomas, for copy editing; Rebecca Lane for the production of this text; and ArtPlus for design and page make-up.

The industrial and commercial firms that supplied necessary illustrations and references.

Table of Contents

About the Authors

Freda Crunden is a professional draftsperson who was educated and trained in England with the Bristol Aeroplane Co. and Rolls Royce Ltd. After emigrating to Canada and raising a family, she started a second career in teaching, combining her technical knowledge with her interest in young people. Mrs. Crunden became the first female Technical Director in the Province of Ontario and served on the executive of the Ontario Technical Director's Association for eight years. She became president of that organization during the O.S.I.S. year. Mrs. Crunden taught Architectural Drafting and Mechanical Drafting at College Avenue Secondary School, Woodstock, Ontario. She is interested in skill training and has worked with provincial and local committees to encourage young people, especially females, to undertake technical training. Freda Crunden is also on the Technical Advisory Committee for Fanshawe College, London, and served as co-chair for the 1989 Architectural Course Review for that college.

Maurice Cosyn was a professional artist and designer for 16 years before beginning his teaching career. Mr. Cosyn received his art and design education in Detroit, Michigan. He has been involved in many areas of design including automotive, advertising, industrial, interior, and architectural. Throughout his career, he has designed and drafted numerous houses, as well as commercial and industrial offices. After several years of operating his own design studio, Maurice Cosyn decided to become a secondary school art teacher, in order to help encourage young people talented in design. Mr. Cosyn has been a visual arts teacher at College Avenue Secondary School, Woodstock, for more than 20 years and is presently Head of the Visual Arts Department.

Maurice Cosyn and Freda Crunden met while on a teachers' training course at Althouse College of Education, London. They began teaching during the same year at College Avenue Secondary School, Woodstock, Ontario, and for many years team-taught the architectural drafting courses at that school. Both authors have experienced the advantages of teaching a project-oriented approach curriculum and have collaborated in developing ideas for this new teaching method. As reflects their particular areas of expertise, Freda Crunden focused on writing the drafting elements of this text, while Maurice Cosyn focused on the design elements.

Introduction
to the Student

THE PURPOSE OF THIS TEXT is to teach you how to design a house that is suitable for a specific lot. Through a project-oriented method of study, you will learn how to select a site, make presentation drawings, and complete a set of working drawings. While doing this, you will also be shown how to improve your basic drafting skills, design concepts, and construction knowledge.

This book is divided into four main sections, which are sub-divided into chapters that introduce you to the basic skills required for the design and drafting process. Each chapter is further sub-divided into units that deal with specific topics.

Part 1 provides an introduction to drafting methods and the use of drafting tools, including computer-aided drafting (CAD). If you are a beginner, Part 1 is designed so that you can work through the text and assignments with minimal guidance. If you have previous drafting experience, this portion of the book will serve as a review.

The project for this text involves designing a house through a step-by-step process. It is introduced at the beginning of Part 2. The development and design of a house continues throughout the remaining three parts of the text. The steps regarding development of the project are outlined at the end of certain chapters as applicable.

Part 2 introduces you to the preliminaries of house design, such as how to select a suitable site, how to do the related survey work, and how to correctly orient the house on the lot. Design theory and the history of architectural design are discussed. Landscaping plans and facilities required for vehicles are also covered in this section and will be of interest to students who are studying surveying, landscaping, and traffic control.

Part 3 assists you in preparing a preliminary design using a step-by-step method and in developing that design into a set of presentation drawings suitable for showing a prospective client. This section could also be studied by students interested in interior design.

Part 4 teaches you how to complete a set of working drawings from the presentation drawings. The technical aspects of a structure, such as foundation and roof design, are covered.

Career opportunities that include educational requirements and job descriptions are provided at the end of this book.

To help you enlarge your technical and non-technical vocabulary, a glossary is included at the back of the text. The appendix also contains selected mathematical tables that will be required for some of the assignments.

Related assignments, review questions, and a "What Do You Think?" section appear at the end of each unit. These questions allow you to practise the skills learned and to test your comprehension of the material covered by the unit.

The text contains material that is essential for completing the assignments and that supplies the necessary drafting background required for related subjects. Individual topics in the text may be selected for use in related careers such as interior design, landscaping, surveying, etc. Extensive illustrations are used to reinforce concepts that are presented in the text.

New terms are shown in second colour when they first appear. An explanation of these terms is given directly after the word and in the glossary.

This book is written using both metric and imperial systems of measurement. The systems are soft converted. However, use of the appropriate scales and recognized standard sizes of materials do not make the conversion of the two systems consistent throughout.

Design for Residential Construction: A Project-Oriented Approach is intended to give you basic skills in the drafting and design process of designing a house. The skills that you learn will be invaluable as they will be transferable to several areas of construction.

INTRODUCTION TO ARCHITECTURAL DRAFTING

Part One is intended for those of you who have not had any previous drafting experience. It will familiarize you with the basic concepts and will assist you in the development of practical skills.

You will be introduced to drafting tools and their uses; a brief outline of the capabilities of computer-aided drafting (CAD) equipment is provided. All the work may be done in either metric or imperial systems of measurement.

If you are a beginner, you can work through this part of the text and assignments with a minimal amount of guidance. If you have previous drafting experience, this portion of the book will serve as a useful review and resource guide.

The ultimate goal of this text is to enable you to draw a full set of house plans using a step-by-step method of instruction. Part One will provide you with the initial skills you require to do this.

CHAPTER 1

Introduction to Drafting

DRAFTING EVOLVED FROM the need of a society to accurately plan and maintain records of the buildings that it constructs and of the products that it makes.

Initially, drafting was used for architectural purposes. Ancient structures such as the pyramids in Egypt and the temples in Greece show that their builders had a knowledge of the properties of materials and a well-developed skill in their use. Those builders almost certainly used some form of graphic representation to guide their workers.

The ancient Romans left us the earliest known book on architectural design. This book was the work of an architect named Vitruvius who lived in the first century A.D. He set down strict rules as to the size of and the method of construction for columns, which were the major structural device of that time.

The Renaissance architects of the fifteenth and sixteenth centuries made great advances in the number and the size of secular and religious structures they built. Plans and drawings of world-famous structures such as St. Peter's Basilica in Rome and the Louvre in Paris were recorded and survive to enrich our knowledge today.

FIGURE 1-1
Early decisions on architectural design
Reproduced by permission of Punch

"I like this one. It's simple."

FIGURE 1-2

Two devices by Leonardo da Vinci to help in the construction of buildings. The machine on the left was used for lifting marble or stone columns into position. The derrick on the right is mounted on a four-wheeled vehicle.

The Bettmann Archive

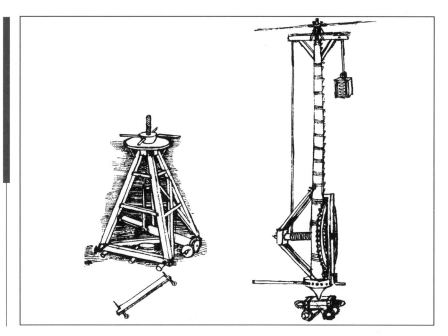

Leonardo da Vinci was the most prolific drafter of this period. His works include practical and imaginary designs for weapons of war as well as designs for buildings and illustrations of scientific developments. He knew the value of drafting both as a basis of design for conveying information to workers and as a means of recording the details of his many inventions.

The design and drawing of mechanical products proliferated during the Industrial Revolution of the seventeenth and eighteenth centuries. Machinery capable of producing components in large quantities was invented. This in turn required standardization of the method by which information was conveyed to large numbers of workers. **Orthographic layout**, a means of conveying exact information in graphic form, evolved as the universal language of technical communication. Modern industry, which now spans the globe, could not function without the use of orthographic drafting. Its main purpose is to convey technical information in the clearest and most concise way. For people who work in the manufacturing or construction industries, it is crucial that they interpret correctly the symbols and methods of graphic communication which appear on the drawings from which they will work.

FIGURE 1-3 *This drawing of a steam engine was published in 1727.*

The Bettmann Archive

UNIT 1 | Drafting Tools and Methods

OBJECTIVES

- To understand the purpose of drafting
- To learn to use drafting equipment correctly
- To understand the importance of good linework and lettering
- To learn how to convey accurate information graphically

DRAFTING MEDIA

There are several types of standard media used in drafting.

PENCIL

The most frequently used drafting medium is the **pencil**. It is cheap and adaptable, and pencil drawings can be altered readily when necessary. Pencils are identified by the grade or graphite content of the lead. The grade is marked on one end of the pencil. For this reason, it is important that only the opposite end be sharpened. The most common pencil in everyday use is grade HB. However, it is not the best pencil to use for drafting as the point will wear down rapidly on the hard surface of the drafting paper. One of the H grades of pencil should be used for drafting. The range is from H to 9H; the higher the number, the harder the lead *(see Fig. 1-4)*.

Most draftspersons will use three or four different grades of lead depending on the task. A 2H is usually used for lettering; a 4H makes a strong, dark line suitable for the subject of a drawing. A 6H will give a sharp, fine line such as that needed for dimensioning. The selection can be influenced by the type of paper that is to be used, as the tooth or roughness of the paper affects the quality of the linework. The pencil grade you choose for a certain task reflects your personal preference.

Drafting pencils should be sharpened with a special pencil sharpener that trims only the wood, leaving an extended portion of lead unsharpened. A long, slim point should then be made by using a small sandpaper block designed for this purpose. A pencil can be sharpened to a **conical point**, suitable for most linework and lettering, or to a **chisel point**, excellent for drawing long lines *(see Fig. 1-5)*.

Many draftspersons prefer to use lead holders, which come in two main types. The first type uses the same thickness of lead that is found in a wooden pencil; it requires sharpening. The second type uses very fine lead, 0.5 mm in diameter or less. This does not have to be sharpened and is

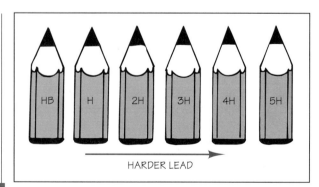

FIGURE 1-4 *Grades of pencil*

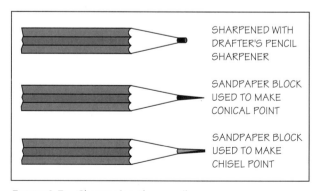

FIGURE 1-5 *Sharpening the pencil*

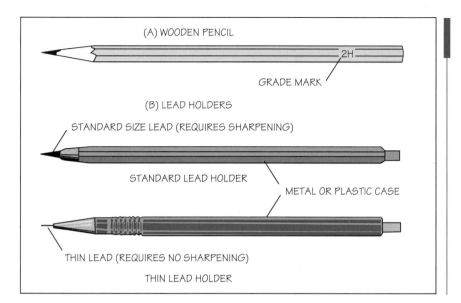

FIGURE 1-6
Pencil holders

available in most H grades of lead *(see Fig. 1-6)*. However, skill is required in using this type of lead holder as the lead will break readily if uneven or excessive pressure is applied to the point. You should try a variety of pencils so that you can determine which performs best for you.

When you put a pencil down on a drafting board, place it in a vertical position so that it will not roll off because of the slope. Do not drop a drafting pencil on a hard surface as the H leads are more brittle than other grades and the lead may break throughout the pencil.

Grip your chosen pencil firmly between your thumb and finger and then incline it at an angle of about 15° in the direction of the hand movement *(see Fig. 1-7)*. Rotate the pencil between your finger and thumb as you draw a line so that you maintain a conical point and thus keep pencil sharpening to a minimum. A chisel point must be held flat against a ruling edge. When drawing long lines, keep your hand in a uniform position relative to the ruling edge, or your lines will not be straight and even in pressure. Hold the lead close to the ruling edge at all times.

INKWORK

Drawing uniform lines in ink is easier and faster with the modern **technical pen** than with the old style ruling pen.

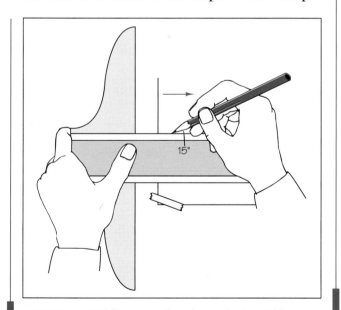

FIGURE 1-7 *Holding a pencil to draw a horizontal line*

FIGURE 1-8 *A technical pen*

Courtesy of Staedtler-Mars Limited

Hold technical pens upright and move with a light steady motion. Inks used with these pens dry rapidly. To avoid smudging, a right-handed draftsperson should start work at the top left-hand corner of the paper and work towards the bottom right-hand corner. A left-handed person will start at the top right-hand corner. Starting at the top has an added advantage: completed parts of the drawing may readily be seen for reference purposes.

Drafting equipment such as set squares and templates are now made specifically for inkwork; they have bevelled edges or small projections throughout the under-surface that raise the ruling edge from the drawing paper and safeguard against smudging. When you purchase equipment, it is a good idea to select this type because it is suitable for pen or pencil work. To raise flat equipment from the drawing surface when doing inkwork, you can apply adhesive plastic lifts that are sold in packages or place a set square partially under the edge being used as a ruling guide.

Do not leave ink in technical pens that are likely to be out of use for more than two or three days at a time. Special cleaning fluid must be used to ensure that all traces of ink are removed so that the pen tips will not become clogged. Electronic cleaning machines are very efficient for cleaning ink pens, but are relatively expensive.

It is much more difficult to correct errors or make changes to inkwork than to a pencil drawing. When you are working on a very complicated design or if you are a less experienced draftsperson, make the initial drawing in pencil and then trace over it in ink on a fresh sheet of vellum stock. Do not attempt to draw in ink directly on top of a pencil drawing. Ink does not adhere well to graphite and you will have difficulty making your lines dense enough to reproduce well.

As an ink drawing is both sharp and dark, any copies are generally superior to those made of a pencil drawing. As a consequence, the proportion of drawings done in ink has increased considerably in recent years.

ERASERS

Erasers come in various shapes and sizes to make the job of correction as effortless as possible.

For general drafting use, an eraser core that is contained in a holder similar to a pencil is a worthwhile investment. A white vinyl core is used for pencil, a blue core for ink. Electric erasing machines are also available for commercial use. Stainless steel erasing shields are valuable aids for clean erasures as they protect the rest of the drawing. Cleaning pads contain a grit-free powder that, when sprinkled over the surface of the paper prior to drawing, will help to keep your work clean.

A drafting brush is a long thin brush that is used to clean off residue left from erasures.

LINE THICKNESS

A draftsperson should be able to draw four distinct types of lines depending on a combination of the weights and thicknesses of the lines. These are:

- light and fine,
- dark and thick,
- dark and medium,
- dark and fine.

Important factors when drafting with a pencil are: how the pencil is sharpened; the amount of pressure applied to the pencil; and the grade of lead used.

When using ink pens, different weights of lines can be readily maintained by using different thicknesses of pen *(see Fig. 1-9A)*. Draw the finer ink lines first and then progress through the other weights of

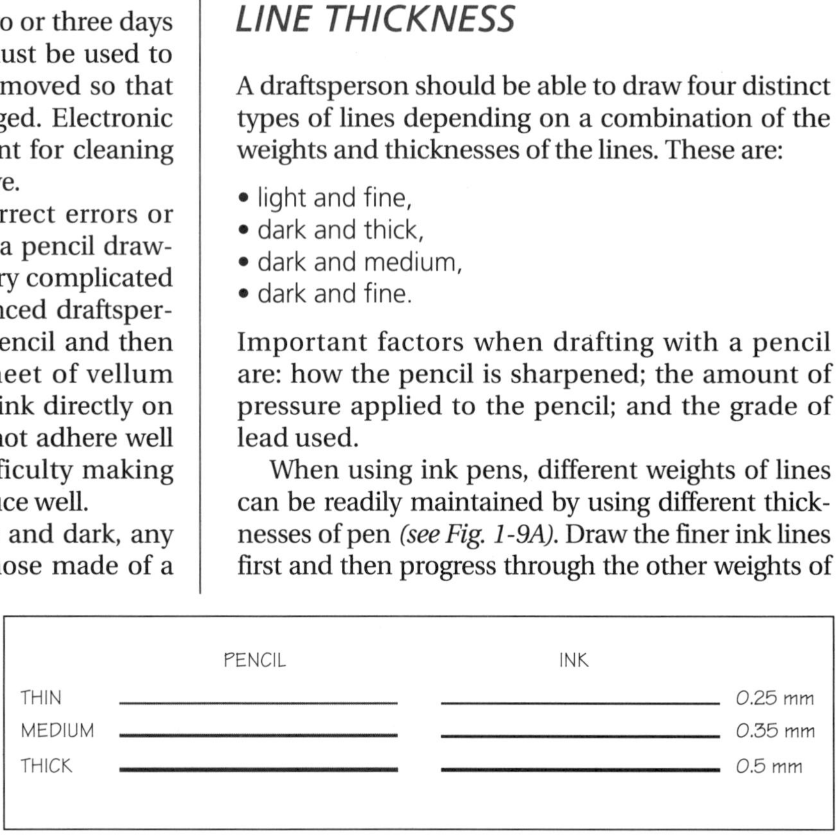

FIGURE 1-9A
Line thickness

	PENCIL	INK	
THIN	————————	————————	0.25 mm
MEDIUM	————————	————————	0.35 mm
THICK	————————	————————	0.5 mm

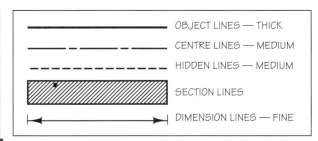

FIGURE 1-9B *Line types*

line that are required in drafting. In this way, the constant interchange of pens is not necessary.

There are several different line types *(see Fig. 1-9B)*.

Construction Lines – These very *light lines* are only just visible to the eye. They are used to block in a drawing or as lines on which to measure distances. The linework will be darkened in later when the drawing has been verified. Construction lines are not reproduced when the drawing is printed because they are light. Therefore, it is not necessary to erase them once the drawing is completed. This is the only type of line that is drawn lightly. All other lines should be dark so that they can be reproduced.

Object Lines – These *strong, thick lines* are used to darken in the surfaces of the subject of the drawing. It is important that you maintain uniformly dark, dense lines of a constant thickness throughout the drawing. Object lines should be readily distinguishable from all other types of lines.

Centre Lines – These lines are *dark lines of medium thickness*. Centre lines are alternate long and short dashes that always start with a long dash and end with a long dash. The long dashes are approximately 25 mm (1") long and the short dashes are 3 mm (1/8") long. Spaces of 2 mm (1/16") should be maintained between dashes. Intersecting centre lines are used in circles with short dashes crossing at the centre point.

Hidden Lines – These lines are *dark lines of medium thickness*. Hidden lines are used to indicate surfaces that are behind the surface of the

view being drawn. The dashes should be approximately 5 mm (1/4") long with a 2 mm (1/16") space between them. In architectural drawings, lines made up of longer dashes are used in plan views to indicate items that are above the level of the plan view being drawn such as roof lines, beams, and upper kitchen cupboards.

Section Lines – These lines are *medium weight and dark* and are always drawn at an angle of 45°. They are used to indicate an imaginary cut through material in order to show the composition of some element of a building such as a masonry wall.

Dimension Lines – These lines should be *fine and dark* so that they differentiate the dimensions from the actual object lines. This is best achieved by using a chisel point with a 4H or harder grade of pencil lead. Drawing dimension lines requires frequent pencil sharpening to ensure that the sharpness of the linework is constant throughout the drawing.

The most common errors made in linework are found in dimension lines that are drawn either too lightly or too thickly, and in object lines that appear to be dark but are actually blurred so that they do not reproduce well. Regular practice is necessary to ensure that all linework is of good quality.

STOCK MATERIALS

There are several basic types of material used in drafting.

Bond Paper – Bond paper comes in a variety of thicknesses and qualities. Inexpensive bond paper can be used for preliminary planning, layout work, or for short-term drafting needs. This type of paper is not a long-lasting material and its erasing qualities are poor. Light does not pass through it so prints cannot be made from drawings on this type of stock.

Vellum – Vellum is a translucent paper that comes in a great range of styles and qualities.

Vellum that is more expensive has a better **tooth**, or surface roughness, which causes ink or pencil to adhere more readily. Many types of vellum have only one side suitable for drawing. The better quality papers facilitate erasures of both ink and pencil lines. They are usually more translucent than less expensive stock and produce a higher quality copy.

Cloth – Cloth is a strong and long-lasting material with good translucent characteristics. It is more expensive than paper.

Film – Film is made from sheets of clear synthetic material often known by the name of *Mylar*. This material is practically indestructible. It has superior erasing qualities; it is very translucent; and it does not age. It is also expensive. Film is used by architectural firms, where accurate records may be needed for reference purposes in the distant future. It is also used by aircraft and automotive designers and in many other manufacturing fields where drawings must have a long life.

STOCK SIZES

Standard stock sizes are used throughout the drafting industry. Each size of stock is in proportion to that which precedes it, so that prints, however large, can be folded to one basic size for easy filing on the job site. Metric and imperial sized stock are similar but not identical to each other.

METRIC STOCK SIZES	IMPERIAL STOCK SIZES
A4 – 210 mm x 297 mm	A – 8 1/2" x 11"
A3 – 297 mm x 420 mm	B – 11" x 17"
A2 – 420 mm x 594 mm	C – 17" x 22"
A1 – 594 mm x 841 mm	D – 22" x 34"
A0 – 841 mm x 1189 mm	E – 34" x 44"

REPRODUCTION METHODS

Many copies of a drawing must be made for the various people who are involved in the construction process. The purchasing agent, the building inspector, the subtrades, and the sales departments will all require prints of the drawing, as well as the contractor who is going to use the drawings to do the construction work. Therefore it is important that the print that has been reproduced is clear and legible. The original drawing is always filed in the engineering and architectural offices for reference and for record-keeping purposes.

Blueprints are copies of original drawings that are used to convey information to the person who will do the work. They are called *blueprints* because early methods of reproducing drawings produced a white line print on a dark blue background *(see Fig. 1-10)*. Visually, these prints are

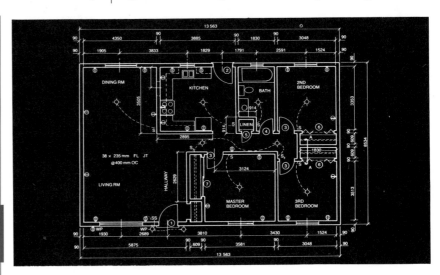

FIGURE 1-10
Blueprint

very hard to work with. Today, improved processing chemicals allow us to make **whiteprints** cheaply *(see Fig. 1-11)*. These prints are much easier to read because a dark line is printed on a white background. However, the generic term *blueprint* is still widely used.

Large drawings are reproduced most often by a **diazo print machine** *(see Fig. 1-12)*. This method of printing transfers the drawing onto sensitized paper by shining a light through the translucent stock on which the drawing is made. A special chemical activator develops and stabilizes the print. Because of the nature of this printing process, all linework and lettering must be dark and dense throughout. Any lines,

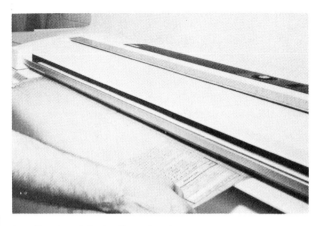

Loading in original vellum drawing

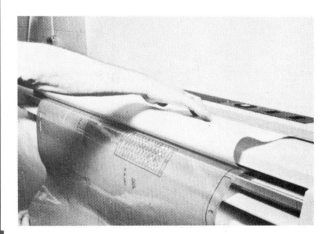

Whiteprint being developed

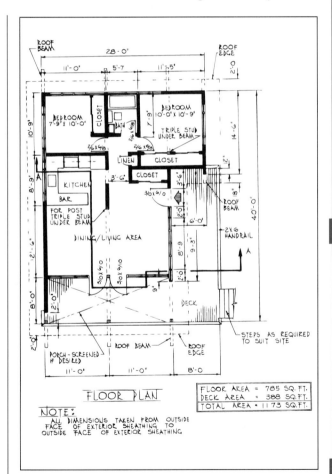

FIGURE 1-11 *Whiteprint*

This drawing is the property of MacMillan Bloedel Limited

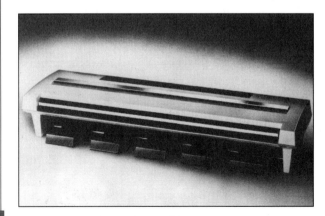

FIGURE 1-12 *Diazo print machine*

AM International Inc. (Canada)

Courtesy of Bruning, a division of AM International

FIGURE 1-13
A CAD drawing

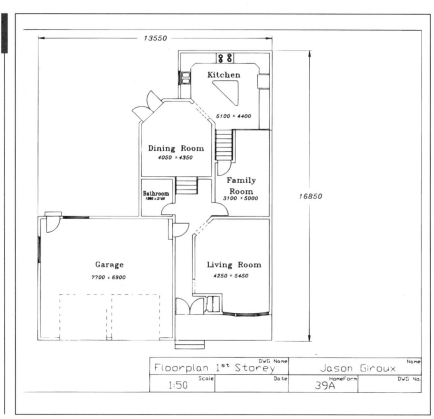

numerals, or lettering that are not solid will not print clearly.

Modern technology has developed **computer-aided drafting** or **CAD** systems that produce computerized drawings that are plotted on an electronic printer *(see Fig. 1-13)*, and **fax** or **fac-simile** machines that now allow us to transfer drawings across the country or across the world via telephone lines and satellites. *However, the same universal drafting conventions are used to produce working drawings.*

Frequently, drawings are changed while a job is in progress; therefore it is essential to keep a record of those who receive a print so that all previous prints can be recalled and amended copies reissued in their place. This procedure prevents the possibility that errors will occur as a result of someone working from an outdated print.

DRAFTING EQUIPMENT

A standard **drafting board** has a fixed slope, set at an angle of 15°. The commercial drafting table usually has a surface that can be adjusted to any desired horizontal or vertical angle. When using this type of table, most draftspersons prefer to work standing up, especially if the board is a large one.

Standard drafting equipment consists of two **set squares** and a **t-square**. These items are designed to allow you to draw horizontal and vertical lines that are perpendicular to each other. Angles of 30°, 45°, and 60° can also be drawn with this equipment.

Drafting machines consist of two plastic scales at right angles to each other, attached to a head that can be locked into any angular position desired. These machines can be moved around the drafting board *(see Fig. 1-14)*.

FIGURE 1-14
Drafting machine
Courtesy of Vemco Corp.

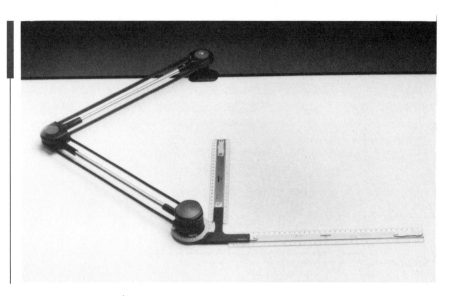

They are used mainly on large boards that can be adjusted to form acute angular slopes on which it would be difficult to maintain the position of a t-square. Some table-top boards can be purchased with a small version of the drafting machine already attached so that together they form a compact portable drafting unit.

A **parallel rule** is a replacement for the standard t-square. The parallel rule is designed to maintain a permanent horizontal straight edge that can be moved up or down along the surface of the board by a system of pulleys and guide ropes. It is used in much the same way as a t-square but, by being attached to the board, it will stay in position even if the slope of the board is steep.

Computer-aided drafting or CAD programs are a contemporary method of making drawings with the aid of a computer. These programs speed up the process of conveying a designer's ideas to the workplace.

The standard concepts of drafting must be understood completely before any equipment can be used effectively. Elaborate drafting equip-

FIGURE 1-15
Computer-aided drafting station

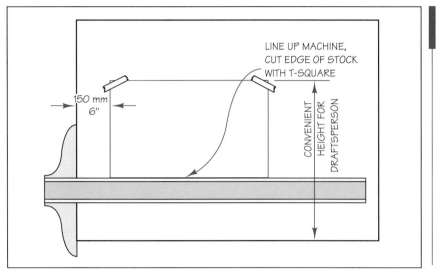

FIGURE 1-16A
Lining up new stock on the board

LINE UP MACHINE,
CUT EDGE OF STOCK
WITH T-SQUARE

150 mm
6"

CONVENIENT HEIGHT FOR DRAFTSPERSON

FIGURE 1-16B
Lining up a drawing on the board

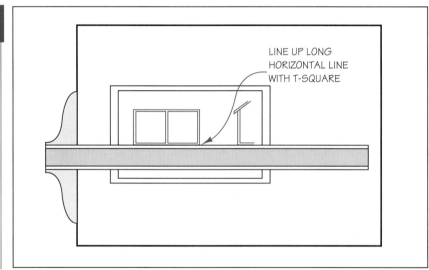

LINE UP LONG
HORIZONTAL LINE
WITH T-SQUARE

ment is not essential for producing a good drawing. A simple t-square and set square used on a flat table with a square edge will produce satisfactory results.

USING DRAFTING TOOLS

The t-square is shaped like a capital letter T. It consists of a head that is moved along the metal or plastic sides of the drafting board, and a blade that is the long straight edge of the t-square and is used for drawing horizontal lines. The head

ensures that the blade lies in a horizontal position across the board.

Use the t-square to line up the edges of a fresh sheet of paper on the board *(see Fig. 1-16A)*. However, when placing an unfinished drawing on the board, align the t-square with the lines of the existing drawing rather than the edge of the paper so that any new lines drawn will be perpendicular or parallel to the lines already drawn *(see Fig. 1-16B)*.

When you are making a pencil drawing, the continuous movement of the square's blade over the drawing can transfer pencil lead from one

FIGURE 1-17
*To draw an intersection at 90°
(vertical and horizontal lines)*

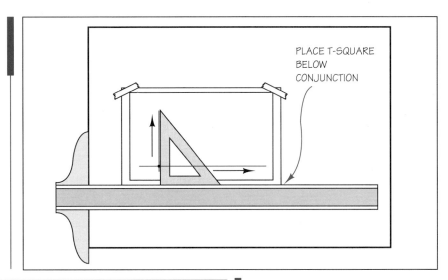

PLACE T-SQUARE
BELOW
CONJUNCTION

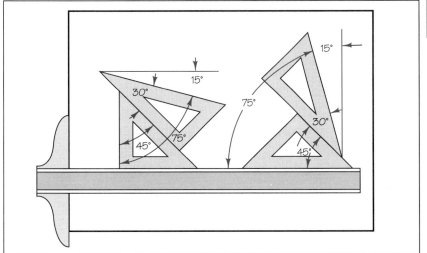

FIGURE 1-18
To draw angles of 15° or 75°

part of the sheet to another. To avoid this, you should apply a slight amount of pressure to the head when moving the t-square. This will slightly raise the blade from the work and will minimize smudging.

The set squares are used to set your work *square* or perpendicular to lines drawn with the t-square. Each of the two set squares is in the form of a right-angled triangle. The first set square has two sides that are of equal length, one on each side of the right angle. The other two angles of the set square triangle are 45°. The second set square has unequal sides and the angles of this triangle are 30°, 60°, and 90°.

Set squares are used in conjunction with the t-square for drawing perpendicular lines. When drawing a vertical line that intersects a horizontal line, make sure that the t-square is placed slightly below the horizontal line before placing the set square in position in order to produce a clean joint *(see Fig. 1-17)*.

Set squares may also be used to draw angles of 30°, 45°, and 60°. If both set squares are placed on top of each other on the t-square, it is possible to draw lines at angles of 15° or 75° *(see Fig. 1-18)*. For any other angle, you will need a protractor or adjustable set square *(see Chapter 1, Unit 2)*.

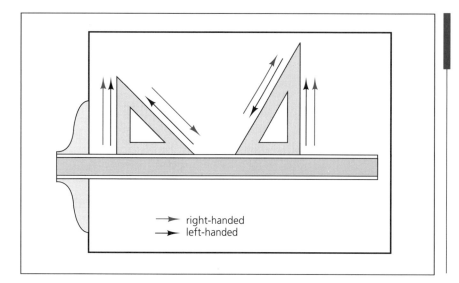

FIGURE 1-19
Direction for drawing vertical and angular lines

Generally the direction in which lines should be drawn is as follows *(see Fig. 1-19)*.

1. Horizontal lines should be drawn from left to right by a right-handed person and from right to left by a left-handed person.
2. Vertical lines should be drawn upwards.
3. Angular lines that run from the bottom left-hand corner to the top right-hand corner should be drawn with an upward motion by a right-handed person and a downward motion by a left-handed person.
4. Angular lines that run from the top left-hand corner to the bottom right-hand corner should be drawn with a downward motion by a right-handed person and an upward motion by a left-handed person.

SCALES

Scales are measuring devices that are used in drafting. They are marked with several systems of gradations that facilitate measurement either at full size or at several reduced sizes. Reduced scales are used for drafting a large item such as a house, an aircraft, or a boat. An example of a reduced metric scale is 1:50, which means a drawing is 50 times smaller than actual size. (In imperial measurement, this would be 1/4" = 1' - 0", which means that 1/4" on a drawing represents 1' - 0" on the object.)

The most popular shape for a scale is triangular in section and it will have many different scale graduations marked upon it. Scales that are colour coded on each side to assist identification are more expensive. *Note:* A scale should never be used to rule lines.

Metric Scales – There are several different metric (SI) scales. The ratios refer to the reduction of measurement which can be made by these scales.

1. Mainly used by engineers
   1:1, 1:2, 1:5, 1:10, 1:20, 1:50
2. Mainly used for architectural work
   1:20, 1:25, 1:50, 1:75, 1:100, 1:125
3. Mainly used by surveyors
   1:500, 1:1000, 1:1250, 1:1500, 1:2000, 1:2500

The 1:1 scale produces full-size measurements. If your scale does not include a 1:1 marking, the scale of 1:10 or 1:100 can be adapted easily. The scale of 1:50 is the scale that is most often used for drawing house plans *(see Fig. 1-20)*. If you require more detail, for instance when drawing a wall section, use a larger scale such as 1:20.

All metric measurements on technical drawings are shown either in millimetres or in metres. The centimetre, although commonly encountered in everyday use, is not a recognized unit of

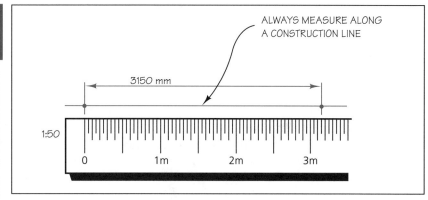

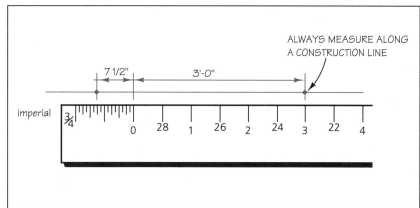

measurement for technical drawings. By stating measurements in millimetres, the possibility of a decimal point being overlooked by a blueprint reader is avoided.

Imperial Scales – Scales in the imperial system are designated as being either an architect's scale or an engineer's scale.

The architect's scale has 11 systems of measurement marked on it. The actual or full-sized graduations have the number 16 at the left-hand end of the scale. It is divided into inches with subdivisions 1/16" apart. The remaining scales are divided into fractions of an inch, each representing one foot, for example, 3/4" = 1' - 0". At the opposite end of the same side, a scale of 3/8" = 1' - 0" is printed, which is half the size of the former scale. The two scales run in different directions from either end of the architect's scale.

The first portion of each imperial architect's scale represents 1' - 0" no matter what its actual size. This portion is then divided into 12 equal sections, each of which represents 1". These divisions on the larger scales are further subdivided to represent fractions of an inch.

At the end of this first portion is a line marked 0 (zero). If we read the figures on the other side of the zero, they represent whole feet according to the scale that is being used. *Fig. 1-21* illustrates this.

In order to measure a distance of 3' - 7 1/2" *(see Fig. 1-21)* with the scale of 3/4" = 1' - 0", you must read the measurements of 3' - 0" from the markings to the right of the zero line which are in an ascending order. Then read the measurements of 7 1/2" from the markings to the left of the zero and read from right to left.

All other scales except the full-size graduations are read in a similar manner, but some scales are read primarily from the left and some primarily from the right, according to which end of the scale the size of the graduations are given.

House drawings are usually based on a scale of 1/4" = 1' - 0" or a 1:48 reduction ratio. This scale is very close to the metric scale of 1:50 so that a house drawing made to either scale will be roughly the same size.

The engineer's scale can be identified readily by the numbers 10, 20, 30, etc. at the ends of the scale. In this system of measurement, each inch is divided into the number of divisions stated at the end of the scale. The scale that has 10 at the left-hand end can be used for measuring decimals of an inch at actual size or decimals of a foot if a scale of 1" = 1' - 0" is required.

MEASURING DISTANCES

When measuring distances, you should first draw a construction line in an appropriate location and then make the measurement by placing small dots at either end of the distance on the line. When you have made your measurement, draw short perpendicular construction lines through the dots so that you will be able to identify the measurement points more readily.

REVIEW QUESTIONS

1. What are three main media using for drafting?
2. Name the main tools used in drafting.
3. What is the main purpose of drafting?

WHAT DO YOU THINK?

1. What is the value of drafting to industry?
2. Apart from drafting for industry, what use might a person make of this skill?

ASSIGNMENTS

1. On an A3/B size sheet of paper taped to a drafting board, draw the following in pencil using a t-square, and a parallel rule, or a drafting machine.
   a. Draw two horizontal lines approximately 10 mm (3/8") apart across the top of the paper.
   b. Below those lines draw two dashed lines approximately 10 mm (3/8") apart.
   c. Repeat these two styles of line using each of the four weights of lines indicated below.
      • light and fine
      • dark and thick
      • dark and medium
      • dark and fine
2. Repeat Assignment 1 in ink, using an appropriate selection of pen thicknesses.
3. The following assignment provides practice in using the standard board instruments or a drafting machine and in making measurements.

   Draw a 10 mm (3/8") border around an A4/A size sheet. Divide the sheet into six equal spaces (two rows of three rectangles) as follows.

   Start by dividing the short side of the paper in half. To do this, place the scale at any angle across the page so that the zero of any convenient scale rests along the top border and a number that can readily be

Figure 1-22A
To divide a sheet in half horizontally

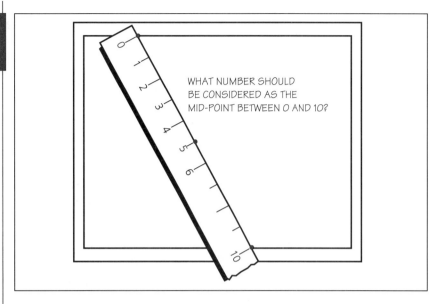

WHAT NUMBER SHOULD
BE CONSIDERED AS THE
MID-POINT BETWEEN 0 AND 10?

divided by two rests on the bottom border *(see Fig. 1-22A)*. Mark the position of the number that is the result of dividing the original number by two. A line drawn through this point will indicate the horizontal centre of the sheet no matter what numbers are used.

To divide the sheet vertically into three equal portions, place the scale at any angle across the sheet so that the zero of any scale rests along the left-hand border and a number that can readily be divided by three rests on the right-hand border *(see Fig. 1-22B)*. Mark the numbers that will result in dividing the original number by three. For example, if 12 is selected, mark 4 and 8. These points will be in the correct

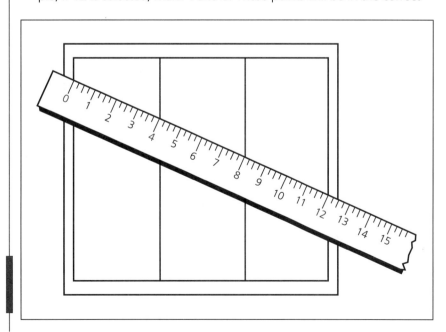

Figure 1-22B
To divide a sheet into three equal spaces

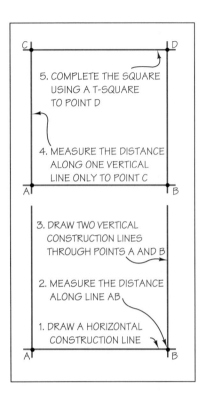

5. COMPLETE THE SQUARE USING A T-SQUARE TO POINT D

4. MEASURE THE DISTANCE ALONG ONE VERTICAL LINE ONLY TO POINT C

3. DRAW TWO VERTICAL CONSTRUCTION LINES THROUGH POINTS A AND B

2. MEASURE THE DISTANCE ALONG LINE AB

1. DRAW A HORIZONTAL CONSTRUCTION LINE

FIGURE 1-23

Construction for drawing a square

vertical position for dividing the paper into three equal columns. Draw lines vertically through these points.

The sheet should now be divided into six equal areas. This method of division can be adapted for any number of equal spaces as required.

Do the exercises below following the directions. Place one exercise in each space.

a. Draw a square 50 mm (2") at actual size. Begin by drawing a construction line any length towards the bottom of the first space with a t-square. Measure the distance of 50 mm (2") along this line. Follow the instructions for drawing a square shown in *Fig. 1-23*. *Note:* Only two measurements should have been made when drawing the square.

b. Draw a rectangle 55 mm x 90 mm (2 1/8" x 3 1/2"). Begin by drawing a construction line of any length towards the bottom of the first space. Measure the shorter distance along this line. Draw two vertical construction lines of any length through each of these points. Measure the longer distance along one of these vertical lines. Each of the measurements should be made only once. The rest of the rectangle is completed by using the t-square and a set square.

c. Draw an equilateral triangle; that is, a triangle having all sides equal and each angle 60°. Begin by drawing a construction line of any length above the base of the space you are using. Make a measurement of 80 mm (3 1/16") along this line. Using the 30°/60° set square, draw a 60° angular construction line through each measurement point. Then, with a sharp pencil, outline the equilateral triangle with dark object lines making neat joints at each point. *Note:* Only one measurement should have been made when drawing the equilateral triangle.

d. Draw a 48 mm (1 7/8") square with sides at 45° to the perpendicular. Begin by drawing a construction line of any length above the base of the space in which you are going to draw. Pick the midpoint and draw two construction lines through this point at 45°, making an included angle of 90°. Measure the correct distance along each of these lines and complete the square by using the t-square with the 45° set square to draw construction lines through the measured points. With a sharp pencil, outline the square.

e. In one of the remaining spaces, make a right angle with two construction lines of any length. From the apex of the 90° angle, draw angles at intervals of 15°, using the set squares in conjunction with the t-square. With a sharp pencil, darken the lines, making each angular line 60 mm (2 1/2") long.

f. In the last space, draw a parallelogram with the vertical sides at 75° to the horizontal. This figure may be any size you wish.

UNIT 2

Additional Drafting Tools and Methods

OBJECTIVES

- To understand orthographic projection
- To dimension with clarity
- To learn to letter clearly
- To make working sketches
- To use compasses and angular measuring devices correctly

ORTHOGRAPHIC DRAWING

The object of drafting is to communicate technical information graphically so that drawings will be interpreted in exactly the same way by everyone who is skilled at reading blueprints. To ensure that this goal was attained, it was necessary to develop a standard method of drafting which would describe the shape of an object completely and accurately.

This method of drawing is called **orthographic projection** *(see Fig.1-24B)*, and its accuracy depends on two factors:

1. Each view of the object has to be drawn perpendicularly to the line of sight so that the shape is not distorted.

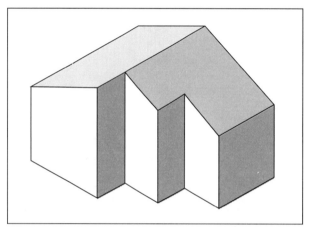

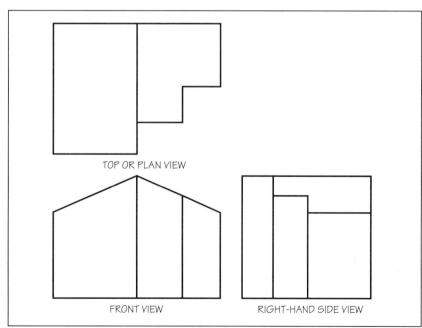

FIGURE 1-24A *(above)*
Pictorial drawing

FIGURE 1-24B *(right)*
Orthographic drawing

TOP OR PLAN VIEW

FRONT VIEW

RIGHT-HAND SIDE VIEW

FIGURE 1-25 *Six orthographic views of a house*

2. A number of two-dimensional views are drawn in a specific relationship to each other in order to give complete information about an object.

Rectangular objects have six sides. The sides relate to each other in much the same way as the sides of a cardboard cake box when it is flattened out. *Fig. 1-25* shows the orthographic relationship of the sides of a house.

When drawing a rectangular object, three orthographic two-dimensional views are usually required to describe the shape. These are the front view, the top view, and the right-hand side view. The front view of an object is the side with the most information.

The views are kept in line with each other both horizontally and vertically, so that the surfaces of the object may be projected from one

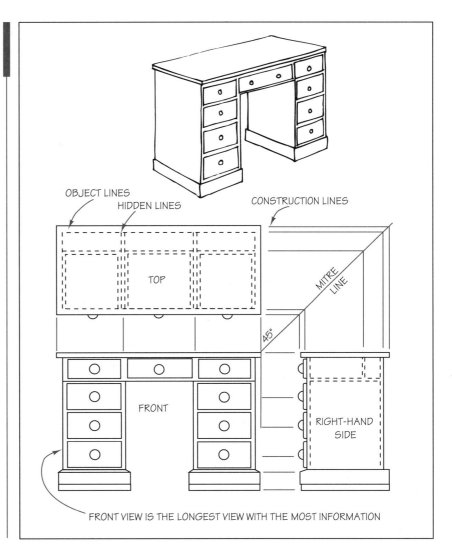

FIGURE 1-26
Orthographic projection using a mitre line

OBJECT LINES
HIDDEN LINES
CONSTRUCTION LINES

TOP

MITRE LINE

45°

FRONT

RIGHT-HAND SIDE

FRONT VIEW IS THE LONGEST VIEW WITH THE MOST INFORMATION

FIGURE 1-27
Blocking in an orthographic drawing

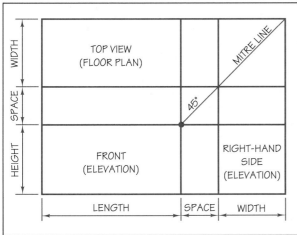

view to the other without additional measurement *(see Fig. 1-26)*. When it is necessary to project lines from the top view to the side view, a **mitre line** is used. This is a 45° line that is drawn from the top right-hand corner of a box which will contain the front view *(see Fig. 1-27)*.

When an object is viewed orthographically, all the surfaces will appear to be on the same plane as the paper, therefore the object will appear to be flat and not three-dimensional. The shape of the object can be determined only by comparing the three orthographic views. In *Fig. 1-28*, the front view of the house appears flat, and it is only when you look at the plan or top view that you can see there is a

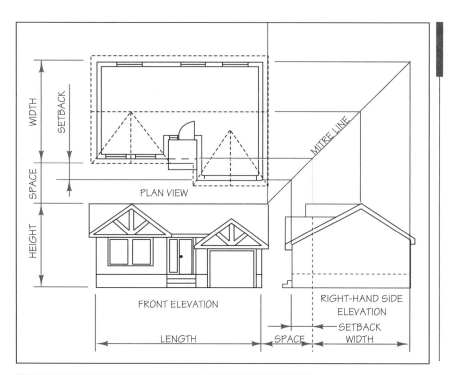

FIGURE 1-28
Three views required to indicate shape

WIDTH
SETBACK
SPACE
HEIGHT
MITRE LINE
PLAN VIEW
FRONT ELEVATION
RIGHT-HAND SIDE ELEVATION
LENGTH
SPACE
SETBACK
WIDTH

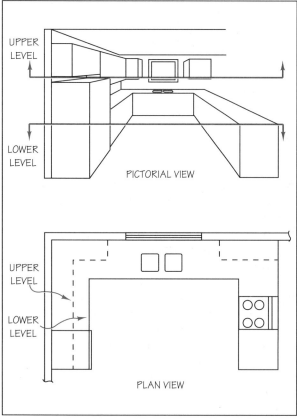

UPPER LEVEL
LOWER LEVEL
PICTORIAL VIEW

UPPER LEVEL
LOWER LEVEL
PLAN VIEW

setback. However, the vertical lines on either side of the door on the front view are clues that some change in shape occurs along the surface. Likewise, the side view must be observed to determine that the roof is a gable. On plan views, structures such as kitchen cabinets and stairs appear as lines on a flat surface and their heights will be seen only on a vertical sectional view *(see Fig. 1-29)*.

To compensate for the size of a house compared to the size of the drawing paper, house plans are drawn to a greatly reduced scale. The scale that is most often used is 1:50 (1/4" = 1' - 0"). Even at this small scale, the plan views of a house are usually large enough so that each has to be drawn on a separate sheet. Therefore, the orthographic relationship of the plan view to the front or side views of the house is not as apparent as they would be if all views were drawn on the same sheet of paper. However, the four elevations, which are vertical views of the sides of the house, are often drawn on one sheet and should be shown in the correct orthographic relationship to each other *(see Fig. 1-30)*.

FIGURE 1-29
Showing different levels of a kitchen for a plan view

FIGURE 1-30
*Orthographic relationship
of elevations*

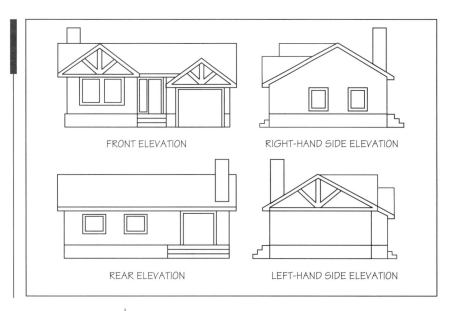

FRONT ELEVATION   RIGHT-HAND SIDE ELEVATION

REAR ELEVATION   LEFT-HAND SIDE ELEVATION

DIMENSIONING

Before a house can be built or an object manufactured, its size must be shown accurately on a drawing. To facilitate this, dimensions are given on a drawing by extending lines from each side of the detail of the object being measured. To make a distinction between the lines of the object and the extension lines, a gap of approximately 2 mm (1/16") is left between them.

A dimension line is then drawn between the two extension lines a minimum of 10 mm (3/8") away from the object and an arrowhead or a slash mark is used to indicate the actual extent of the dimension *(see Figs. 1-31A and 1-31B)*. **Extension** and **dimension lines** are fine, dark lines that should be readily distinguishable from the thick, dark lines of the object.

When dimensioning a drawing, the greater dimensions should always be placed furthest from the object. This avoids the possibility of confusion in reading the smaller dimensions.

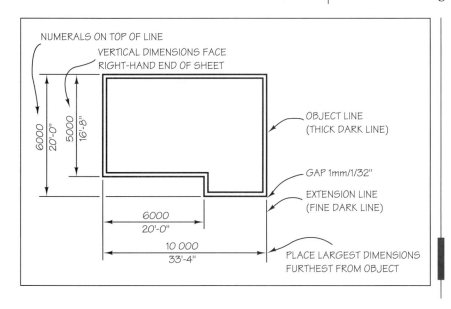

NUMERALS ON TOP OF LINE
VERTICAL DIMENSIONS FACE
RIGHT-HAND END OF SHEET

6000
20'-0"

5000
16'-8"

OBJECT LINE
(THICK DARK LINE)

GAP 1mm/1/32"

EXTENSION LINE
(FINE DARK LINE)

6000
20'-0"

10 000
33'-4"

PLACE LARGEST DIMENSIONS
FURTHEST FROM OBJECT

FIGURE 1-31A
Dimensioning — arrowheads

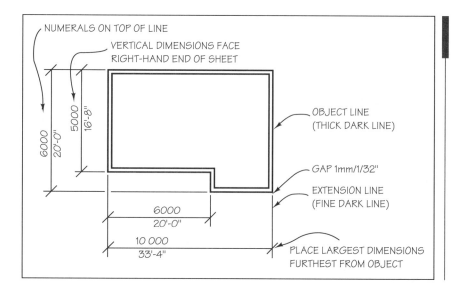

NUMERALS ON TOP OF LINE
VERTICAL DIMENSIONS FACE
RIGHT-HAND END OF SHEET
6000
20'-0"
5000
16'-8"
OBJECT LINE
(THICK DARK LINE)
GAP 1mm/1/32"
EXTENSION LINE
(FINE DARK LINE)
6000
20'-0"
10 000
33'-4"
PLACE LARGEST DIMENSIONS
FURTHEST FROM OBJECT

FIGURE 1-31B
Dimensioning — slashes

LETTERING

One of the most important skills you as a draftsperson must develop is to letter clearly and neatly. The numbers and notations on a drawing are equally as important as the drawing itself, and they must be legible on a printed copy.

The letters must be large and of such a shape that they can be read easily under conditions at the job site, conditions that will usually be inferior to those of a drafting office. For example, there may not be a convenient place to spread out the drawings, and the work may be conducted outdoors on a windy, snowy, or rainy day. Dimensions and notations must be completed with such clarity that a worker can interpret the drawings without difficulty even under these conditions.

Single-stroke Gothic lettering is the style of lettering that should be used on drawings because of its clarity of form *(see Figs. 1-32A and 1-32B)*. Lettering can be drawn upright or sloped at an angle of 22 1/2° to the vertical. Fancy scrolls and flourishes should never be a part of technical lettering. However, this does not prevent you from developing a unique and attractive style of lettering with practice.

ABCDEFGHIJKLMNOP
QRSTUVWXYZ
1234567890

ABCDEFGHIJKLMNOP
QRSTUVWXYZ
1234567890

ABCDEFGHIJKLMNOPQRSTUVWXYZ
1234567890

FIGURE 1-32A   *Single-stroke vertical Gothic lettering*

ABCDEFGHIJKLMNOP
QRSTUVWXYZ
1234567890

ABCDEFGHIJKLMNOP
QRSTUVWXYZ
1234567890

ABCDEFGHIJKLMNOPQRSTUVWXYZ
1234567890

FIGURE 1-32B   *Single-stroke sloping Gothic lettering*

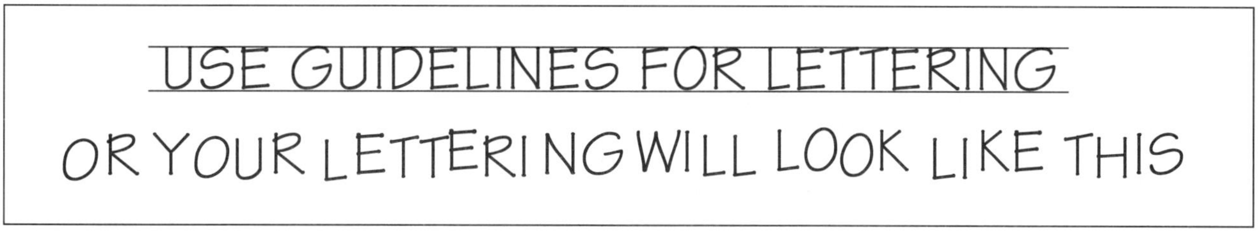

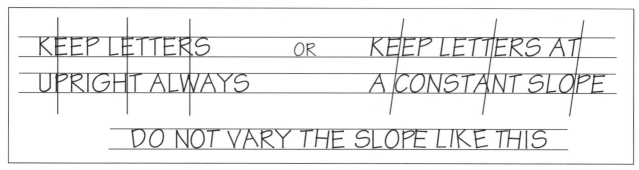

USE GUIDELINES FOR LETTERING
OR YOUR LETTERING WILL LOOK LIKE THIS

FIGURE 1-33A   *Horizontal guidelines for lettering*

KEEP LETTERS   OR   KEEP LETTERS AT
UPRIGHT ALWAYS   A CONSTANT SLOPE

DO NOT VARY THE SLOPE LIKE THIS

FIGURE 1-33B   *Vertical guidelines for lettering*

The accepted size of lettering is 3 mm (1/8") high. This size is easily readable, but it is not so large that the dimensions and notations will dominate the drawing. All lettering should be in upper case or capital letters except for the metric symbols, which are in lower case. All lettering should be the same size with the possible exception of the title, which may be larger if desired. Guidelines should always be used to ensure that the letters are the same height. Guidelines are drawn in light construction lines because these lines are not erased when the lettering is completed. When drawing vertical or sloping letters, it is helpful to draw an occasional vertical or sloping (22 1/2° to the vertical) guideline so that it is easier to maintain a consistent angle for the upright lines of the letters *(see Figs. 1-33A and 1-33B)*.

You should apply a considerable amount of pressure to the pencil when lettering so that it will still be clear and legible when the drawing is copied as a whiteprint. You should also raise the pencil from the paper after each stroke rather than form letters with one continuous line. In this way, the lettering will appear neater and you can maintain an even pressure. When you are lettering, your pencil will require frequent sharpening.

Lettering guides are available from commercial sources to help you draw guidelines; they are especially helpful for lettering blocks of notes. Stencil-type lettering guides are not recommended as it takes much longer to letter with them and it is not possible to compress or extend the width of the lettering when desirable. Also the use of stencil-type guides prevents you from developing your own style of lettering.

Individual letters should appear to be spaced equally apart. To do this, it is necessary to space letters with vertical sides farther apart from each other than those that have open or curved sides *(see Fig. 1-34A)*, so that the area of the space between the letters is approximately the same. At

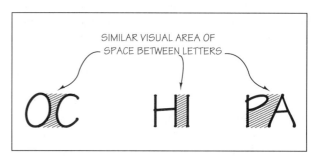

SIMILAR VISUAL AREA OF
SPACE BETWEEN LETTERS

OC   HI   PA

FIGURE 1-34A   *Spaces between letters*

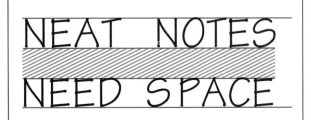

FIGURE **1-34B** *Spaces between words*

FIGURE **1-34C** *Spaces between lines*

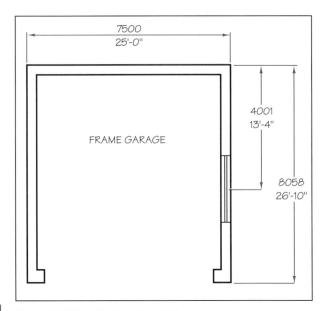

FIGURE **1-35A** *Unidirectional dimensioning system*

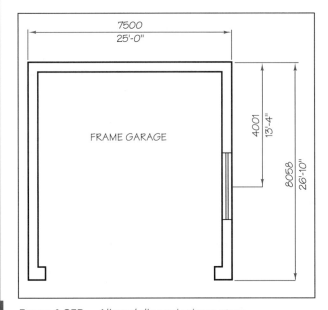

FIGURE **1-35B** *Aligned dimensioning system*

least one letter width should be allowed between words *(see Fig 1-34B)*.

For clarity and neat appearance, rows of lettering should be spaced apart from each other by half the height or even the full height of a letter *(see Fig. 1-34C)*. Numerals should be placed on the drawing so that all dimensions can be read from the bottom of the sheet – this is called **unidirectional dimensioning** (usual on CAD drawings) – or so that vertical dimensions can be read from the right-hand side of the sheet – this is called **aligned dimensioning** (common on hand-produced drawings) *(see Figs. 1-35A and 1-35B)*.

SKETCHING

The ability to make free-hand sketches is essential for a draftsperson. Spur-of-the-moment drawings are frequently required. For instance, a client may wish to see what differences a double door or a bay window would make to the appearance of a house. Ideas like this are often brought up in discussion with clients, and a quick sketch will settle the matter without getting involved in the expense of a formal drawing. This type of change can also be done quickly with CAD if a computer is available.

An addition to an existing structure may be required. If there are no drawings available, all measurements of the existing structure will have to be taken and recorded on a sketch at the site so that a fitting design can be developed and an accurate drawing made at a later date.

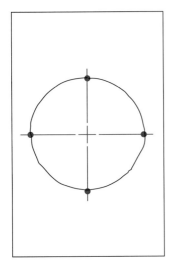

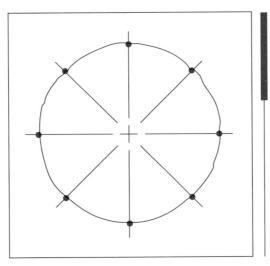

You may feel reluctant to try sketching because you think that your free-hand drawing will be inadequate and will look unprofessional. However, with practice and patience, you can attain a reasonable proficiency, and you will find that this skill will be useful in many situations. A simple graphic sketch is much easier to understand than a verbal description.

Sketching should be done with a softer type of pencil than that used for formal drafting. For example, an HB lead is suitable for sketching. A pad of paper that is approximately letter size should be used so that the pad is easily held and the sketch is a good size.

Graph paper is an asset and will help by providing guidelines for the sketch. Always use the reverse side of the graph paper; the printed squares show through the paper and your sketch will be more clearly seen on the blank surface.

To practise sketching, begin by drawing a series of horizontal lines on a piece of scrap paper. These lines can be drawn continuously with your hand held in a uniform position or the line can be made up of short strokes. The lines should be drawn fairly rapidly.

Then, practise vertical lines and angular lines. You can, if you wish, turn the paper as you work so that you can draw each line in a way that is most comfortable for you.

If it is necessary to sketch circular figures, it is a good idea to draw in a set of centre lines perpendicular to each other. Then mark an equal distance representing the radius along each arm as a guide for the free-hand circle *(see Fig. 1-36A)*. If it is a large circle, it may be advisable to draw additional diagonal guidelines as well *(see Fig. 1-36B)*.

A sketched line will not have the sharpness or accuracy of a line drawn with drafting instruments but it can nevertheless appear neat and stylish.

The same rules that are used for drafting should be followed when sketching. Decide on the number and type of views required, then block in your work with light construction lines. Darken these lines only when you are satisfied that the sketch will clearly convey the information required.

It is particularly important that you are able to draw the various elements in your sketch proportionately because you will not be using any form of measuring device when you are sketching. Judge the relationship of sizes before you begin. For example, is a wall twice as long as it is high? Is a window square or rectangular? Are the tops of the doors and the windows the same height? A few simple observations will make your sketch much more useful and accurate *(see Fig. 1-37)*.

A sketch must be well planned and clear if it is to be of value. Never think of or refer to a sketch as a rough drawing. In the workplace, the same dependability is required when conveying information on a sketch as on a formal drawing.

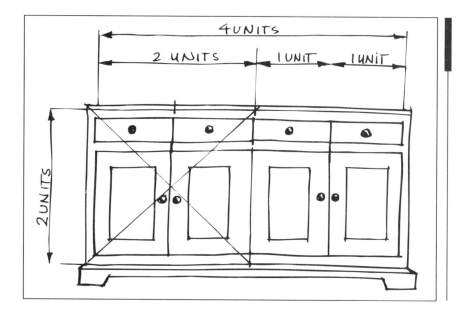

FIGURE 1-37
*Establishing proportions
for sketching*

ADDITIONAL DRAFTING TOOLS

COMPASSES

There are three compasses for drawing circles.

1. The **spring bow compass** is used to draw circles from approximately a 20 mm (3/4") radius to a 130 mm (5") radius. It is the most commonly used compass in drafting *(see Fig. 1-38A)*. It should be held by the knurled top only. The compass should then be inclined in the direction in which it is being rotated. This avoids putting pressure directly on the lead, which would cause it to be pushed back into the holder resulting in a circle with a double line.

2. The **drop compass** is used to draw very small circles such as 1 mm (1/32") radius *(see Fig 1-38B)*.

3. The **beam compass** is used to draw circles with very large diameters. The length of the beam controls the extent of the radius that can be used. It must be held at either end of the bar in order to draw a large circle *(see Fig. 1-38C)*.

All of these compasses use lead, which must be frequently sharpened. The lead should be sharpened on one side only to give it a long slim point *(see Fig. 1-39)*.

Before drawing a circle, draw a pair of centre lines to determine the centre point. This practice

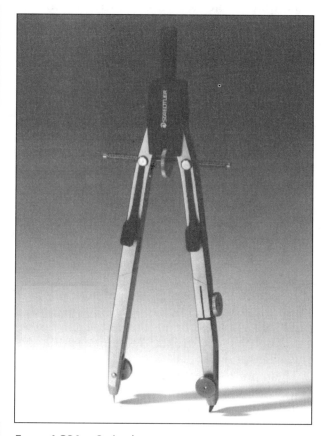

FIGURE 1-38A   *Spring bow compass*

Mars Drawing Instruments and Accessories. Courtesy of Staedtler-Mars Limited

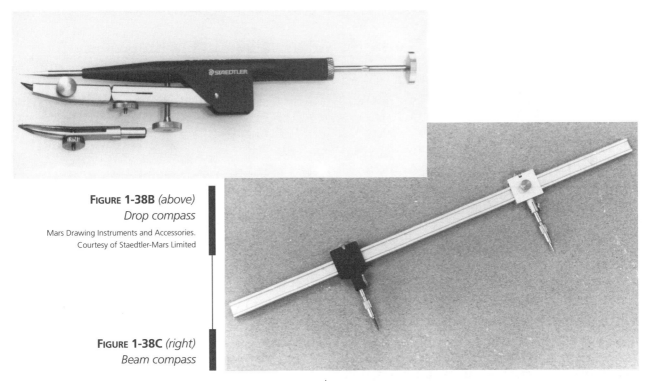

FIGURE 1-38B *(above)*
Drop compass

Mars Drawing Instruments and Accessories.
Courtesy of Staedtler-Mars Limited

FIGURE 1-38C *(right)*
Beam compass

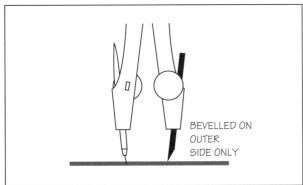

BEVELLED ON
OUTER
SIDE ONLY

FIGURE 1-39 *Sharpening the compass*

will ensure that the circle will be in the correct location and will be truly concentric with any other circle that has the same centre point. In order to draw a circle accurately, first measure the required radius from the centre points along one of the arms of the centre lines. Adjust the compass to this measurement on the paper. Do not adjust the compass directly on the scale as this will damage the scale and it will not be as accurate as the paper measurement method *(see Fig. 1-40)*.

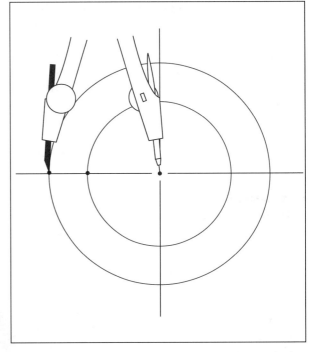

FIGURE 1-40 *Adjusting the compass to a radius marked on the centre line*

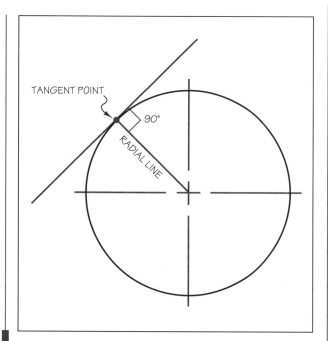

FIGURE 1-41 *Tangent line*

Compasses or circle templates are often used to draw tangent arcs. **Arcs** are portions of the circumference of the circle. **Tangent arcs** are found on objects that have rounded corners in order to maintain a smooth curved outline. A **tangent** is a line that touches a circle at one point only, and when that point, which is called the **tangent point**, is joined to the centre of the circle by a radial line, this line will be at a 90° angle to the tangent line that has been drawn *(see Fig. 1-41)*. To draw a tangent arc in a 90° angle, follow the steps shown in *Fig. 1-42*.

DIVIDERS

A **divider** is a drafting instrument that is very similar in appearance to a compass but it has two metal points instead of one *(see Fig. 1-43)*. It is

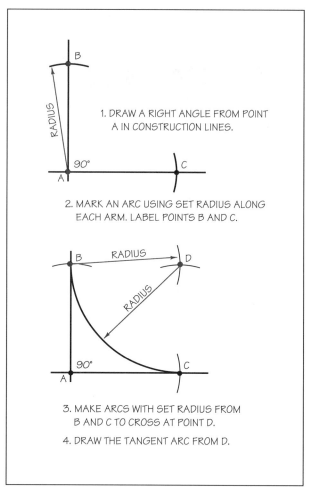

1. DRAW A RIGHT ANGLE FROM POINT A IN CONSTRUCTION LINES.

2. MARK AN ARC USING SET RADIUS ALONG EACH ARM. LABEL POINTS B AND C.

3. MAKE ARCS WITH SET RADIUS FROM B AND C TO CROSS AT POINT D.

4. DRAW THE TANGENT ARC FROM D.

FIGURE 1-42 *Construction for a tangent line*

used to transfer dimensions from one area of the drawing to another or onto a separate drawing.

Proportional dividers can be used to transfer a distance that is to be two or more times the size of the original dimension. Regular dividers can also be used to enlarge.

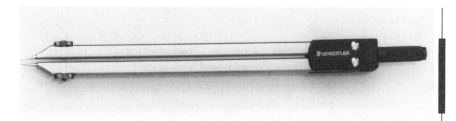

FIGURE 1-43
A divider

Mars Drawing Instruments and Accessories.
Courtesy of Staedtler-Mars Limited

FIGURE 1-44

These are some of the drafting tools you will become familiar with.
From left to right:
(A) Adjustable set-square;
(B) French curve; (C) T-square;
(D) Flexible curve

Compliments of PiCo Design

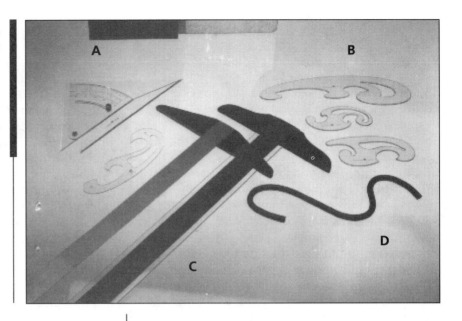

FRENCH CURVES

French curves come in a variety of shapes and sizes and are used to draw irregular curves *(see Fig. 1-44)*. The French curve must be lined up carefully with the points that have already been plotted on the drawing. To ensure a smooth curve, the position of the French curve you are using should face the same direction as the curve that will be formed by the plotted points on the drawing so that the degree of curvature increases or becomes more gradual as required. Join at least three points at a time with the French curve and attempt to achieve a smooth overlap.

PROTRACTORS

Protractors are used to measure angles *(see Fig. 1-45)*. Most protractors are semi-circular, others are circular, and some are marked on a flat scale or ruler.

A protractor is an instrument that is frequently used inaccurately. Follow the steps below to obtain accurate angles.

1. Draw a set of centre lines of a sufficient length in the correct location on the paper so that the protractor can be lined up along these lines.
2. Identify the centre point of the protractor by following the angular lines from the edge of the

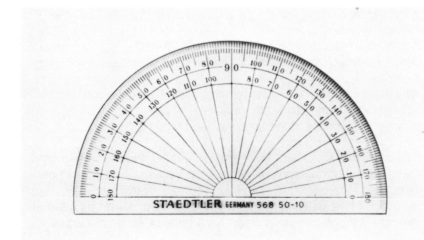

FIGURE 1-45

A protractor

Mars Drawing Instruments and Accessories.
Courtesy of Staedtler-Mars Limited

protractor to discover where they will meet. This point is sometimes not too clearly marked.

3. Line up the centre point on the protractor with the centre point on the drawing.
4. Turn the protractor so that *zero* is on one of the centre lines from which you wish to make the angular measurement.
5. Measure the angle on the exterior edge of the protractor.
6. Join this point to the established centre point on the paper to form the required angle.

ADJUSTABLE SET SQUARES

An **adjustable set square** is an instrument that can also be used to measure or draw angles. This set square is split and has a radial scale joining the two parts, which can be set at any angle. It is not necessary to locate the apex point when drawing an angular line with the adjustable set square *(see Fig. 1-44)*.

TEMPLATES

Many different types of **templates** can be purchased for drawing various small shapes that are frequently found on drawings.

The **circle template** is ideal for drawing small circles *(see Fig. 1-46)*. Take care to match both the centre lines on the template with those on the drawing so that the circles will be concentric with

the centre point and with other circles drawn from the same centre point. To obtain a perfect circle, the pencil point must always be in contact with the edge of the template. A circle template can be used for drawing small tangent arcs or rounded corners of an object.

An **architectural template** has cut-outs for drawing doors, sinks, toilets, stairs, etc. It can be obtained to scale in both metric and imperial systems.

You will find a visit to a drafting supplies store interesting. An up-to-date manufacturer's catalogue will inform you of the variety of equipment available to assist you in drafting.

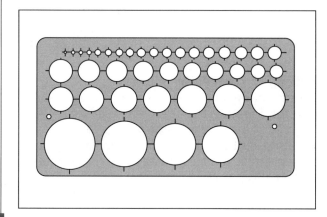

FIGURE 1-46 *A circle template*

***R**EVIEW QUESTIONS*

1. What type and size of lettering is usually used in drafting and how should the letters be spaced?
2. What should you consider before making a sketch?
3. Describe how to use a protractor. List the sequential steps.

***W**HAT DO YOU THINK?*

1. Why is it important to use orthographic projection when conveying technical information to another person?
2. Why is it useful to be able to make a good sketch?

***A**SSIGNMENTS*

1. Your instructor will provide you with a sheet showing four drawings. Complete the orthographic views of each drawing. Use construction (light) lines for projection and mitre lines where necessary.
2. Select one of the drawings from Assignment 1. Using instruments, draft the three orthographic views on an A4/A sheet of vellum as follows:

a. Draw a 10 mm (3/8") border around the vellum using dark lines.

b. Make the drawing at a scale of 2:1 (twice the size of the original drawing).

c. Block in all three views in construction lines starting at 20 mm (3/4") from both the left-hand margin and the bottom margin.

d. Add details using a mitre line and projection lines. Make all projection lines *very light* so that they will not print. Darken all object lines.

e. Show the three overall dimensions in fine dark lines. Place dimensions between views where possible and show one dimension on each view.

f. At the bottom of your drawing neatly letter the title, the scale, and your name.

g. In the top right-hand corner of your drawing, draw in a series of ten guidelines 3 mm (1/8") apart, each approximately 100 mm (4") long. Then neatly letter the following in upper case letters:

ON MY FIRST ORTHOGRAPHIC DRAWING

CONSTRUCTION LINES ARE VERY LIGHT

OBJECT LINES ARE THICK AND DARK

DIMENSION LINES ARE FINE AND DARK

GUIDELINES USED FOR LETTERING ARE LIGHT

h. Make a whiteprint of your drawing.

3. Select a drawing from Assignment 1 (other than that used for Assignment 2). Make a free-hand sketch of that drawing at approximately twice the full size using accepted drafting techniques. Show the overall dimensions, taking the measurements from the original drawing.

4. To practise using compasses and angular measuring devices, divide an A4/A size sheet of bond paper in half vertically.

a. In the left-hand section, draw a set of centre lines.

b. Measure a 50 mm (2") radius and a 25 mm (1") radius from the centre point along one of the centre lines.

c. Adjust the compass to these measurements and draw two concentric circles. Darken these circles.

d. With a protractor or an adjustable set square, measure increments of 15° from the centre point of the circles. Draw and darken the angular lines between the two circles only.

e. In the right-hand section, draw two lines at right angles. Join these lines with a tangent arc that has a radius of 35 mm (1 3/8"). Use the method described in this chapter.

UNIT 3

Pictorial Drawing and Rendering Techniques

OBJECTIVES

- To understand pictorial drawing materials
- To learn pictorial formats
- To understand drawing methods
- To learn rendering techniques

A **pictorial drawing** is a drawing that shows a three-dimensional view of how a house will look after it is built on a lot. The drawing usually shows trees and landscaping or other items around the building to create a picture of the finished structure. Most pictorial drawings are done in pencil because this technique is faster and easier, and it still allows a wide range of tones and textures to be used. You should also learn to use other materials for more variation in pictorial drawings.

DRAWING MATERIALS

PENCILS

The difference between drafting pencils and drawing pencils is the lead. **Drawing pencils** have softer lead and are graded by a number and the letter B. The higher the number, the softer the lead *(see Fig. 1-48)*. It is recommended that you use 2B and 6B pencils for doing pictorial drawings.

There are also wide, flat drawing pencils available in B grades. This style of pencil is similar to the carpenter's pencil. The soft B leads are ideal for shading large areas of a drawing. If the flat sketching pencil is used on its narrow side, the width of the lead creates brick effects *(see Fig. 1-49)*.

Drawing pencils should be sharpened slowly to avoid breaking the soft lead. A straight-back razor blade is an appropriate instrument to use for

FIGURE 1-47 *Pictorial rendering in pencil*

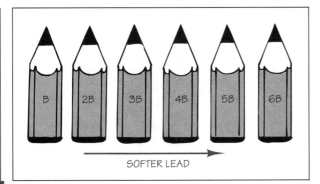

Figure 1-48 *Grades of drawing pencils*

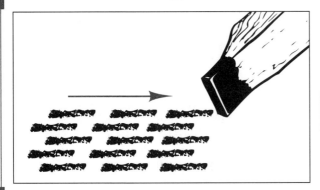

Figure 1-49 *Using the flat sketching pencil to create brick tones*

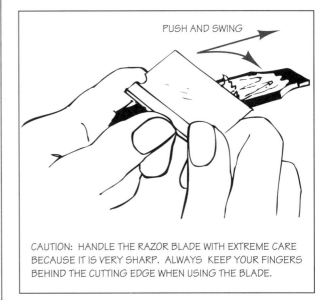

CAUTION: HANDLE THE RAZOR BLADE WITH EXTREME CARE BECAUSE IT IS VERY SHARP. ALWAYS KEEP YOUR FINGERS BEHIND THE CUTTING EDGE WHEN USING THE BLADE.

Figure 1-50 *Sharpening the flat sketching pencil with a straight-back razor blade*

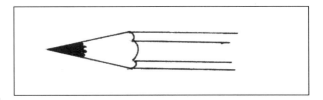

Figure 1-51A *The sharp point*

sharpening these pencils *(see Fig. 1-50)*. There are three types of points that are used with the drawing pencil. The **sharp point** is used for small details and fine natural textures *(see Fig. 1-51A)*; the **rounded** or **blunt point** is used for heavier textures, wide lines, or smaller shadows *(see Fig. 1-51B)*; and the **chisel** or **square point** is used for brick, boards, broad lines, and shading *(see Fig. 1-51C)*.

ERASERS

The flexibility and textural capabilities of using different erasers are quite often overlooked. An eraser can be used as a drawing instrument as well as for simply erasing errors.

Kneaded Erasers – The kneaded eraser is intended to be kneaded, stretched, and shaped in order to self-clean. This flexibility also allows you to shape the eraser to a fine point for erasing small areas or to flatten it to clean large areas.

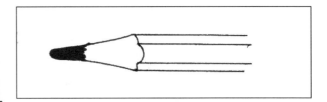

Figure 1-51B *The rounded or blunt point*

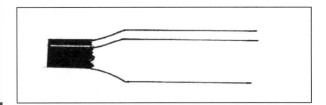

Figure 1-51C *The chisel or square point*

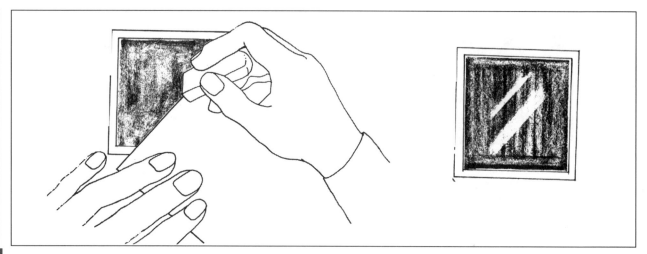

FIGURE 1-52 *Using the eraser to create shine*

A unique quality of the kneaded eraser is that it will lift off excess pencil lead. This is done by simply pushing the eraser down on the area and then lifting it off. This technique is very useful for creating textural effects such as clouds, bushes, or soft materials. The kneaded eraser can also create the effects of reflected light on shiny materials *(see Fig. 1-52).*

You would be well advised to obtain a kneaded eraser made of raw rubber, usually grey in colour, rather than the plasticised kneaded erasers, usually blue or green in colour. The rubber compound works more efficiently and remains more pliable.

Art Gum Erasers – These erasers are usually creamy yellow in colour and are quite soft. They are designed to crumble into small pieces when rubbed over the drawing. Although they will erase most pencil lines, their prime function is to act as an overall cleaning and smudge-removing eraser. For this reason it is best to leave the crumbs on the drawing. Then, using your fingertips, gently rub the crumbs around in a circular motion to evenly clean the open clear areas of your drawing. Remove the dirty crumbs with a drafting brush.

Sand Erasers – Sand erasers are available in block form as well as in pencil form. They are designed to be abrasive to remove dark lines as well as ink lines. The sand eraser can be effectively used to create textures and reflected light on blueprints or whiteprints, since careful erasing will allow you to remove blueprint lines. Sand erasers should be used gently and slowly to avoid tearing holes in the drawing paper.

PENS AND MARKERS

Pen-and-ink techniques are often used for pictorial renderings when there are several drawings to be done and when these drawings are going to be reproduced *(see Fig. 1-53).* Since the ink lines are black and white rather than grey, the picture is reproduced more economically. Light and dark tones are optically created by drawing lines closer together and farther apart, or by using thick and thin ink lines.

The same techniques are used for drawing with nylon-tipped black markers. Both pen-and-ink and marker drawings require careful planning of tones and textures because it is difficult to correct mistakes.

Pens – Two styles of pens are commonly used. The **dip-type pen** uses interchangeable nibs of various sizes. The nibs are graded numerically so that if the number is larger, the nib will produce a wider line. Some pen nibs are designed to be flexible so that they can draw a fine line or, by slightly increasing finger pressure, produce a wider line. When using dip-type pens, you should use a good quality waterproof India drawing ink.

FIGURE 1-53 *Example of an ink drawing*

The second style of pen used in drafting as well as in pictorial drawing is called a technical pen. Technical pens operate with tubular nibs that are also available in nine sizes. The sizes range from a fine line 0.13 mm, to a broad line 2.0 mm. For the beginner, the best three sizes to use are the 0.35 mm, the 0.5 mm, and the 0.7 mm. The width of the line remains constant to the width of the nib being used because the ink is discharged from a tubular nib.

There are several advantages to using technical pens for ink drawings. Each nib has an ink-reservoir cartridge that allows continuous drawing for a long period of time. These reservoirs are also refillable. The ink used for technical pens is shellac-free so that the ink flows easily and will not gum up the tips. Technical pens do not drip or spatter and can be used with set squares and t-squares without the ink smearing under the instrument. They are expensive and delicate drawing instruments, so you must take extreme care in handling, storing, and cleaning these pens.

BRUSHES

Architectural drawings that are produced by brush painting require a great deal of practice. These pictorial drawings are usually done by artists who specialize in architectural illustration in all media. Two types of brushes are used. They are watercolour brushes that are fine pointed, and watercolour brushes that have flat chisel ends. Both styles of brushes are graded in size by number. A larger number indicates that the end of the brush will also be larger. The best quality brushes are made with pure sable bristles and are very expensive.

You should develop a thorough understanding of textures and shading in pencil before attempting to do painted pictures.

COMPOSITION FORMATS

When planning your pictorial drawing, you should consider the general proportions of the building as well as the design characteristics.

There are three basic composition formats:
1. a **square format**, in which the width is approximately the same as the height,
2. a **portrait format**, which is taller than it is wide,
3. a **landscape format**, which is wider than it is tall.

Two-storey houses may look larger and more elegant displayed in a portrait format, whereas drawings of a ranch or split-level house may be better suited to a landscape format. A square format is not used very often because it creates a less interesting pictorial drawing.

The placement of the building within the format should also be carefully considered. Avoid having the horizon divide the format in the middle. You may choose between a high horizon *(see Fig. 1-54A)*, and a low horizon *(see Fig. 1-54B)*. It is more appealing if there is more sky and less ground, or more ground and less sky, than to have equal areas of sky and ground.

DRAWING METHODS

All pictorial drawings use one or a combination of three main methods. The three main methods are dots, lines, and solids. Although each method may be used alone to create a certain texture or a style of drawing, they may also be combined to create a technique that best suits the material for the drawing.

Dots can be very effective in ink drawings as they suggest textures or the gradual shading of an object. This is called a **stipple technique** and is a very slow but effective method of drawing or shading *(see Fig. 1-55)*.

Lines are most commonly used because they quickly suggest three-dimensional form. Lines can also be varied to suggest texture and can be used for shading in pencil or in ink *(see Fig. 1-56)*.

Solids are used to suggest massive areas. These areas may not be done in pencil or ink but could

FIGURE 1-54A *High horizon or bird's eye view*

FIGURE 1-54B *Low horizon or worm's eye view*

FIGURE 1-55 *A drawing rendered by stipple technique*

FIGURE 1-56 *Pencil lines for texture and shading*

be large open areas of clear paper. When large areas of dark materials or areas in shadow are to be shown, solid tones of pencil or ink are most effective *(see Fig. 1-57)*. A night scene can be created by using the solid technique *(see Fig. 1-58)*.

RENDERING TECHNIQUES

In order for you to make a complete pictorial drawing, you should first experiment with shading and creating textures in various ways. A step-

FIGURE 1-57 *Line and solid technique*

by-step procedure for drawing pictorials in different media is explained in Chapter 13, Unit 1. The following diagrams and suggestions will help you to learn the use of the pencil, pens and markers, and the blueprint machine in creating shading and textures.

Pencil Shading – You will learn to observe and examine light and shade through practice. The effect of light from a single source on an object is easier to understand if the object is placed near the source of the light. An example is the sun or a lamp. The areas closer to the source are lighter while those areas farther away are darker.

Various tones of grey, white, or black can be made by using B pencils with a sharp point, a rounded point, or a chisel end. If you carefully rub the pencil point back and forth on the paper with various finger pressure, you will notice light grey, dark grey, or very dark areas of pencil tone. Another way to create tone is to use the side of the lead by tipping the pencil so that it is almost parallel to the paper surface. This technique gives a smoother tone without showing lines *(see Fig. 1-59)*.

Lines can be intentionally used for shading by drawing light lines, darker lines, or thick and thin lines *(see Fig. 1-60)*. Since most buildings are box-shaped, it is recommended that you practise shading box-like forms.

Here are three important suggestions to help you create professional-looking drawings.

1. Always use at least three to five different tones in your drawing, from very light to very dark.
2. Shade the light grey tones first and the dark tones last. It is easier to darken tones than it is to lighten tones.
3. Draw shading lines in the same direction as the surface of the object *(see Fig. 1-61)* and in the same perspective as the object.

FIGURE 1-58 *Using solids to create a night scene*

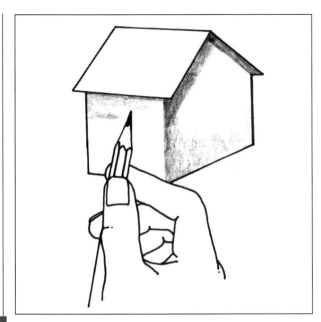

FIGURE 1-59   *Shading with the side of the lead*

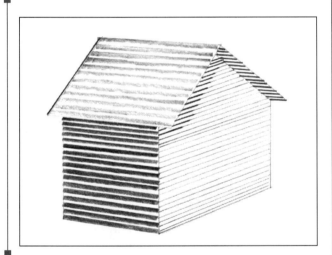

FIGURE 1-60   *Shading using thick and thin lines*

Pencil Textures – To create the illusion of wood, brick, shingles, stones, grass, clouds, etc. with a pencil requires choosing the correct pencil point. *Figures 1-62A, B*, and *C* show examples of the various textures made by each type of pencil point. Practise these textures in various sizes and tones. For textures that are smooth or have soft blurred edges, the pencil tones can be smudged with the fingertips or the kneaded eraser. This

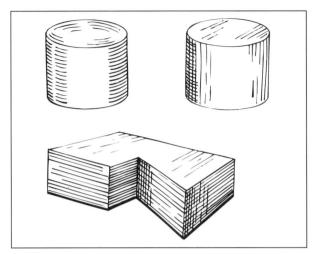

FIGURE 1-61   *Line shading in the direction of the surface*

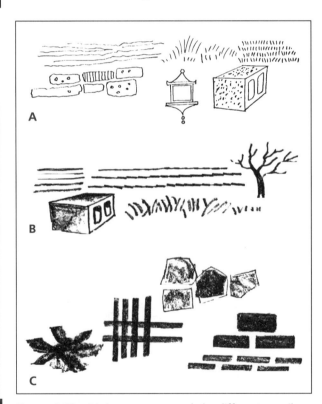

FIGURE 1-62   *Various textures made by different pencil points*

A   *Sharp point textures*
B   *Blunt point textures*
C   *Chisel point textures*

FIGURE 1-63 *Creating textures by smudging*

FIGURE 1-64 *Using torn paper to create clouds*

rubbed effect is ideal for water, clouds, or shrubs *(see Fig. 1-63)*. An effective method of indicating cloudy skies is to use torn cloud-shaped pieces of paper. Use these pieces as masks and then rub the pencil lead with your finger from the edges of the paper mask. By using two or three torn shapes, you can easily produce a dramatic cloud effect *(see Fig. 1-64)*.

Ink and Marker Shading – The understanding of light and dark shading tones on an object is the same for ink or marker drawings as it is for pencil drawings. There is an important difference, however, as to how you create the illusion of grey tones with ink or black marker.

Ink lines will be black, regardless of their thickness, so the illusion of a grey tone is made by leaving white spaces between the lines. The eye will combine the white spaces and black lines and will see areas that are either light or dark grey tones. If the lines are closer together, the grey tone appears darker *(see Fig. 1-65A)*. Ink lines for shading may be drawn parallel to each other or at various angles to each other to create optical tones of grey *(see Fig. 1-65B)*. When they are used at angles to each other the technique is known as **cross-hatching**

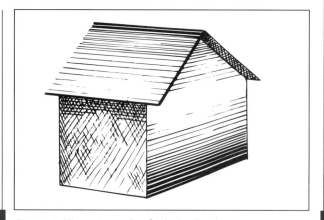

FIGURE 1-65A *Example of ink shading lines*

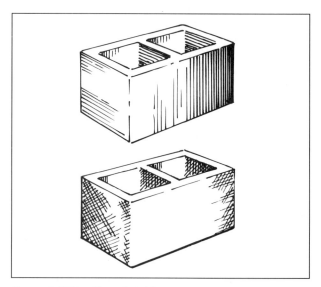

FIGURE 1-65B *Cross-hatching*

Pen-and-ink or black marker drawings may be done entirely with the aid of rulers and instruments or in a combination of freehand strokes. Always shade the light-tone areas first because more ink lines can be added easily; removing excess shading strokes is difficult.

Ink and Marker Textures – A variety of textures can be drawn similar to the pencil method. Where a softer or blurred effect is desired, the dot or stipple effect may be used *(see Fig. 1-65C)*. *Figure 1-66* illustrates commonly used ink strokes.

USING THE PRINT MACHINE TO CREATE EFFECTS

The diazo print machine can be used as an aid to make pictorial drawings for many effects. For example, if you would like to illustrate a house in order to compare various colours of brick, the outline of the house could be blueprinted several times and various colours could be rendered on the prints using coloured pencils.

A dramatic combination drawing can be achieved by shading the landscaping in pencil but leaving the outline of the house in simple lines. This drawing is then blueprinted, and the house is completely rendered on the print in pencil or in ink, leaving the landscaping in blue tones for a two-colour effect. The reverse of this technique is also possible.

To create a night effect or an illuminated effect, the designer may render the drawing in pencil with a complete range of tones and then blueprint the drawing at a dark setting. The resulting print will have an overall blue appearance. Using white opaque watercolour paint and a brush, the areas to be illuminated are painted white. This technique is best suited to interior drawings.

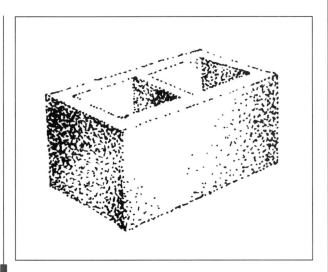

FIGURE 1-65C *Stipple*

FIGURE 1-66 *Ink strokes*

REVIEW QUESTIONS

1. List and explain briefly each of the most common methods used in drawing.
2. What is the difference between a portrait and a landscape format?
3. Describe the most important difference in drawing grey tones with a pencil and drawing grey tones with pen and ink.

WHAT DO YOU THINK?

1. Which medium do you prefer for a pictorial drawing: pencil, pen and ink, or paint? Give reasons for your choice.
2. Do you think a pictorial drawing is a necessary part of a set of plans to present to a customer? Explain the reasons for your decision.

ASSIGNMENTS

1. Using a t-square and a set square, draw four rectangles 60 mm x 90 mm (2 1/2 " x 3 1/2 ") on an A4/A sheet of paper. Using your 2B drawing pencil, render the following textures putting one texture on each rectangle:
   brick
   wood
   cut stone
   shingles
2. Your instructor will supply you with a diagram with the drawing space divided into six equal rectangular spaces. Shade three of the boxes to show different light direction: one using pencil tones; one using pencil lines; and one using pencil tones and lines combined.

   Shade the remaining three boxes in pen-and-ink or marker using different techniques.

CHAPTER 2

An Introduction to Computer-Aided Drafting

COMPUTERS USING computer-aided drafting (CAD) software programs have changed the approach to graphic communication and have revolutionized the method of designing and producing architectural presentation and working presentation drawings. Many CAD programs have been developed that will assist you in making drawings directly on the monitor and then reproducing them on a plotter.

You cannot presume that you need only to press a button and the computer does all the work. The use of computer software must be carefully learned in order that it can be effectively applied. It is still essential that the theories, rules, and practices of drafting be fully understood prior to working with a CAD program. CAD is a drafting tool just like the drafting machine. However, it is much more sophisticated and can save a draftsperson a lot of time if the operator is familiar with the program.

CAD allows the construction of accurate details that are capable of being modified more readily than is possible on a conventional drafting board using standard equipment. Although it is true that many draftspersons will continue to use drafting boards, t-squares, drafting machines, and other conventional equipment for some time to come, in the future the majority of drafting will be developed from the sketch phase and transferred directly to the computer screen by means of a software program.

UNIT 1 | Using a Computer for Architectural Drafting

OBJECTIVES

- To examine some of the main operational steps in using a computer-aided software program
- To investigate and produce computer-aided solutions to sample practical assignments

THE CAD APPROACH

The CAD approach is an *aid* to graphic communication. *Fig. 2-1* shows that:
1. the screen represents the drawing paper,
2. the lines and text are applied by means of the software program,
3. the solution or resulting graphic is reproduced on drawing paper by using a plotter or a printer that is designed to be used with the computer.

The floor plan shown in *Fig. 2-1* can readily be produced using conventional drafting equipment and techniques. The advantages of the CAD process become evident when it is discovered that graphic details can be quickly and efficiently moved or modified. Details can be erased, added, moved, copied, scaled, zoomed, etc. by the use of the software menus *(see Fig. 2-2)*.

One of the major advantages of an architectural CAD software program is the use of a symbols library. Since a large part of the presentation and working drawings includes the use of symbols such as windows, doors, wall textures, electrical, and plumbing fixtures, etc., it is evident that if a prepared library of standard symbols is available, the symbols can be readily selected and added to the drawing as needed. They can also be moved and copied within the design as required

FIGURE 2-1
A sample floor plan produced by computer software
Courtesy, Drafix CAD by Foresight Resources Corp.

FIGURE 2-2

Right: A sample elevation view
Below: A zoomed (magnified) view
of the front entrance

Courtesy, Drafix CAD by Foresight Resources Corp.

(see Fig. 2-3). As well, you have the option of preparing and adding symbols to the library as desired.

As you study this brief overview of CAD, you should become familiar with and practise the following Guidelines for Effective CAD Application:

1. To develop a planned approach before applying CAD hands-on,
2. To prepare a sketch of your design, including scale, paper size, and specifications,
3. To remember that architectural standards must be used throughout the work,
4. To know and understand the capabilities of your CAD system by learning, practising, and applying all of the menus when possible,

FIGURE 2-3

A kitchen layout showing an application of symbols. Note the symbol for stove.

Courtesy, Drafix CAD by Foresight Resources Corp.

5. To remember that drawing modification is much easier because items can be copied, moved, or rotated,
6. To save your work on a regular basis every 15 to 20 minutes. This will prevent the need to redraw the project if the system fails,
7. To discuss information with fellow students. Someone may be more familiar with some aspects of CAD and may be able to show you additional ways to use the system,
8. To keep a written record of things you need to know in a format that you understand and is convenient for you.

CAD SOFTWARE TERMINOLOGY

Many commercial CAD software programs are available, some of which are

Drafix, AutoCAD, DesignCAD, CADApple, CAD, VersaCAD, CADTutor, Autosketch, and *CADKey.*

These programs vary in both cost and complexity.

Although they also vary in the way they are applied by the user, all programs produce a graphical end result. Information learned on one system can, in many cases, be carried over to another system.

Much of the menu application and visual screen results are self-evident, but it is important to understand some of the more common terms used within the software programs. It is possible that these terms vary slightly from program to program but the result of the application is much the same.

There are many menu commands that are used within a software package and each needs to be understood and applied. It is true, however, that some commands are used on a more regular basis than others and are needed to create even the most basic graphic display.

The following information is an attempt to clarify those menu details that need to be understood for general operations. The terms are arranged in a sequence similar to the way in which they might be used. These terms are not necessarily related to any specific software package.

• **Logon** – The means whereby you can access the software program. This usually means identifying yourself and giving a secret password.

• **Default** – The preset values of the CAD software parameters, which present such things as line style, sheet size, scale, text, pen colour, etc. These defaults can be changed as needed by use of the menu commands.

• **Scale** – The default scale is normally full size (1:1) but may be changed as required.

• **Grid** – A series of visible points on the screen that can be turned on or off. This provides an easy method of construction by using the points in order to plot the diagram on the screen. The distances between grid points are referred to as values that can also be changed as required.

• **Lines** – Selecting and applying straight lines on the screen is normally constructed by using the grid to the distances from grid point to grid point. The default style uses solid lines but may be changed as necessary.

• **Arc** – A partial circle may be constructed by one of several methods such as finding the end points and selecting a third point on the arc or by selecting a portion of a circumference of a circle.

• **Absolute Co-ordinates** – Points located on the horizontal (X axis) and the vertical (Y axis) at a distance from a preset (0, 0) origin. Normally the bottom left-hand corner of the screen represents the intersection of the X and Y axis or the point (0,0).

• **Zoom** – The process of magnifying a portion of the drawing in order to make details of small parts more visible. This menu command should not be confused with **SCALE**.

• **Pan** – The process of moving to and viewing an area of the drawing different from that displayed on the screen after zooming in.

• **Copy** – The ability to reproduce a detail in a new location while leaving the original detail in its preset position.

• **Move** – The ability to transfer the position of a detail to a new location.

• **Rotate** – The ability to locate the detail at a different angle by moving it in a clockwise or counter-clockwise direction.

• **Dimension** – The process of adding the dimensional values to the drawing. Normally the size is automatically dimensioned based on the chosen scale. If a change in value is required, the text can in most cases be overwritten to show the value required. Dimensions are normally presented in unidirectional form but may be changed to the aligned method.

• **Text** – The application of notes and specifications normally in upper and/or lower case. The text style and the size of the lettering can be changed as required.

• **Layer** – A layer or plane on which a drawing or part of a drawing is constructed. When several layers are used, one or more may be switched on or off to clarify the drawing. For example, it may be necessary to show drawings with and without dimensions. These drawings can both be made by using layering.

You can find many other menu commands within the specific CAD software program that you use. Each system requires that you select the appropriate menu option. Different software programs vary in method whereby the commands are made operational.

Using a CAD system to its full potential takes time and effort but as you become accustomed to the system you will find faster ways of achieving results.

REVIEW QUESTIONS

1. What is the advantage of using CAD compared to the more conventional drafting tools?
2. Why is the use of a CAD symbols library an advantage?
3. State any four of the Guidelines for Effective CAD Application outlined in this chapter.

WHAT DO YOU THINK?

1. Arrange the Guidelines in order of importance.
2. Assuming that you are presently able to access a CAD system,
   a. List the menu items you are familiar with and the menu items you must learn.
   b. How do you intend to become knowledgeable about these new commands?
3. Prepare a comparison list of operations, methods, and results for the conventional drafting approach and the CAD approach.

ASSIGNMENTS

The following practical assignments using CAD are offered as a means of encouraging you to apply some of the basic operations that are required when using a CAD program. As outlined, it is necessary to plan the steps that you will use to ensure a measure of success and to reduce frustration.

Each assignment in this chapter generally indicates the operations and CAD menus that were used. Remember that since there are differences between software programs, this text indicates a general procedure only. The actual terms and program steps related to the CAD program you are using need to be applied. Assignments in other chapters can also be undertaken by CAD as well as the major project if computer time is available.

Once you have developed an appreciation for the use of the CAD system, any selected assignment or project drawing in this course can be constructed with the CAD program.

1. This CAD assignment is to partially design a single-storey dwelling so that you can follow it step-by-step using the pictorial sequence. Each stage is accompanied with some indication of the procedure and menu commands. The scale used is relative to the grid size chosen in this example.
   a. Display the default settings for the *grid* and *paper size (see Fig. 2-4)*, and, if necessary, change these defaults:

   > Metric – grid 10 mm, paper A3
   > Imperial – grid 1/4", paper B

   b. Check that *grid lock* and *snap* are on before entering *lines*. Note that some systems draw one line at a time while others are capable of drawing double lines. Block in the general design of the dwelling *(see Fig. 2-5)*.
   c. Select *zoom* and enlarge part of the design. In *Fig. 2-6*, the top right corner, which will be the kitchen, was chosen. At this stage, it is possible to *modify* or *trim* the corners and to delete any lines that may overlap.

FIGURE 2-4

This represents a grid and paper size for construction of an on-screen detail.

Courtesy, Drafix CAD by Foresight Resources Corp.

FIGURE 2-5

The general layout of the dwelling is blocked in.

Courtesy, Drafix CAD by Foresight Resources Corp.

FIGURE 2-6

*Parts of the design can be zoomed
or enlarged for modification.*

Courtesy, Drafix CAD by Foresight Resources Corp.

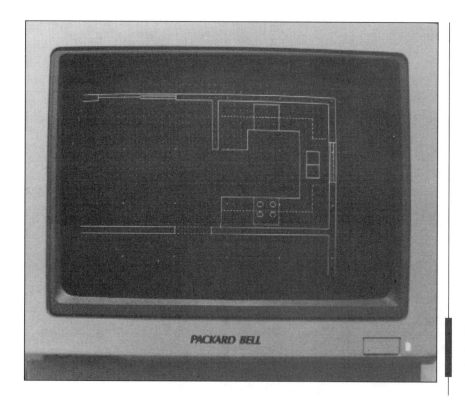

FIGURE 2-7

Adding fixtures to the dwelling.

Courtesy, Drafix CAD by Foresight Resources Corp.

FIGURE 2-8
Using the symbol library to identify details.
Courtesy, Drafix CAD by Foresight Resources Corp.

d. Several construction operations can now be carried out. The *grid* can be changed to 3 mm (1/8") so that details may be drawn. Remember to change *grid snap*. The walls can be broken so that doors can be located. Fixtures should now be constructed *(see Fig. 2-7)*.

e. By using line modification, it is possible to indicate in dashed lines the overhead cupboards and archways. *Text*, that is written notation, may be added at this stage if required. The inclusion of some symbols is also possible by selecting from a *symbol library*. Sink, refrigerator, and range details are typical of symbols that could be stored in the symbol library *(see Fig. 2-8)*.

To show the full construction of a single-storey dwelling such as this would occupy a lot of space; therefore only a brief overview is shown.

You are encouraged to construct a project similar to this and experiment with the CAD program that is available. Remember that at this stage, you must concentrate on learning to understand the operation of your program rather than to be concerned with actual design accuracy.

2. Unlike the previous assignment, you are asked to produce a design format for producing the symbol as outlined below. Some suggestions will be offered with respect to the construction but you must choose the most suitable order of operations for your CAD program.

Fig. 2-9 shows an example of a north symbol design that would be used for application on architectural site plans. You are asked to draw this symbol at full size as shown and then save the resulting diagram in the symbol library. This symbol may be recalled as required and copied onto any drawing as needed.

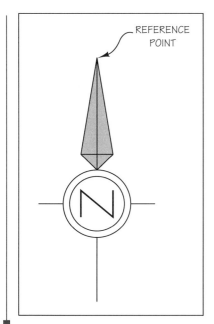

FIGURE 2-9
North symbol

Figure 2-10

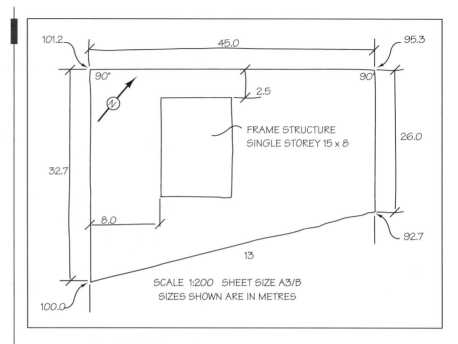

Scale: Full size as shown
Grid Spacing: 3 mm (1/8")

It will be necessary to select a reference point on the symbol for location purposes so that when the symbol is copied from the file you can position it exactly. Once it has been copied onto the drawing as displayed on the monitor, it can be moved and/or rotated into any convenient location.

3. On an A3/B size sheet of paper, redraw the site plan as shown in *Fig. 2-10* using CAD. Specification notes and dimensional information are to be included. For the purpose of this assignment, sizes are shown in metric units.

   You will need to consider the CAD program you are using, the *scale* setting, the *grid* setting, and the *paper size*. Copy the north symbol as an addition to this drawing (see Assignment 2). Remember that the north symbol was drawn and saved at the full-size scale.

PART 2

ARCHITECTURAL DESIGN

Part Two introduces the main project, which may be done sequentially with the assignments or undertaken at a future time according to instructions from your instructor. At the end of all relevant chapters, you will find the appropriate steps to take in order to proceed with the design of a full set of presentation and working drawings for a house design.

Part Two covers the selection of the site and the orientation of the structure. Surveying, theory of design, and general feasibility are also studied so that when you reach Part Three you will have all the preliminary knowledge required to begin designing a house.

Your instructor will acquaint you with the units and assignments that are applicable to your course of study.

EXPLAINING THE PROJECT

THE PROJECT

The project is to design a house to suit a particular lot. This text has been compiled to assist you in completing that task.

Your instructor will advise you as to which assignments will be the most beneficial in providing the necessary back-up data. You may do the assignments and the project sequentially or you may be asked to attempt the major project at the end of the course or during a subsequent course.

Your instructor will provide you with a choice of lots. Your house design project must be related to one of these lots. As an alternative to designing a house yourself, you may select from a magazine a house plan that is suitable for the lot and revise that plan in accordance with ideas that you acquire as you work through this book.

The project may be done in metric or imperial measurements and may be drafted by hand or by CAD if sufficient computer time is available.

Your house design may be very simple or it may involve a great deal of creative work and research. If it is to be successful, any creative house design must be based on knowledge of graphic communication through drafting, sound construction techniques, and the needs of your supposed client.

The steps in the project are outlined at the end of each chapter where applicable.

	Steps	Page
Chapter 3	1	74
Chapter 4	2-5	110
Chapter 9	6-10	228
Chapter 10	11	242
Chapter 11	12-16	267
Chapter 12	17	281
Chapter 13	18-19	296
Chapter 14	20-24	347
Chapter 15	25-30	384

CHAPTER **3**

Making a Site Plan

THERE ARE MANY FACTORS that will influence the choice of location for a new home. A major consideration will be the distance from the workplace for those who work outside of the home. For some people, proximity to a suitable school or daycare centre and a shopping centre may be of prime importance; some people want easy access to a community centre complex, outdoor sport facilities, or other social activities; and some consider easy access to arterial roads and major highways desirable.

Other factors to be considered are:
• What type of lifestyle does the household enjoy?
• Do members of the household prefer the amenities of the town or do they like country living?
• What size and style of house can the family afford?
• What sports and/or hobbies does the family enjoy?
• Will transportation be available for outside activities?

If an urban setting is chosen, certain general requirements must also be met by the community. Dependable **public services** must be available such as water mains, sewage lines, hydro, natural gas, and telephone connections. The municipality must provide maintenance services including garbage collection, regular road repair and cleaning, snow removal, and street lighting of adequate intensity. The existence of **protective services** such as an effective police force and an efficient firefighting unit should also be confirmed.

If a rural area is chosen, take note of the services that may not be provided in that area.

Figure 3-1 *Community requirements*

UNIT 1 | Selecting the Site and House Plan

OBJECTIVES

- To recognize the alternatives in lot selection
- To appreciate why a lot should be selected prior to choosing a house plan
- To recognize the various options available for selecting house designs
- To determine the maximum size of a building for a specific lot
- To appreciate the local by-laws with regard to positioning the house on the lot

SELECTING THE LOT

After identifying the community and location that will best meet the needs of the purchaser, the next step in planning to build a house is the selection of the lot. There are many more options for house designs than there are available lots on the market. Therefore, a house should be designed after a lot has been chosen to take advantage of the size, shape, and orientation of that particular lot. It is unwise to build a house that is too large for the lot and that is not compatible with those in the immediate vicinity. A house that is larger or smaller than those nearby or of a very different style or

FIGURE 3-2 *A planned residential community*

relative cost will look awkward and will affect the resale price of that house and of the houses on adjacent lots.

VARIOUS HOUSE DESIGN OPTIONS

PLANNED RESIDENTIAL COMMUNITIES

The most effective way to purchase a lot is by selecting land that is part of a planned residential community. These communities are designed by a developer, and the layout of the subdivision is approved by the local municipality before the lots come onto the market. Essential services such as water, sewers, hydro, telephones, and roads will usually be installed prior to the start of construction. Quite often, subdivisions have a number of houses that are already constructed and on display as model homes. The buyer may then select a suitable design. Normally, one particular contrac-

tor is chosen to do all the construction. Legal matters, land titles, and all relevant professional fees are arranged so that the purchaser is relieved of many of the small details usually involved with the building of a house. Naturally, the cost of these conveniences and of the installation of utilities and roads will be reflected in the relatively higher cost of the lots.

INDIVIDUAL LOTS

Many people prefer to find a lot themselves, by obtaining land in a rural area or by buying an undeveloped lot in an urban area. In either case, the essential services will have to be installed specifically for that lot, which will be an additional cost.

When a lot is to be purchased other than as part of a planned residential community, it is advisable to employ the services of a **lawyer**, a **surveyor**, and eventually a **contractor**.

FIGURE 3-3 *An individual lot*

A lawyer will **search the title** before the purchase of a piece of real estate. This is to ensure that the new owner will have clear title to the land as described on the deed and that no previous legal involvements will prevent this. The lawyer will also discover if there are any **liens** registered against the property. A lien is any charge or debt shown at the registry office against the property, such as a mortgage or a financial court judgement against the current owner. For example, if there is a mortgage outstanding against a property, the lender of that mortgage owns a portion of that real estate. A lawyer will also advise the buyer of any **easement** on the land. An easement is the legal right given to public utility companies to come onto the land to do repairs and maintenance work to their installations, which either run through or can be accessed only through that property. In return for this right, the utility company agrees to restore the land to the condition that it was in before their entry. A buyer should be aware of these factors before signing an agreement to purchase as they will affect land use and value.

Upon purchase of the land, the lawyer will require a survey plan to be drawn up by the surveyor. This will be considered a legal document that will be used to register the plan and deed at the local registry office under the new owner's name. The surveyor will also stake out the lot at this time.

A contractor will build the house by a certain date for a certain price to the **specifications** and working drawings. The contractor's responsibilities will include hiring electricians, carpenters, and other subtrades, as well as purchasing materials. You should select your contractor on the basis of reputation rather than the lowest quotation for the job. The buyer's satisfaction depends on the contractor's integrity and good will. It is not possible to cover all details in writing, although it is wise to see that as many as possible are included in the specifications.

Some people elect to build a house themselves, acting as their own general contractor. In this case, more capital must be available before commencing work because lumber yards and other suppliers who extend credit will not be as generous to an individual as they are to an established contractor.

EXISTING HOUSES

Instead of building a new house, a buyer might consider an existing new house or an older house that has already been occupied. Here the advantage could be early occupation of a property where all utilities and necessary amenities are in place. The land on an older property is probably landscaped with a lawn and fully grown trees. Another positive factor is that the buyer can observe the house and its environs in a developed state.

Some knowledge of house design and construction will assist the buyer in making many of these decisions by giving that person the confidence of a well-informed consumer.

FINDING THE RIGHT DESIGN

There are several options available to enable a person to select a suitable design. The decision is important, and you should take sufficient time to ensure that the house plan is suitable for the people who plan to live in the house and also that the house will be compatible with other houses in the immediate vicinity.

As a house is the largest investment that many people will make in a lifetime, the matter of potential resale value must be given serious consideration. Most people will move four or five times during their adult lives.

MAGAZINE PLANS

Many design magazines contain **presentation drawings** for a wide range of designs from which a plan may be selected. A set of presentation drawings shows a basic **floor plan** and a **perspective rendering**, which gives an artist's impression of how the house could look on a site. These drawings give adequate information for selecting a suitable house layout (*see Fig. 3-4*).

A full set of **working drawings** providing specific details of how the house will be constructed and what materials are to be used can then be purchased from the publisher.

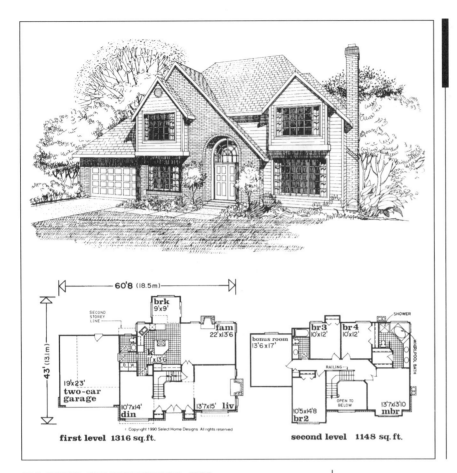

FIGURE 3-4
Presentation drawing

first level 1316 sq.ft.

second level 1148 sq.ft.

PLANS SUGGESTED BY A CONTRACTOR

A contractor is knowledgeable about which houses have proved most popular and economical to build in the chosen area and can make suggestions regarding the selection of a plan. The contractor may be able to point out a similar house that the company has built locally that will give the client a realistic idea of how the house will actually appear when it is built.

AN ARCHITECT-DESIGNED HOUSE

An architect may be hired to design a home. The architect can design a house that will meet the needs of a household with several different interests. The architect will also be familiar with the latest building materials, heating and cooling devices, and contemporary designs. An architect-designed house will probably be unique and up-to-date, but this will not necessarily make it readily resalable. Fewer buyers will be attracted to a house with an unusual layout or decor.

The architect will also supervise the construction throughout the entire building process and deal with all legal matters in connection with the building. In this case, the person for whom the house is being built is not obligated to visit the site until the house is completed. This is a definite advantage for a busy person or someone who lives at some distance from the site. However, an architect-designed house will be more costly than building from any other type of plan. The architect's fees are usually based on a percentage of the total cost of the project.

YOUR OWN DESIGN

It is quite possible to adapt a ready-made plan or to design a house yourself. If you are not experienced, have your plans checked over by a building consultant or a reputable general contractor before applying to the municipality for a permit to build. The local building inspector will have to approve the plans before a building permit will be granted.

Many new house designs take time to develop fully to the satisfaction of a client, and a series of changes to the plan are requested by most purchasers. Also, if unusual materials or windows are specified, it may take a lot of time to locate and obtain these items. Therefore, it is necessary to allow three to six months from the time your design criteria are set to commencement of the actual building of the house.

MAXIMUM SIZE OF STRUCTURE

After the type of house has been decided on, the next thing to determine is the size of the house that can be built on a particular lot. Largely, this will be controlled by the municipal by-laws for that building area. The by-laws specify a setback that determines how far back the house must be placed on the lot. Sometimes the building line must be adhered to rigidly, so that the fronts of all the houses on a specific street will be in line. Some municipalities allow a variance, provided the minimal setback is observed.

A house is also required to have side yards. The requirement varies according to the type of house. A one-storey structure requires a smaller side yard than a two-storey structure, and a house without a garage will usually require a wider side yard on one side for parking. You should be aware that if a corner lot is selected, setbacks usually apply to the roads on the two sides of the lot. As setbacks are larger than side yards, this will mean that there is less area on which the house can be built. Most municipalities require a minimum back yard also.

Typical figures for setbacks and yards in a medium-sized urban area such as a community of 50 000 or less would be as follows:

POSITIONING OF HOUSE ON THE LOT	TYPICAL MINIMUMS	
	Metric	Imperial
Setback	6000 mm	20' - 0"
Side yards – one storey	1200 mm	4' - 0"
– two storey	1800 mm	6' - 0"
– no garage (one side of lot only)	2400 mm	8' - 0"
Back yard	7500 mm	25' - 0"

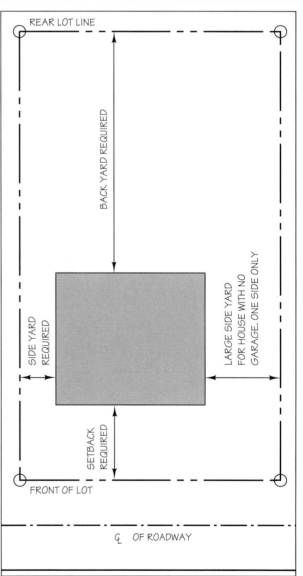

FIGURE 3-5 *Yard definitions*

ZERO-LOT-LINE

Some municipalities allow **zero-lot-line planning** in selected locations. Zero-lot-line planning allows greater density of single-dwelling housing in these areas; houses can be built on the lot line so that the lots are smaller and less costly. Cars are usually allowed to be parked in front of the house in order to further conserve space. Local authorities must be consulted before this type of planning is permitted *(see Fig. 3-6).*

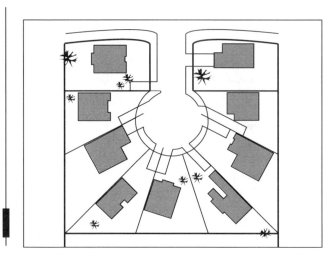

FIGURE 3-6 *Zero-lot-line planning*

REVIEW QUESTIONS

1. What factors make it necessary to select a lot before deciding on the house design?
2. What professionals will you need to hire if the house is not part of a planned residential community?
3. How is the maximum size of the house which can be built on the lot controlled? Who sets these conditions?

WHAT DO YOU THINK?

1. How can a purchaser's lifestyle affect the choice of a lot and house design?
2. Would you prefer to buy a lot in a standard subdivision or to buy an individual lot? What are the reasons for your choice?
3. What consideration will you give to the resale value when planning a house design?

ASSIGNMENTS

1. Collect at least six presentation drawings from newspapers or magazines. Try to include different styles and types of houses in the collection. If you can obtain some presentation drawings from publications that are several years old, you can make comparisons between the designs.
2. Collect at least ten current real-estate advertisements for new houses and for older homes. Compare the value of these homes considering their condition, size, amenities, and location. Select the one you feel is the best buy and state why.
3. Interview some homeowners and determine what made them select the home they currently occupy. Have them consider such aspects as location, community amenities, house design, etc. Find out what features were the most significant for them in making their choice. Write a one-page report.
4. Determine the maximum frontage for a two-storey house without a garage which is to fit on a lot plan supplied by your instructor. Draw to scale the standard setback and side yards appropriate to the house. Do not draw the house, but merely determine the maximum area of land that can be used for building. Dimension the maximum frontage of the house on the drawing of the lot.

UNIT 2

Orientation and Energy Conservation

OBJECTIVES

- To understand the effect that organic and solar orientation have on house design
- To orient a house in order to maximize advantages and minimize disadvantages of a lot
- To understand the difference between active and passive solar heating
- To appreciate the need for ecological concern and energy conservation

Some inconsistencies may exist between metric and imperial measurements in the following chapters because professional scales for metric

and imperial do not coincide. This will not affect the outcome of the assignments.

ORGANIC ORIENTATION

A house should be designed to take advantage of the physical features of the lot. The position of the roadway and structures on adjoining property will have an effect on the positioning of the new structure and the driveway leading to it. Windows should be placed to take advantage of more attractive views and to avoid unattractive views such as a factory or a parking lot. For example, a summer

FIGURE 3-7 *House avoiding an unattractive view*

FIGURE 3-8A   *Front elevation: side-split on sloped lot;*
B   *Side elevation: back-to-front split on sloped lot*

cottage will likely have its main room and large windows overlooking a lake, whereas a house in the city should be designed so that the main room and windows face away from any unpleasant view. The orientation of rooms will therefore be determined by such physical features.

General land conditions are important in the orientation and design of a house. For example, a side-split plan might be considered for a wide lot that slopes in the same direction as the front or roadside of the lot. A back-to-front split plan would be practical for a narrow lot sloping in the opposite direction *(see Figs. 3-8A and 3-8B).* Today, one-storey houses are often constructed with the narrow side facing the street because of small lot frontages. A narrow lot with not much depth will often mean that a two-storey house is the only possible design for that site.

SOLAR ORIENTATION

Between 1930 and 1970, when fossil fuels were comparatively inexpensive, North American builders tended to disregard some aspects of solar orientation for they could provide a house with economical heating and cooling. The advent of the energy crisis in the mid-seventies and the rise in the cost of electricity and fossil fuels forced architects to look more carefully at the orientation of their structures in order to conserve fuel. As a result, present-day houses are being designed with a greater regard for fuel conservation.

In the northern hemisphere, there are three types of climatic conditions to be considered when orienting the house on the lot:

1. The sun moves from east to west in a southerly arc and therefore will warm different areas during the day *(see Fig. 3-9).*

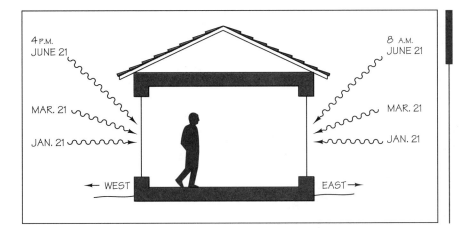

FIGURE 3-9

Sun angles at different times of the year

2. The sun is higher in the sky in the summer than it is in the winter.
3. The prevailing winter wind is from the northwest and makes the house cold by actually sucking the heat out of the northwest corner of the structure.

In consideration of these factors, several design ideas can be formulated:
1. Bedrooms and kitchens should have windows facing east to take advantage of the morning sun.
2. Garages, which are normally unheated, should be placed on the northwest side when possible.
3. Sunrooms and patios should have a south or southwest aspect in order to take advantage of the afternoon and evening sun.
4. All large windows should be placed on the south or west sides and windows should be limited in size and number on the north and east sides of the house. This arrangement allows sunlight to warm the house in the winter and will provide a through draft in the summer.

CONTROLLING THE MICRO-CLIMATE BY LANDSCAPING

The landscaping and design of a particular building can maximize or minimize the climatic effects or physical conditions. Evergreen trees appropriately placed can form year-round protection from winds, noise, and odours. The changing nature of deciduous trees can be used to shade the house in summer and to allow the sun to per-meate through the branches in the winter and help warm the structure *(see Fig. 3-10)*. Wide overhangs on the south and southwest sides can also screen out the sun in summer and allow the lower winter sun rays into the house later in the year *(see Fig. 3-11)*.

In this way, a **micro-climate** or a small localized area where the climate has been manipulated can be created so that the effect of the general weather pattern will have been altered to the advantage of the house built upon the lot. Not all the factors mentioned can be used in the same house, but the more that these advantages and constraints are taken into consideration, the more comfortable and economical the house will be. Further landscaping ideas are explained in Chapter 7, Units 1 and 2.

SOLAR HEATING

Because of the vast number of dwellings that require heating, the drain on irreplaceable fossil fuels is considerable. Two methods of using solar energy for domestic heating were developed.

1. **Passive solar heating** attempts to maximize the heat that the structure absorbs by correct orientation and by special design features of the house itself *(see Fig. 3-12A)*.
2. **Active solar heating** collects heat from the rays of the sun in panels and transfers this heat to storage tanks to be used on demand *(see Fig. 3-12B)*.

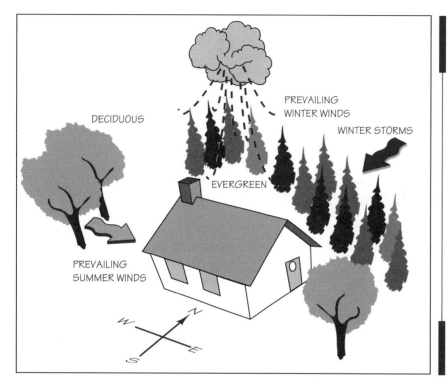

FIGURE 3-10
Orientation and landscaping to improve the micro-climate

DECIDUOUS

PREVAILING
WINTER WINDS

WINTER STORMS

EVERGREEN

PREVAILING
SUMMER WINDS

FIGURE 3-11
Roof overhang to control solar heating

JUNE 21

MARCH 21 OR
SEPT. 21

DECEMBER 21

The effectiveness of solar heating depends on the general climatic conditions in the area. In some parts of the world, solar heating may be the only system of heating required. However in Canada, where it is often overcast or where there are a high proportion of cold days, supplementary heating is necessary.

PASSIVE SOLAR HEATING

The house itself can be used as a heat trap, making heating a product of nature rather than of technical devices. Primarily, it is essential to insulate the house so that heat loss is minimal. Thicker studs of 38 mm × 148 mm (2" × 6") may be used in exterior walls to allow for additional insulation. The house should be enclosed in a vapour barrier with a minimal number of breaks and should be sealed with weather stripping and caulking to prevent energy loss. Insulating a house will be further discussed in Chapter 8, Unit 3.

A house that will benefit most from passive energy techniques will be one that is built with the principal façade within 30° of due south. In order to absorb the maximum amount of solar

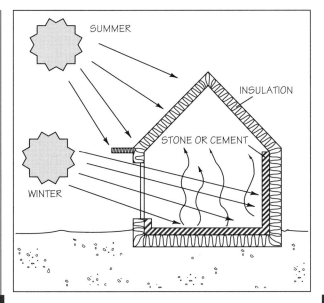

FIGURE 3-12A *Passive solar heating*

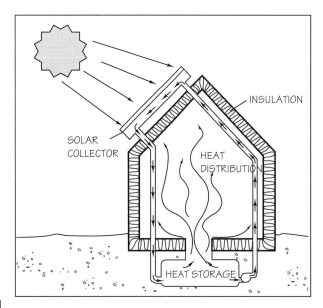

FIGURE 3-12B *Active solar heating*

radiation, the house should be shaped so that it is elongated along the east-west axis with the longer walls facing north and south *(see Fig. 3-13)*.

When the basic orientation of the house has been decided upon, attention can then be turned to the design of the house itself as a solar collector. To do this, large masses of masonry should be introduced along the south wall. This masonry mass will absorb the heat of the sun during the day and give it off during the cooler hours of the night *(see Fig. 3-14)*. A chimney correctly positioned can serve this purpose. A stone patio immediately outside a large window with a southern exposure or a tiled floor inside a large window will absorb the sun's rays and will produce the same effect.

Large areas of glass also assist in the retention of heat inside the house because of the **greenhouse effect**. This is caused by light rays that pass through glass being transformed into heat rays

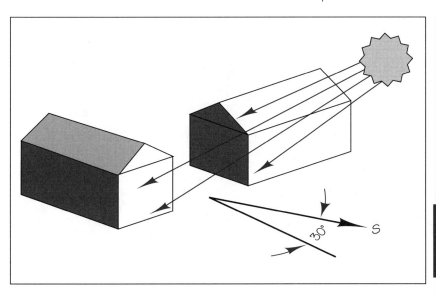

FIGURE 3-13

Optimum shape and orientation for absorbing radiation from the sun

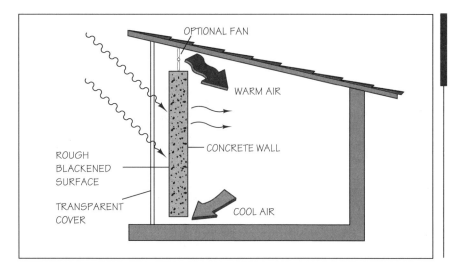

FIGURE 3-14
Passive solar heating design

OPTIONAL FAN

WARM AIR

CONCRETE WALL

ROUGH BLACKENED SURFACE

TRANSPARENT COVER

COOL AIR

that are unable to pass back through the glass. A common example of the greenhouse effect is the great amount of heat generated inside a car that has been parked in the sun.

The construction industry has developed a range of glass that can resist the amount of heat absorbed in the summer yet minimize the heat loss during the winter. This type of glass is valuable in avoiding extremes of temperatures in some locations. Manufacturers should be con-sulted for advice on the best locations for their products.

It is advisable to consult someone with solar heating experience before making any radical changes to the construction of a house in order to ensure that the building's heating system will be cost effective. The additional cost of installing aids for the reduction of heating costs must be returned in savings on conventional heating bills over a reasonable period of time.

FIGURE 3-15 *Solar house*
Home built by R.L. Meuser Construction Company. Home owned by Mrs. John Black. Designed by Clif Carey, AIA

FIGURE 3-16
*How the active solar-heating
system works*

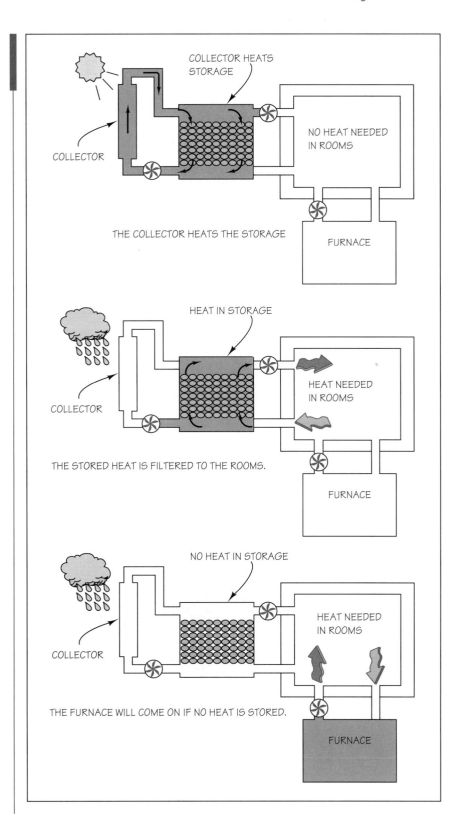

ACTIVE SOLAR HEATING

Placing collectors on the roof and storing the heat collected in tanks filled with water or rocks maximizes the heat collected. This heat can then be used on demand.

An active solar-heating system consists of at least two closed loops. One is a **collector/storage loop** *(see Fig. 3-16)* made up of flat-plate collectors that are directly connected to the storage tanks. The collector has an absorber plate, usually painted matte black, which absorbs the sunlight and transfers the heat to a liquid or the air. The liquid most often used is water that either trickles over the collector plate or is run through pipes that are an integral part of the absorber plate. It is important to have facilities for a down drain to avoid the water freezing in cold weather and when the system is not in operation. Air is also used as a transfer medium in flat-plate collectors and causes fewer problems (such as freezing or leaking) than a water system does. The front of the collector plate is usually glass to prevent the loss of heat and the back is covered with insulation for that same reason *(see Fig. 3-17)*.

Most active solar-heated homes have collectors that face south or up to 10° west of south. The tilt of the panels from the horizontal should be 15° greater than the latitude where the house is located for best winter heating. In Ontario, this means that the panels are approximately at a 60° slope.

The storage medium for a water system is usually a tank of water, which offers direct heat transfer. The tank must be well insulated to avoid loss of the heat that has been collected. Storage for an air system is usually rocks. Rocks are not as efficient for storage of heat as water is and to be effective, this system requires two-and-a-half times more volume of storage than water does. Storage tanks are usually sunk into the ground because of their size and weight.

The size of solar collectors and the volume of storage required will depend on the local climate and can be determined mainly by trial and error.

So that heat can be moved to other areas of the house as required, a **second** or **transfer loop** consisting of a heat exchanger, thermostat, and fans is needed. A forced-air system is useful for distributing the heat, and this system can also be used by the back-up conventional heating system.

Solar power can also be used to heat water for domestic use and for swimming pools by incorporating extra transfer loops. Solar energy can be engineered to provide a cooling system, as well.

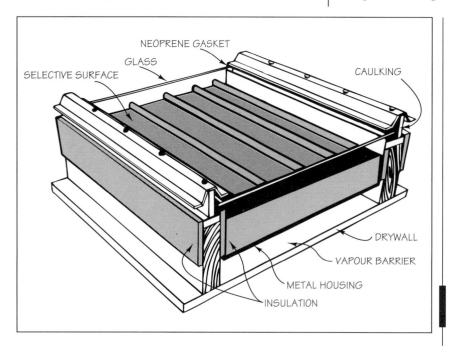

FIGURE 3-17
Typical flat-plate collector

Heat pumps are another method of producing natural energy for heating and cooling. A heat pump uses exactly the same technology as refrigeration, which takes heat out of food and passes the heat back into the kitchen. Heat pumps can also work in reverse, moving heat to cold and also cold to heated areas for air-conditioning.

Both heat pumps and active solar systems are costly to install so care should be taken to ensure that they will be cost effective by properly insulated construction of the original building. Active solar heating is most effective when installed in a passive solar house.

REVIEW QUESTIONS

1. What effect does the climate have on house design?
2. How might landscaping enable you to maximize the advantages and minimize the disadvantages of your lot?

WHAT DO YOU THINK?

1. What are the advantages in selecting the correct orientation of a house?
2. What factors should you consider if you plan to build a house incorporating either active or passive solar heating?

ASSIGNMENTS

Note: When drawing a site plan or a plan for a house, the front (or street side) is always positioned at the base of the paper.

1. Sketch an orientation plan of your own home or a friend's home showing how the house is located on the lot. (Pace out the size of the lot and house to estimate the sizes.) Use graph paper for the sketch.
   a. Determine the orientation of the house by observation of the sun. Place a north symbol on the plot plan and indicate nearby physical features of the lot.
   b. Briefly comment on the orientation of the house on the lot and state how the micro-climate might be improved by landscaping or altering the structure.
2. On the site plan provided by the instructor, determine the layout of the one-storey house shown in order to maximize the advantages and minimize the disadvantages of the orientation of the lot. Do this by indicating the living, sleeping, and dining areas as well as the kitchen, garage, etc., in the appropriate location and by suggesting some landscaping improvements. Retain this lot plan for future assignments.

SELECTION AND ORIENTATION

THE PROJECT

You are now about to start the project, which is to design step-by-step a set of presentation and working drawings for a house to suit a particular lot. The house design may be made using metric or imperial systems of measurement and may be drafted by hand or by CAD if sufficient computer time is available.

Step 1

a. Select a lot for a house that you will design as the major project for this course. Make an accurate drawing of this lot on an A3/A sheet of vellum at a scale of 1:125 (1 " = 10' - 0").

In construction lines, draw in the side yards and setback and determine the maximum size for the frontage of the type of house you wish to design.

b. Print a copy of this drawing, sketch the approximate size of the house, and indicate the orientation of the major areas of the house by showing living, sleeping, and service areas in the appropriate locations.

CHAPTER 4

Preparing Site Plans

SURVEYING IS THE NAME given to the science of measuring and describing in graphic form the physical properties of a piece of land. The original explorers of the North American continent recorded their discoveries as surveys. Early surveyors encountered several major difficulties in making accurate typographical two-dimensional drawings. These difficulties concerned the curvature of the earth and the large distances that had to be measured.

Geodetic surveying is a branch of surveying that deals with large land masses and the inherent spherical shape of the earth. **Land surveying**, which deals with relatively small areas of land, does not take into account the curvature of the earth.

In the past, surveys were made with instruments much less efficient than those used by professional surveyors today. Until recently, measurements of distances were made with a steel tape or chains.

The inequities between these surveys of the past and the highly accurate electronic measurements made today must be reconciled to the satisfaction of the official records and the present owners of the property. The relationship of current surveys to past records results in many legal disputes over land claims, as valuable pieces of property could be in question.

When we purchase a piece of property and build on it, we become involved with the survey process in order to ensure that the land we own is registered under our name and the building we place upon that site obeys the regulations that are set down in the municipal by-laws. These regulations concern location, zoning, and the adherence to the national and provincial building codes.

UNIT 1 | Introduction to Survey Plans

OBJECTIVES

- To recognize and understand symbols commonly used by surveyors
- To be able to read survey notes
- To calculate the interior angles and bearings of a lot from given data
- To be able to draw and interpret survey plans
- To determine the maximum building size for a lot

PREPARING SITE PLANS

Once a piece of property has been identified as suitable for a project, the next step in designing the building is to prepare a **site plan**. The purpose of the site plan is to confirm the correct orientation of the building and the maximum size of a structure that can be built on the site.

When a piece of property changes ownership, the local authorities have a method of recording the transfer of that property from the present owner to the purchaser. The location, boundaries, and area of the lot must be confirmed by a surveyor and then the deed and survey plan, which describe the lot, must be registered in the new owner's name at the local registry office by a lawyer.

THE SURVEYOR'S FIELD NOTES

The surveyor's primary measuring instrument is a **transit**, a small telescopic device set on a tripod. With this instrument, the surveyor can measure vertical and horizontal angles and judge distances and heights relative to a stable established height called a datum line. The universal **datum line** is sea level, which is constant.

The surveyor relates the measurements to **survey iron bars (S.I.B.s)**, which are semi-permanent markers that have been placed in the ground so that the top protrudes. These markers are numbered and their location recorded at the local registry office.

The surveyor's readings are recorded in **field notes** that are made after walking around, or traversing, the lot. These field notes are translated into bearings, elevations, and contours that appear on the **traverse** or **survey plan** of the property.

FIGURE 4-1 *A transit*

Courtesy of Construction Surveys

SURVEY CALCULATIONS

Surveying calculations make use of trigonometry, which is the study of triangles. Some understanding of this type of mathematics is necessary in order to comprehend and work with the information on a survey plan. The exercises that follow will assist you in gaining confidence in your calculations.

To draw the site plan, it is necessary to recreate the survey plan at a suitable scale. To do this, you must understand the relationship between azimuths and bearings and the relationship of bearings to each other.

BASIC CALCULATIONS

To *convert bearings* to *azimuths*, study the formula for each quadrant *(refer to Fig. 4-2)*. It is important, however, to remember the following:

An **azimuth** is an angle taken from the north in a clockwise direction *(see Fig. 4-3)*.
A **bearing** is an angular deviation from the north or the south meridian *(see Fig. 4-4)*.
The **meridian** is an imaginary line from the north to the south *(see Fig. 4-5)*. All bearings are measured from this line.
A **quadrant** is one-quarter of the full compass and therefore contains 90° *(see Fig. 4-6)*.

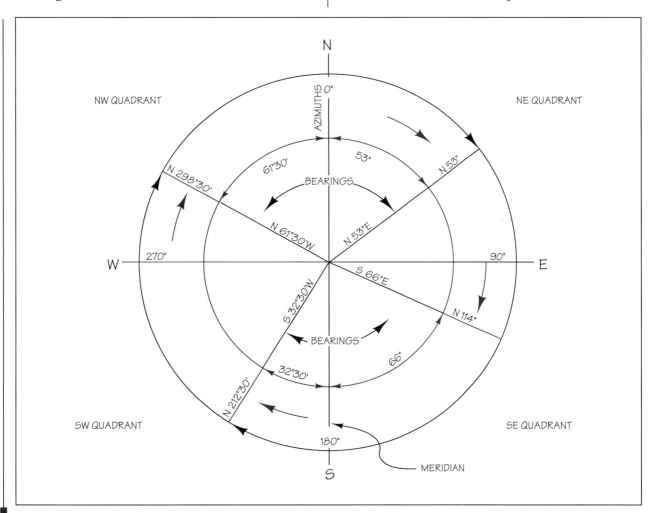

FIGURE 4-2 *Compass*

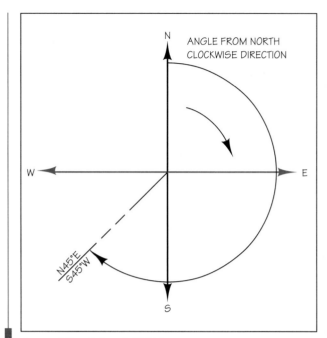

FIGURE 4-3   *Azimuth N 225°*

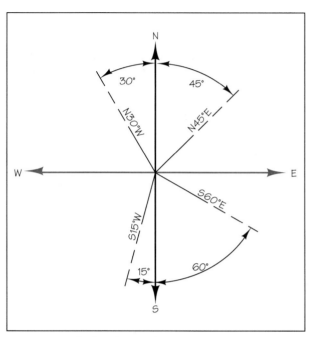

FIGURE 4-4   *The bearing angles*

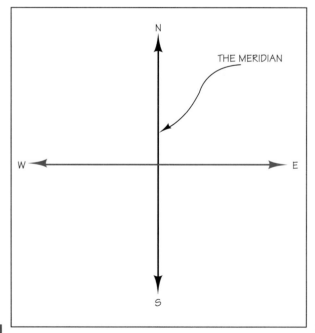

FIGURE 4-5   *The meridian*

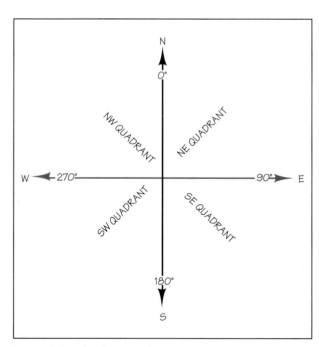

FIGURE 4-6   *The four quadrants*

NE QUADRANT

NE Bearing	=	The Azimuth
N 30° E	=	N 30°

SE QUADRANT

180° – SE Bearing	=	The Azimuth
180° – S 40° E	=	N 140°

SW QUADRANT

180° + SW Bearing	=	The Azimuth
180° + S 30° W	=	N 210°

NW QUADRANT

360° – NW Bearing	=	The Azimuth
360° – N 40° W	=	N 320°

DEGREES, MINUTES, SECONDS

Up to this point, we have worked with measurements in whole degrees. Degrees are further subdivided into minutes and seconds. There are 60 minutes in one degree and there are 60 seconds in one minute, similar to the division of time periods. In angular measurement, a minute is indicated by the symbol ' after the number and a second is indicated by the symbol " after the number. For example: 40° 30' 15". The base set is no longer 10 (or a decimal), so the calculations for bearings cannot be carried out on a simple calculator. Sophisticated scientific calculators are designed to do trigonometry and can be used throughout the survey calculations. If you do not have a scientific calculator, examples of manual addition and subtraction are shown below. Study them carefully before you proceed.

ADDITION

Deg.	Min.		Deg.	Min.	Sec.
89°	45'		23°	16'	30"
26°	15'		17°	45'	45"
116°	00'		41°	02'	15"

SUBTRACTION

Deg.	Min.		Deg.	Min.	Sec.
89°	00'		23°	16'	30"
26°	15'		17°	45'	45"
62°	45'		5°	30'	45"

CONVERTING AZIMUTHS TO BEARINGS

To convert azimuths to bearings, determine the quadrant in which the azimuth lies by referring to the following expressions and *Fig. 4-2*:

A NE Quadrant Azimuth is < 90°

A SE Quadrant Azimuth is > 90° < 180°

A SW Quadrant Azimuth is > 180° < 270°

A NW Quadrant Azimuth is > 270° < 360°

Study the following formulas and their application (*refer to Fig. 4-2*):

NE QUADRANT

Azimuth	=	NE Bearing
N 40°	=	N 40° E

SE QUADRANT

180° – Azimuth	=	SE Bearing
180° – N 120°	=	S 60° E

SW QUADRANT

Azimuth – 180°	=	SW Bearing
N 240° – 180°	=	S 60° W

NW QUADRANT

360° – Azimuth	=	NW Bearing
360° – N 290°	=	N 70° W

ASSIGNMENTS 1 AND 2

Conversion problem sheets 1 and 2 will be assigned by your instructor.

CALCULATING INTERIOR ANGLES

To calculate the interior angles of a polygon from given bearings:

The shape of a traverse (or lot) usually takes the form of a mathematical figure called a **polygon**. A polygon is a closed figure that can have any number of sides. The relative angles of the sides of a polygon must be such that the sum of the interior angles equals $(n – 2) \times 180°$, where n equals the number of sides.

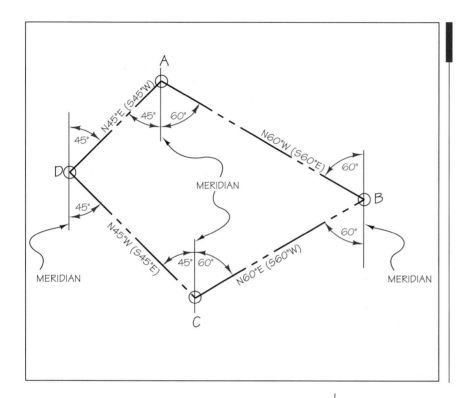

FIGURE 4-7
Calculating interior angles

Example: The interior angles of a triangle equal
$(3 - 2) \times 180° = 180°$
The interior angles of a rectangle equal
$(4 - 2) \times 180° = 360°$

To determine the interior angles of a traverse, draw in the meridian, or north-to-south line, through each corner of the property as indicated in *Fig. 4-7.* Indicate the angles to which the bearing angles refer. To calculate ∠A:
Add the two bearing angles,
therefore, $45° + 60° = 105°$
To calculate ∠B:
$180°$ – the sum of the two bearing angles,
therefore, $180° - (60° + 60°) = 60°$
To calculate ∠C:
Add the two bearing angles,
therefore, $45° + 60° = 105°$
To calculate ∠D:
$180°$ – the sum of the two bearing angles,
therefore $180° - (45° + 45°) = 90°$
∠A + ∠B + ∠C + ∠D = $360°$
The interior angles = $360°$

The sum of the interior angles of a four-sided polygon equals
$(n - 2) \times 180°$
$(4 - 2) \times 180° = 360°$
Therefore, the answer is correct.

ASSIGNMENTS 3 AND 4

Determine the interior angles of the traverses for calculation problem sheets 3 and 4, which will be assigned by the instructor. These exercises will give you confidence in later calculations.

CALCULATING BEARINGS AND INTERIOR ANGLES

To calculate bearings and interior angles of a traverse:

Sometimes not all of the bearings are stated on the field notes *(see Fig. 4-8).* Interior angles are given instead and the bearings must be calculated from these angles. To do this for a traverse, draw the meridians at each corner of the lot. Traditionally bearings, on a survey are always shown from the north.

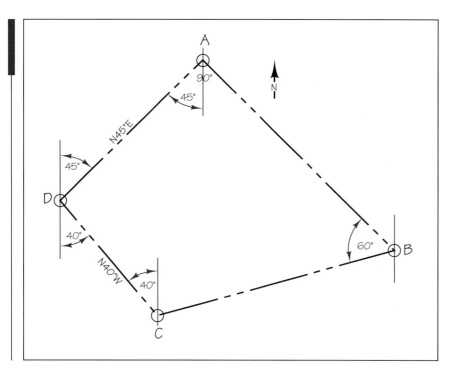

FIGURE 4-8
Calculating bearings and interior angles

To determine bearings AB and BC, which are unknown:

bearing AB = interior ∠A – bearing AD
  90° – 45° = 45°
  As a bearing, this is N 45° W.

bearing BC = 180° – (interior ∠B + bearing AB)
  180° – (60° + 45°) = 75°
  As a bearing, this is N 75° E.
  All the bearings are now known.

To check the correctness of the bearings, find the sum of the interior angles.

To determine interior ∠C and ∠D, which are unknown:

∠C = the sum of the bearing angles BC + DC
  75° + 40° = 115°

∠D = 180° – the sum of bearing angles AD + DC
  180° – (45° + 40°) = 95°

Therefore, the sum of the interior angles is

∠A + ∠B + ∠C + ∠D = 90° + 60° + 115° + 95° = 360°

The sum of the interior angles of a four-sided figure is
  (n – 2) x 180° = 360°

Therefore, the calculations are correct.

CALCULATIONS AND NORTH SYMBOL

To calculate a traverse with the north symbol at any angle:

On a survey plan, north is not always at the top of the paper. It can be at any angle but is always related to the angle of the bearings. To solve a traverse where this is the case, draw a meridian line through each of the points of the traverse parallel to the north symbol, as shown in *Fig. 4-9.*

To determine bearing BC, ∠C, and bearing DE:

bearing BC = interior angle – bearing ∠AB
  115° – 70° = 45°
  As a bearing, this will be N 45° W

∠C = 180° – (bearing BC +CD)
  180° – (45° + 30°) = 105°

bearing DE = 180° – (∠E + bearing AE)
  180° – (132° 30' + 11° 30') = 36°
  As a bearing, this will be N 36° W.

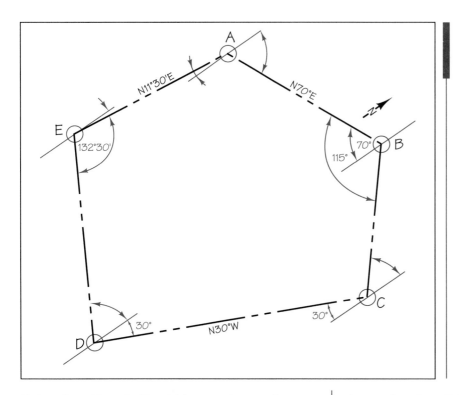

FIGURE 4-9

Calculations for a traverse with the meridian at an angle

Determine ∠A and ∠D, which are unknown, in order to check the interior angles of the traverse:

∠A = (180° − bearing AB) + bearing AE
       (180° − 70°) + 11° 30' = 121° 30'
∠D = bearing CD + bearing DE
       30° + 36° = 66°

∠A + ∠B + ∠C + ∠D + ∠E =
121° 30' + 115° + 105° + 66° + 132° 30' = 540°

The sum of the interior angles of a five-sided polygon is
       (n − 2) x 180° = 540°
Therefore, the calculations are correct.

ASSIGNMENTS 5 AND 6

Do the calculations to solve a traverse for assignments 5 and 6, which will be provided by your instructor.

DRAWING THE TRAVERSE

To draw a traverse of a convenient size for a site plan, it is necessary to use a reduction scale. A suitable scale can vary from 1:100 to 1:500 accord-ing to the size of the lot and the amount of detail required on the drawing.

To draw a property line at the correct bearing, use a protractor or an adjustable set square. Refer to Chapter 1, Unit 2, to ensure that you know how to use these instruments correctly. Draw the meridian and the east-west line in an appropriate location, using construction lines of a sufficient length so that either of the instruments can be lined up accurately. Draw the correct angle, using a construction line, and then measure the distance according to the scale being used. If north is not at the top of the paper, it is often easier to draw the bearing angles correctly if the sheet of paper is turned so that the north symbol points to the top of the bearing.

Property lines must be shown in the appropriate line style, namely long dashes alternating with two small dashes. The long dash should be used around each corner of the boundary line. Each corner or change of direction is further emphasized with a small circle.

Each property line should be dimensioned by a bearing and a distance. On survey drawings, it is

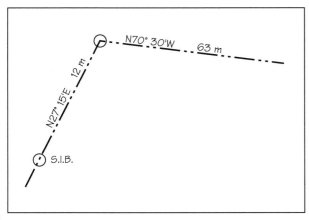

FIGURE 4-10 *Property lines*

common practice to give all bearings in relation to the north. All dimensions should be readable from the bottom right-hand corner of the drawing.

The information that must appear on each traverse or survey plan is as follows:

a. identification of lot
b. scale of drawing
c. date survey was taken
d. name of surveyor
e. north symbol
f. dimensions of bearings and distance for each property line
g. location of S.I.B.s
h. date of drawing
i. name of draftsperson

REVIEW QUESTIONS

1. Why do we call a survey drawing of a lot a traverse?
2. Why is it necessary to give the date when the survey was made?
3. What type of mathematics is used in survey work?

WHAT DO YOU THINK?

1. Why are bearings always plotted from the north on a traverse?
2. Why is it necessary to register the purchase of land at the registry office?

ASSIGNMENTS

Retain all traverse drawings assigned. Additions will be made to these drawings as you progress through this chapter and the chapter on landscaping.

7. A worksheet with a traverse will be supplied by your instructor. Do the following:
   a. Start at point A and proceed in a clockwise direction. Measure the bearings of each property line with a protractor.
      Example: Line AB has a bearing of N 22° E
      For greater accuracy in measuring with a protractor, extend the meridian and EW lines.
      When all the bearings have been determined, check that the sum of the interior angles equals the interior angles of a polygon with the same number of sides.
   b. Measure the length of each property line at a scale of 1:250 (1" = 20' - 0").
      Example: Line AB is 21 300 mm (67' - 0") long.
      Record your findings on the traverse worksheet.
   c. Redraw the traverse from your recorded figures.
      i. Use an A3/B size sheet of bond paper.
      ii. The scale of the traverse is to be 1:125 (1" = 10' - 0").

iii. The starting point A should be located 10 mm (3/8") from the left- hand margin and 100 mm (4") up from the bottom margin so that the drawing can be contained on the paper.
The completed drawing will be twice the size of that shown on the worksheet. Dimension the traverse appropriately. Place a circle in each corner. Give the bearing and distance for each property line and show the north symbol. Add the title "Traverse I" to the title block.

8. Draw a traverse for Lot 53, part of Concession 11, Westville, from the field notes given below, which were made on September 3, 1988, by Mr. Lisowyk.
   a. Use an A3/B size sheet of vellum.
   b. North is to be taken as top edge of the sheet.
   c. Start 25 mm (1") in and 25 mm (1") down from the top right-hand corner.
   d. The scale is to be 1:125 (1" = 10' - 0").
   From the most northeasterly iron bar of Lot 53, proceed S 27° 30' W for 26.5 m (79' - 6"). Turn 90° from this property line and go 27 m (81' - 0") in a northwesterly direction. At this point, the property meets a highway going due north and follows it for 12 m (38' - 0"). Then the property line goes S 71° 15' E and meets the final edge of the property, which is at an angle of 45° from the original property line.
   i. Calculate and show all bearings and determine all property line lengths. Check to see that the sum of the interior angles is correct.
   ii. Locate the survey iron bars and identify the lot.
   iii. Show all appropriate survey data, including the north symbol.
   iv. Add the title "Traverse II" to the title block.

9. Draw the following traverse from survey notes made on November 8, 1989, for Lot 64, part of Lot 4, Concession 10, North Park, by Ms.Balm.
   a. Use an A3/B size sheet of vellum.
   b. Orientation is such that the N meridian is 60° to the right of a vertical line. The assignment will be easier to draw, if the drawing sheet is placed so that the N symbol is upright.
   c. The iron bar is to be 10 mm (3/8") from margin on the left-hand side of the sheet and 75 mm (3") from the top border.
   d. The scale of drawing is to be 1:250 (1" = 20' - 0"). From an iron bar at the most northwesterly corner of Lot 64, proceed N 10° 15' E for a distance of 52 m (156' - 0"). At this point, the lot line bearing is N 57° 15' E and runs for a distance of 42 m (126' - 0"), where it joins a road that forms an angle of 105° with the property line. The property line follows the road for 33 m (99' - 0"), where it is intersected by a road running at right angles to the first road. The property ends along the road where a bearing from the original survey iron bar intersects it at N 74° 45' E.
   i. Calculate and show all bearings and determine all property line lengths.
   ii. Locate survey iron bars and identify the lot.
   iii. Show all appropriate survey data.
   iv. Add the title "Traverse III."

UNIT 2 | Trigonometric Construction and Calculations

OBJECTIVES

- To use trigonometry for practical purposes
- To read mathematical tables accurately
- To draw a traverse using trigonometric construction
- To calculate relevant data on a survey plan to the point of a partial closure

PLOTTING ANGLES FOR A TRAVERSE

It is difficult to maintain accuracy when drawing a bearing angle because even a slight deviation in the placement of the line that defines the angle will become a sizable discrepancy over a longer distance as shown in *Fig. 4-11*. Measuring a distance along a straight line can be done with greater accuracy than measuring an angle. Therefore, if trigonometric ratios are used to determine the relative lengths of the sides of a right-angled triangle that contains the relevant bearing angle, this angle can be drawn more accurately. The lengths of the *opposite* and *adjacent* sides can be plotted on two lines that are at right angles to each other and the *hypotenuse* can then be constructed by joining the ends of these measured lengths. By this method, the bearing angle contained in this congruent triangle will be drawn more accurately than if it had been drafted with a protractor or any other direct method of measuring angles.

THE TRIGONOMETRIC FORMULA

$$\frac{\text{OPPOSITE}}{\text{ADJACENT}} = \text{TANGENT OF THE ANGLE}$$

Therefore, opposite = tangent of the angle × adjacent

To apply the trigonometric method to the drawing of a property line with a bearing of N 60° 30' E, look up the natural tangent of the bearing angle in Table 3 of the Appendix.

The tangent of 60° 30' in the table is 1.7675; therefore if the adjacent line A is assumed to be 10 units long, the length of the opposite line using the formula will be 1.7675 × 10. The answer is 17.675.

Therefore, in plotting an angle of 60° 30' the length of the side adjacent to the angle is 10 units and the length of the side opposite the angle is 17.675 units.

METHOD OF DRAWING A TRAVERSE BY TRIGONOMETRIC CONSTRUCTION

(Follow Fig. 4-12.)
1. The meridian (N-S line) is drawn through the starting point of the property line X , which is to have a bearing of N 60° 30' E.

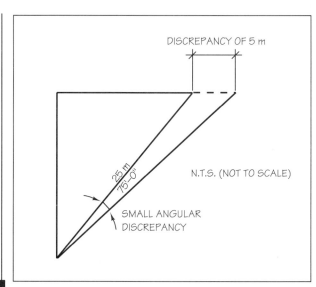

FIGURE 4-11   *Comparative discrepancies*

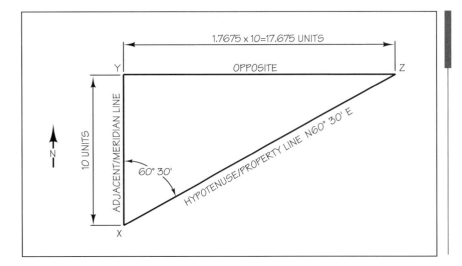

FIGURE 4-12

To draw an angle accurately by trigonometrical construction

2. Then, ten units are measured along the meridian from the starting point X. The ends of this line are X and Y respectively.

Note: A scale of any size can be chosen to measure the units provided that the same unit is used for the *opposite* and the *adjacent* sides of the right-angled triangle. A unit of 10 mm (3/8") is convenient for doing this type of construction on most survey drawings. However, if the bearing angle is greater than 70°, it may be necessary to use a smaller unit for this part of the construction to accommodate the greater numerical value of the opposite side, which will be determined by the larger tangent ratio.

3. From the Y end of the ten-unit measurement, a line is drawn at right angles; it represents the *opposite* or line YZ on the right of the meridian.

4. Measure 17.675 units along line YZ.

5. Join point X to point Z as shown. Line XZ will form the hypotenuse, which will define the bearing angle at point X with reasonable accuracy.

Note: If a northwest bearing is specified, draw the opposite line to the left of the meridian.

The hypotenuse will *not* be the required length of the property line but it is drawn at an accurate angle for the bearing. This line must now be adjusted to the correct length in accordance with the stated scale of the drawing.

This trigonometric method of construction should be followed clockwise around the perime-

ter of the figure until the traverse is completed *(see Fig. 4-13).*

CALCULATING A TRAVERSE TO A PARTIAL CLOSURE

A traverse is a mathematically closed figure. There is a relationship between all the angles and the lengths of each side of the traverse, just as there is for a triangle. Accordingly, the accuracy of all the dimensions of a traverse can be determined by using trigonometric ratios.

A schematic diagram of a traverse is shown in *Fig. 4-14.* It shows the traverse enclosed in a rectangle made up of a series of triangles of which the respective hypotenuses are the property lines. Following the direction of the surveyor in traversing the lot, arrows have been placed along the perimeter of the rectangle in a clockwise direction. It can be seen that if the sides of all the triangles are calculated, the sum of the distances making up the northerly side should equal the sum of the distances forming the southerly side. Also, all the lengths pointing in a westerly direction will equal all the lengths pointing in an easterly direction. If all the southerly distances are subtracted from the northerly distances the answer should be zero, and if all the westerly distances are subtracted from the easterly distances the answer should also be zero. If this is the case

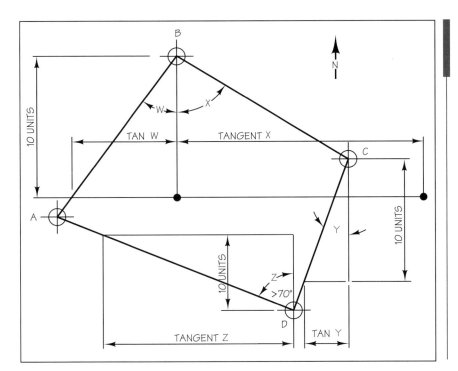

FIGURE 4-13
*Plotting angles for a traverse
with greater accuracy*

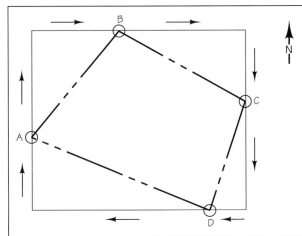

FIGURE 4-14   *Direction around a traverse*

then you have a **closure**. A closure proves that the relationships between bearing angles and distances are correct for the traverse.

To calculate a closure, you will require the following data, which has already been calculated for the traverse:
1. the length of the property lines
2. the bearing angles

A closure chart is shown in *Fig 4.15*. Your instructor will provide you with a working copy. It is simple to make a closure for any traverse if you transfer the relevant information from the drawing to the chart following the procedures listed below.

Start drawing a closure for Traverse I, which you have already completed as an assignment for Unit 1 of this chapter.

1. Letter the points of the traverse on the drawing in a clockwise rotation, starting at A .
2. In the first column of the chart headed *line*, enter the letters that have been placed at each end of the property lines, i.e., AB, BC. Continue until you have listed each property line.
3. Enter the length of each of these property lines in the distance column (2).
4. In column 3, headed "Bearings," enter the appropriate bearing for each property line.
5. From Tables 1 and 2 included in the Appendix, record in the next two columns (4 and 5) the natural cosines and natural sines for each bearing angle.

CLOSURE CHART

					6	7	8	9
					LATITUDE		DEPARTURE	
1	2	3	4	5				
LINE	DIST.	BEARING	COSINE	SINE	+ (N)	– (S)	+ (E)	– (W)

FIGURE 4-15 *Closure chart*

6. Sketch a schematic diagram for the lot on a separate sheet of paper, and place the arrows around the perimeter similar to *Fig. 4-14*.
7. Indicate in which column your answers should be placed according to the direction of the arrows on the schematic drawings. The *latitudes*, columns 6 and 7, will be either northerly plus or southerly minus. The *departures*, columns 8 and 9, will be either easterly plus or westerly minus.
8. Latitudes are calculated by multiplying the distance, which is the property line length, by the cosine of the bearing angle.
   Mathematical formula:
   cosine of the angle × hypotenuse
   = adjacent side.
   Work directly from the figures that you have recorded on the chart and enter your answer in the latitude column.
9. Departures are calculated by multiplying the distance, that is the property line length, by the sine of the bearing angle.
   Mathematical formula:
   sine of the angle × hypotenuse
   = opposite side.
   Work directly from the figures you have recorded on the chart and enter your answer in the departure column.
   Although you can accelerate the calculating process by using a scientific calculator, take care that all trigonometric data is duly recorded as you proceed. In this way, you can discover errors and easily make any adjustments.
10. Total the figures for each of the four columns.

11. Subtract the total northerly latitudes and the total southerly latitudes from each other.
12. Subtract the total easterly departures and the total westerly departures from each other.

In each case, the answer should be close to zero to verify the correct relationship of all lengths and bearings and to complete the closure.

CHECKING DISCREPANCIES

If there is a considerable discrepancy between either of the two *latitude* columns or the two *departure* columns, check the following points:

1. Are the answers recorded in the correct *latitude* or *departure* columns? This is the most probable error.
2. Are the bearings correctly entered against the corresponding property lines?
3. Do the distances correspond to the property lines as given on the traverse?
4. Have the tables been read correctly?

If your work appears to be correct and there is still a discrepancy, it is possible to manipulate the figures by adjusting angles and distances until the answers approximate zero. However, you must ensure that you compensate for any adjustment of an angle so that the sum of the interior angles of the polygon remains unchanged.

If your answer is a low figure, less than 5 for example, your calculations represent a partial closure and are acceptable at this level of study.

REVIEW QUESTIONS

1. Why is trigonometric construction a better method for drawing traverses?
2. How can you check your calculations if you use a scientific calculator?

WHAT DO YOU THINK?

1. Why is it necessary to make a closure?
2. Can you calculate to a closure if one of the sides of the traverse is a curve as might be the case if the property line ran along the side of a highway?

ASSIGNMENTS

1. Redraw Traverse I on vellum using trigonometric construction. Use your original drawing to plan all congruent triangles before proceeding. When completed, superimpose your second drawing over the original drawing to assess the improved accuracy of this method.
2. Using the existing information from Traverse I and with a form obtained from your instructor, calculate to a partial closure.

Notes on trigonometric construction to be used for Assignment 3

   a. If north on the drawing is at an angle, turn the paper on the drafting board so that north is pointing upwards. You will find that this makes it much easier to assess the direction of the bearing angles.
   b. On scrap paper, sketch a rough plan of the traverse by approximating angles and distances to determine the basic shape of the figure you begin to draw.
   c. Calculate all bearings and interior angles and record them on the rough plan. Check the sum of the interior angles.
   d. Decide how to plan congruent triangles on the rough copy.
   e. Look up the tangents of all the bearing angles and record them on the rough copy.
   f. Start drawing the traverse from the given data using trigonometric construction.

3. Draw Traverse IV for Lot 65, part of Lot 9, Concession 12, Brockford.
   a. Use an A2/C size sheet of vellum.
   b. North is to be 30° to the left of vertical.
   c. The starting point 75 mm (3") from the right-hand side border and 160 mm (6 1/2") from the top border.
   d. The scale of the traverse is to be 1:125 (1" = 10' - 0").
   e. Details of the survey are as follows:
      i.   From the iron bar east of Lot 64, proceed 28 m (84' - 0") at a bearing of S 56° 15' W.
      ii. Then go 36 m (108' - 0") at a bearing of N 39° 45' W.
      iii. Turn N 22° E for 25 m (75' - 0").
      iv. The most northerly corner of the lot is a right angle.
   f. The property line proceeds from this point southeast to join a property line from the first iron bar going in a direction of N 5° 30' W. By layout, determine all lengths and calculate the bearings for all property lines. Check with the calculations made previously and see that all the interior angles add up to the correct number of degrees for a five-sided polygon.
4. Using a form provided by your instructor, calculate Traverse IV to a partial closure.

UNIT 3 | Elevations and Contours

OBJECTIVES

- To understand elevations and contours on a survey plan
- To be able to interpolate contours from grid elevations
- To be able to demonstrate landscaping changes made by contour lines on a drawing
- To be able to draw a profile from a survey plan that shows contour lines

MEASURING SYSTEMS

The drawings in this unit are drawn to a scale of 1:250 or 1:125 for metric drawings or a scale of 1" = 20' - 0" or 1" = 10' - 0" for imperial drawings. *Note:* For this unit only, to accommodate imperial as well as metric measurement, the elevation measurements may be read either as metres or as feet. Although the units of measurement are not the same size for both systems, it will not make a difference to the usefulness of the assignments.

ELEVATIONS

In addition to plotting the lengths and bearings of property lines for the land enclosed, a surveyor has to measure the relative heights above a stated datum line. The universal datum is at sea level, as this is constant worldwide. A **bench mark** is a permanent stone survey marker recording a known height above sea level and the location. All subsequent heights can then be measured from this known site. In most municipalities, a prominent site is selected, such as the front of a civic building, and the height above sea level is accurately measured and recorded there.

Although sea level is the most universally used datum line, measurements may be related to some other datum line that is more local and therefore more convenient to use. For example, some municipalities may arbitrarily determine the datum line for various areas under their jurisdiction or a datum line may be set for a particular job by relating all heights to a stable level platform on or near that job site. The datum line, which is deemed to be zero, must be stated on all the related drawings. The surveyor measures the relative heights by using a transit and a measuring rod. Two levels are sighted on either side of the transit and any difference in the grade level can be measured from these readings. A series of such sightings is made to determine the differences in grade levels over a great distance. The recorded figures are then related to the datum line that has been set for that particular survey.

It is customary for a surveyor to measure the elevations for each corner of a property and to record them on the drawing of the lot *(see Fig. 4-16)*. On a survey plan, an elevation is indicated by a cross (+) or the letters *EL*. (Example: + 85.48 or EL 85.48, which indicates that the point is 85.48 metres [feet] above sea level or above the stated datum line.)

When making a plot or site plan, the builders will find it useful if the level of the finished floors of the existing structures is indicated. Also, the elevation of the base of a large tree should be given. This point should be marked on the plan with a cross. If any changes to the grade level of the property are proposed in the future, these figures will be required for reference.

CONTOUR LINES

If the land has a slope, **contour lines** are shown on the surveyor's drawing to indicate the degree of the slope. The closer the contour lines are to

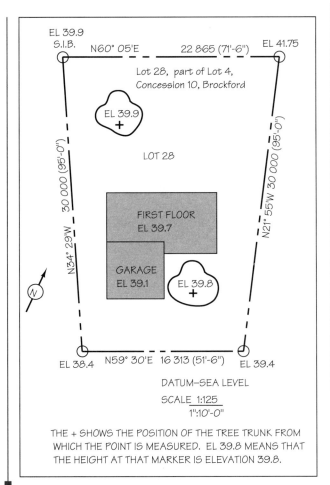

FIGURE 4-16 *Survey plan with elevations (Sample diagram – not to scale)*

each other, the steeper the slope. Contour lines that are far apart indicate a gentler slope.

A contour line indicates all of the points of land having the same height. Contour lines are usually drawn freehand or with a French curve (see Chapter 1, Unit 2). Each contour line is broken in a conspicuous place, and the height for that particular line is inserted in the space. The **contour interval**, which is the vertical distance between any two adjacent contour lines, is constant throughout a drawing and is usually given under the datum information. The size of the contour interval is dependent on the size of the area being drawn, the steepness of the slopes, and the use for which the drawing is made *(see Fig. 4-17)*.

INTERPOLATION

To determine exactly where the contours lie, the surveyor will stake out a square grid of an appropriate size on the property, measure, and record the elevation at each corner of the grid. By **interpolation**, which is the act of introducing new points in a mathematical progression, a draftsperson can then assess where the points indicating the height will fall and draw in the contour lines *(see Fig. 4-18)*.

In *Fig. 4-19A* you are shown a grid with elevations. The aim is to draw the contour lines on this grid by using interpolation. The contour interval for the grid is 2 and any lines you draw must be two units higher or lower than the contour lines on either side of it.

Start by selecting the elevation 102 on the left-hand side of the grid. By interpolation you must find all of the points of land that are 102 high. To do this you must find a figure that is higher than 102 in one corner of the same grid square and a figure that is lower than 102 in an adjacent corner. On the grid the elevation directly above 102 is 103 and, in the opposite corner, the elevation is 101. By interpolation you know that 102 lies half way between 103 and 101 and a contour line can be drawn to connect this point and the elevation 102 *(see Fig. 4-19B)*.

The elevations are decreasing in height so the next contour line will be 100. Continuing down the left-hand side of the grid we find figure 98 below 102. We can interpolate that the half way point on this grid line has the elevation of 100. This point can be connected to the measured elevation of 100 in the upper corner of the same square *(see Fig. 4-19C)*.

To complete this contour line 100, find the elevations on the top line of the grid which are shown as 101 and 98. You can interpolate that 100 will occur one third of the distance from 101 along this grid square. This point can be connected to the contour line 100 which has already been started *(see Fig. 4-19D)*.

The interpolations are continued at intervals of two until all the elevations have been included and the contour lines run off the plan.

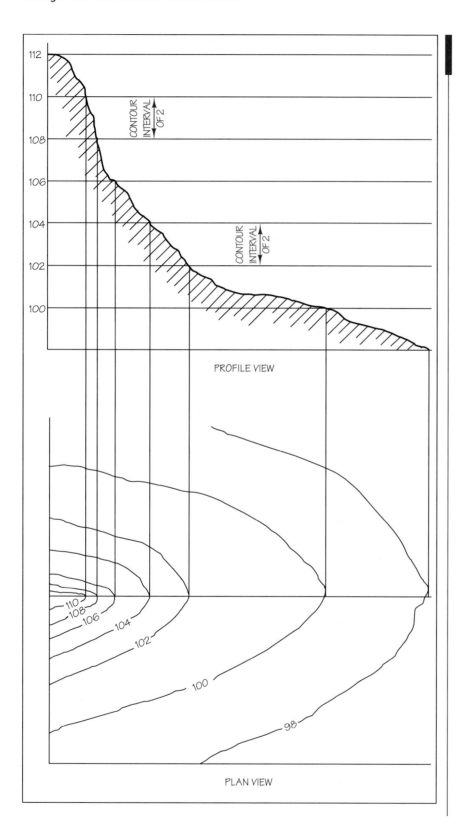

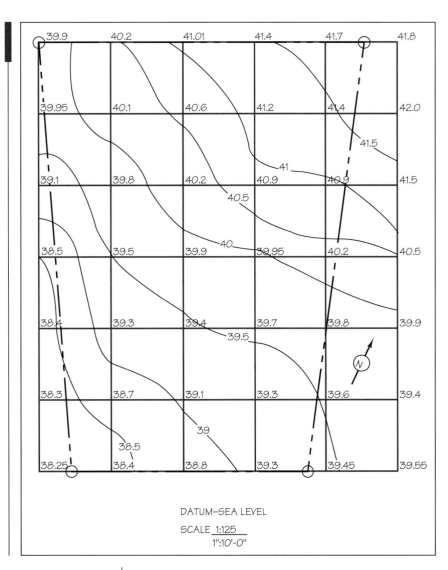

Figure 4-18
Survey grid and contours

DATUM—SEA LEVEL

SCALE 1:125

1":10'-0"

Each contour line must be labelled with the correct height placed in an appropriate gap in the contour line *(see Fig. 4-19E)*.

LAND PROFILES

Where changes have to be made to sewers or waterlines or to the roadbed, the civil engineer in charge will require an accurate drawing of the profile of the land where the work is to be done. This drawing will be an imaginary *cut* through a section of the land in order to show the shape and height of the property along that line, the depths of utility lines, and the levels of the roadbeds.

To draw a profile, first draw a line representing the imaginary cut or the **profile line** on the plan view where the section is required. This will not necessarily be parallel to the bottom of the plan but could be at any angle. On a separate sheet of paper, draw a series of horizontal lines to scale, the same distance apart as the contour interval. The series of lines should include one interval lower and one interval higher than the contours that cross the profile line. The sheet with the contour interval lines you have drawn should be

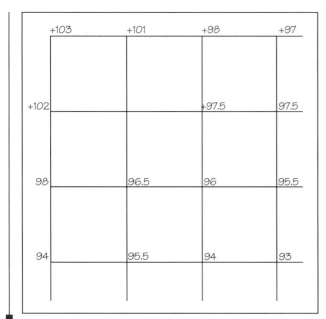

FIGURE 4-19A

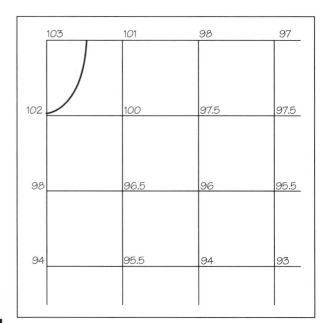

FIGURE 4-19B

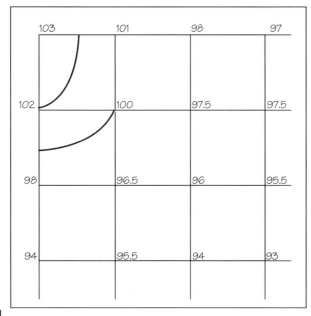

FIGURE 4-19C

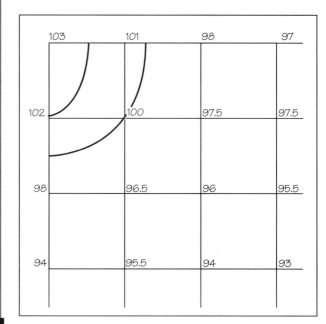

FIGURE 4-19D

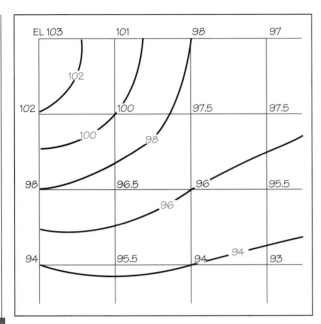

FIGURE 4-19E *Interpolation — grid and contours*

placed on the survey plan, below and parallel to the profile line you have drawn. Project the lines perpendicularly towards the grid from the points where the contours cut the profile line on the original drawing. The **grade level** at any particular point on the profile is where a projected line meets the horizontal line of the same value on the grid *(see Fig. 4-21A)*. Join all the points indicated

on the grid with a freehand line to form a drawing of the profile of the hill or valley. Cross-hatch the land side of the line to make the profile more visible on the drawing.

If you wish to compare two sections of land that lie parallel to each other, the resulting profiles can be placed on one drawing. If a change has been made to the contour of a piece of land, the *before* and *after* profiles may also be shown on one drawing *(see Fig. 4-21B)*.

If a profile is intended to convey a general impression of the slope of the land, as opposed to being used specifically for civil engineering purposes, it is advisable to use a scale for the grid heights that is twice as large as the scale that has been used for distances on the survey plan. As the distances will be plotted directly from the survey drawing, there will be a different scale for height and for distance.

The reasons for using two different scales on a profile drawing are:

1. Height and distance measurements are often unrelated in size, so the resulting profile would not be graphically appropriate if the same scale were used for both measurements.
2. A better visual impression of the slopes results because we tend to perceive slopes as steeper and distances as shorter than in reality.

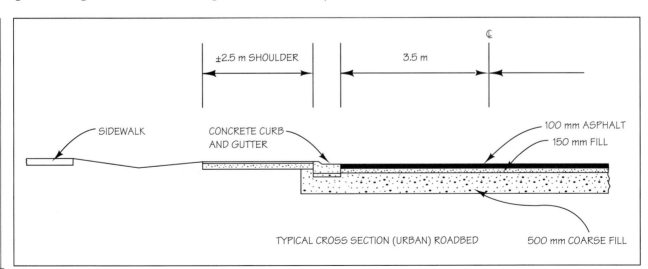

FIGURE 4-20 *Example of civil engineering profiles*

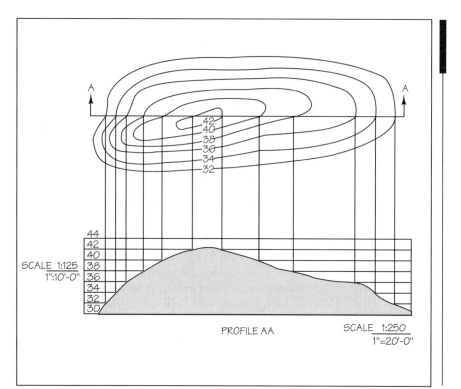

FIGURE 4-21A
*Profile section from contour lines
(sample diagram – not to scale)*

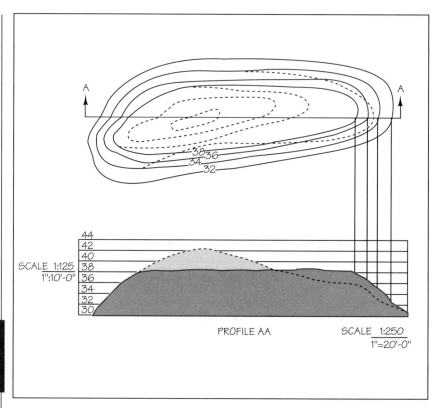

FIGURE 4-21B
*Profiles before and after
removal of hill
(sample diagram – not to scale)*

ADDING ELEVATIONS AND CONTOURS TO THE SITE PLAN

Elevations should be included for each corner of the lot on all site plan drawings. Contour lines should be added to a site plan if the fall of the land is greater than 2 m (6' - 6").

When a house is placed on a sloping lot, it is often necessary to change the gradient of the land to accommodate a specific feature. This feature could be a driveway, improved drainage, or an aesthetic consideration. To indicate such a change of grade, the deviation of the contour lines must be drawn as required. The original position of the contour lines should appear as dashed lines *(see Fig. 4-22)*.

Your notes at the bottom of the site plan should include the level of the datum line that has been used as well as the contour interval for the drawing.

ADDITIONAL INFORMATION REQUIRED ON THE SITE PLAN

1. The distance of the centre line of the roadway from the property line.
2. Locations and depth of water mains, sanitary sewers, storm sewers, hydro lines, telephone lines, cable TV lines.

Information regarding the position of all utility lines and road widths is usually readily available from a local municipal planning office or from the public utilities themselves. Utility lines should be drawn and labelled, and the dimensions of these lines from the property line should be given *(see Fig. 4-22)*.

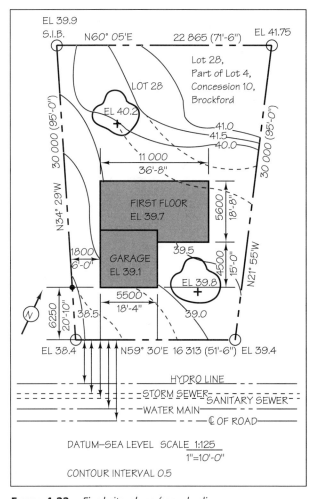

FIGURE 4-22 *Final site plans (sample diagram – not to scale)*

REVIEW QUESTIONS

1. What levels can be used as a datum by surveyors?
2. How are contour lines plotted?
3. Why and when is it permissible to use two different scales on a profile drawing?

WHAT DO YOU THINK?

1. Why is it necessary to draw a site plan?
2. When designing a house, would you prefer to work with a sloping lot? Give reasons for your answer.

ASSIGNMENTS

1. An interpolation grid (two copies) will be provided by your instructor.
   a. Draw in contours at a contour interval of 2. (The figures can be either metres or feet.) Use one copy for rough work and make one good copy to be handed in. All contour lines should be broken to show the height for that particular line.
   b. Make a profile cut along line C and draw the profile for it at the base of the sheet. Use 5 mm (1/4") for each contour interval division. Clearly indicate the heights on the grid lines and show the scales used along each side.
2. Draw contours on Traverse II, which was completed for Unit 1 of this chapter.
   a. Enlarge the contour plan you have just made from the grid to twice the full size. This can be done quickly by drawing an enlarged grid twice the size of the original and then copying the contours or by using a photocopier that will make an enlargement of the original.
   b. Trace the contours onto Traverse II. You may arrange the contour plan in any way you like, provided the contours cover most of the traverse.
   c. Interpolate the elevations for each corner of the lot and enter the figures on your drawing. Place three large trees randomly on the lot and give the elevation for the base of each tree trunk.
   d. Change the contour lines to form a flat area at the lowest contour level you have drawn on Traverse II. The level area is to be at least 10 m x 15 m (30' - 0" x 50' - 0").

UNIT 4

Garages, Driveways, and Parking Facilities

OBJECTIVES

- To appreciate the importance of adequate vehicle parking facilities
- To be aware of the acceptable sizes for garages, driveways, and parking spaces
- To determine the total amount of space required by various outdoor parking patterns and turn-arounds
- To be able to complete site plans by including garages, driveways, and parking facilities

PROLIFERATION OF MOTOR VEHICLES

On a site plan, a designer must allow sufficient space for vehicle parking. Modern private residential parking often has to accommodate automobiles, motorcycles, recreational vehicles, boats, etc.

Until the 1960s, a single-car garage was adequate for a family. A narrow, single-lane driveway gave access to the lot. In major urban areas, a single-lane mutual driveway was often shared by adjacent houses.

During the 1960s, the number of people owning automobiles and various recreational vehicles escalated dramatically. Today, most adult members of a household have their own car, so it is not uncommon to see three or four cars parked outside a single-family dwelling on a regular basis.

In newly built residential areas, two-car and three-car garages are not unusual. Many families who own a boat, for example, prefer to keep it under cover for a large part of the year.

GARAGE LOCATION

The average width of a residential lot now rarely exceeds 18 000 mm (60' - 0"); therefore, a multi-car garage must often be sited in front of the house. This has brought about changes in the design of many modern house frontages and floor

FIGURE 4-23
Houses with shared driveways
Canada Wide

plan layouts. The ranch-style single-storey house with adjoining garage, common in the 1950s and 1960s, is seldom built now because it requires a wide lot.

The best location for a residential garage is on the side of the prevailing wind, which is from the northwest for most of North America. A garage located in this position will partially protect a house from the winter winds. The remainder of the house will stay warmer, and heating costs will be reduced.

To minimize the formation of snowdrifts on a driveway or against the door of a garage facing north, some sort of screen should be provided on the northwest side, perhaps a fence, a wall, or a row of evergreen bushes or trees.

The garage or other parking areas should be located close to the side door or back door of a house to facilitate delivery of groceries and other services to the kitchen and utility areas. Also, the family and their guests will require easy access from parked cars to the front door. These factors should be considered when positioning the garage, parking area, and driveway.

GARAGE STRUCTURES

There are three ways of adding a garage to a residential property:

1. A **built-in garage** adjoins the house. It may have a room above it, in the case of a two-storey house, or additional rooms constructed behind it. The roof will usually form part of the main roof system *(see Fig. 4-24)*. This is the most common type of garage built in contemporary houses.
2. An **attached garage** adjoins one side of the main building only and has a separate roof structure *(see Fig. 4-25)* and requires steps into the main structure because of the difference in the floor levels.
3. A **detached garage** is a structure that is entirely separate and is usually built behind the main house. A covered walkway to the house is desirable. Your design should make the garage appear an integral part of the overall plan. This type of garage is often constructed after the main house is completed *(see Fig. 4-26)*.

FIGURE 4-24
House with built-in garage

Protective features such as fireproof walls and doors are not essential for attached or built-in garages where the housing unit serves only a single-family dwelling. Insulation is desirable whether or not the garage is heated.

A door that gives direct entry into the house from the garage should be weather stripped to prevent car exhaust fumes from entering the house. In some municipalities, the by-laws require an automatic door-closure device on this type of door. An entry from the garage should not be directly into a living room, dining room, or kitchen. It is desirable to have a small entry hall located between the garage and the house where possible, so that fumes will not enter the living area of the house.

GARAGE DIMENSIONS

A full-sized car takes up space measuring 1800 mm (6' - 0") in width by 5100 mm (17' - 0") in length. Even if a small-sized car is initially to be housed in the garage, allowance must be made for the possibility that a full-sized car or van may be owned at a later date. Within the garage, there should be a sufficient amount of clear space on either side of a car so that car doors can be opened fully and that passengers and their baggage can enter or leave the car comfortably. This additional clearance will make it easier to walk beside the car when entering or leaving the garage.

Frequently, a direct entry into the house is situated either at the side or the rear of the garage.

The garage floor must be at grade level if the car is to enter or leave the garage without hindrance; the finished floor of the house is likely to be at least 600 mm (2' - 0") above grade. Provision must therefore be made for a landing and two steps in order to allow access to and from the house. The space required for the steps will be additional to the space required to house the car(s).

Another popular residential feature is a doorway between the garage and the back yard. This feature allows the garage to be used as a toolshed and a store-room for sizable outdoor items such as a barbecue, lawnmower, lawn furniture, or firewood. Some people find it convenient to use the garage as a workshop. This means that more space must be added to the garage.

It is wise to design a garage that is as large as possible within the limits set by budget and lot size.

AVERAGE GARAGE WIDTHS

SMALL SINGLE	*LARGE SINGLE*
3600 mm (12' - 0")	4500 mm (15' - 0")
SMALL DOUBLE	*LARGE DOUBLE*
6000 mm (20' - 0")	7500 mm (25' - 0")
SMALL TRIPLE	*LARGE TRIPLE*
9000 mm (30' - 0")	11 400 mm (36' - 0")

AVERAGE GARAGE LENGTHS

MINIMAL	*GENEROUS*
6000 mm (20' - 0")	8000 mm (27' - 0")

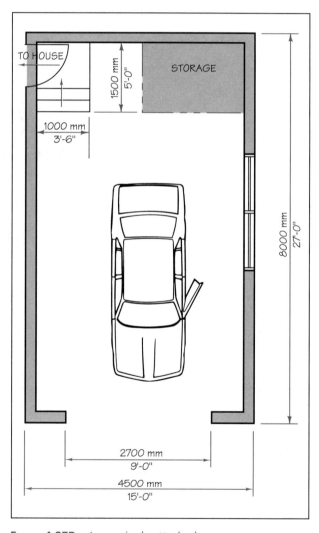

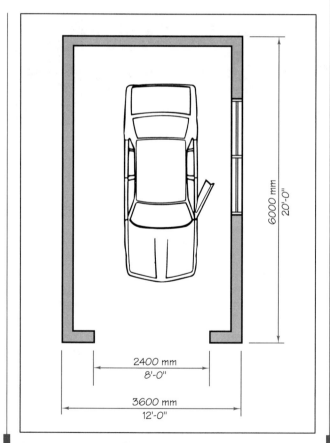

FIGURE 4-27A *Small single garage*

FIGURE 4-27B *Large single attached garage*

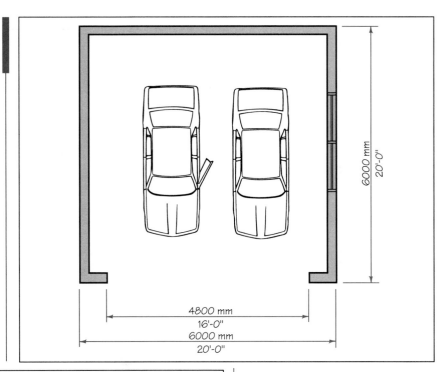

FIGURE 4-27C
Small double garage with double doors

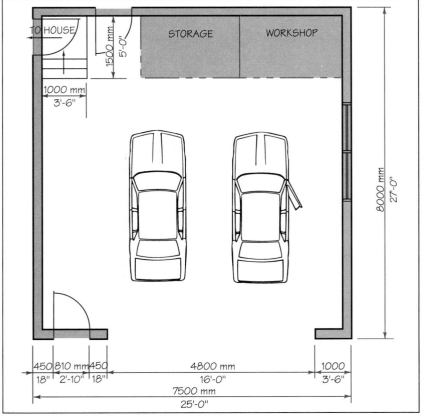

FIGURE 4-27D
Large attached double garage with double doors and side and rear doors

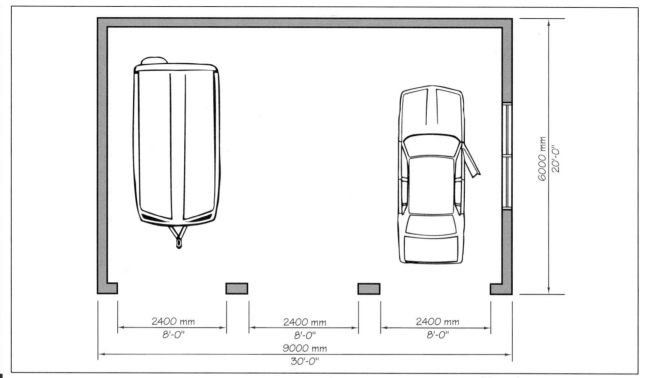

FIGURE 4-27E   *Small triple garage with three single doors*
FIGURE 4-27F   *Large attached triple garage with one double, one single, and a side and rear door*

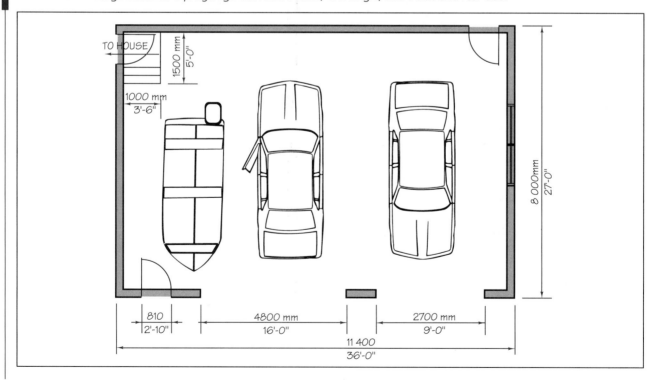

MINIMAL ADDITIONAL SPACE ALLOWANCE REQUIRED

LANDING AND STEPS	*WORKSHOP OR STORAGE AREA*
1000 mm x 1500 mm	1500 mm x 2400 mm
(3' - 6" x 5' - 0")	(5' - 0" x 8' - 0")

GARAGE DOOR SIZES

SMALL SINGLE
2400 mm x 2100 mm (8' - 0" x 7' - 0")

MEDIUM SINGLE
2700 mm x 2100 mm (9' - 0" x 7' - 0")

DOUBLE DOOR
4800 mm x 2100 mm (16' - 0" x 7' - 0")

GARAGE DOORS

Garage doors can be two swing doors, roll-up sectional doors, or overhead doors, the latter being the most common in contemporary houses. These doors can be either single- or double-car width. Aesthetic considerations often control which width of door is selected, as the size of the door affects the appearance of the entire structure. A double door is not as convenient as a single door, especially if it has to be opened by hand. However, automatic electronic door openers can be installed easily and relatively inexpensively. This allows a garage door of any width to be opened by remote control from within a car.

CARPORTS

A carport is a less expensive means of providing a degree of weather protection for a car. A carport has a similar roof structure to a garage and is the same size, but it lacks one or more walls, so it is not totally enclosed. However, a carport will provide shade in the summer and adequate protection from snow and rain at other times of the year.

Carports are usually attached to one side of the house and may provide a covered entry to a side door. They are designed so that a car can drive through them. This feature provides additional off-street parking and/or a turn-around area behind the house *(see Fig. 4-28)*.

DRIVEWAYS

A single-lane driveway should be a minimum of 2400 mm (8' - 0") wide. A double-lane driveway should be a minimum of 3600 mm (12' - 0") wide. A driveway should be even wider if it is fenced

FIGURE 4-28
House with carport and turn-around area at the back

along one or both sides. Fencing that is close to a driveway becomes a psychological barrier for some drivers as it may cause the driveway to appear narrower. All driveways should meet the roadway at right angles so that a vehicle may exit safely in either direction. It is also advisable to have a minimum 1000 mm (3' - 6") radius where the driveway meets the hard top of the road to allow for a smooth entry and exit. This is called a **flare**

A circular driveway must be wider than a straight one so that a driver may negotiate the curve safely. A single-lane circular driveway should be 3300 mm (11' - 0") wide and a double-lane circular driveway should be 4000 mm (13' - 0") wide. The minimum inside radius for a curved or circular driveway is 5400 mm (18' - 0"). The minimum width of a lot that comfortably provides space for a double-lane circular driveway is 20 000 mm (67' - 0").

Every effort should be made to construct a driveway so that it is level along its entire length. Ice and snow can make negotiation of the driveway difficult. A slope of one in three or a gradient of 100 mm:300 mm (4":1' - 0") is the maximum rise acceptable for a driveway *(see Fig. 4-29)*. If a

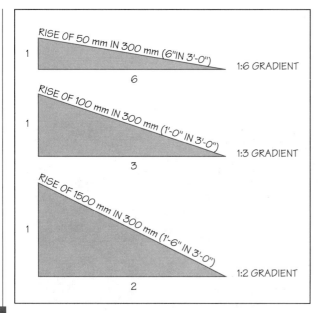

FIGURE 4-29 *Gradients — the slope of the land appears to be steeper than it actually is*

driveway has to be built on a slope, there should be a car-length portion of hard-top without gradient where the driveway meets the street. This will ensure that the car can be turned safely into the driveway from the roadway even when slippery road conditions exist.

In order to provide adequate drainage on the surface of a driveway, the crown, or centre line, of the pavement should be 150 mm (6") higher than the grade at the edges and should gradually slope down each side of the driveway.

ADDITIONAL PARKING

Apart from cars owned by members of the household, additional off-street parking is required for visitors and for delivery vehicles. Two or three parking places should be provided on a medium-sized or large lot, in addition to garage space. These parking places are often on the driveway. This arrangement can be inconvenient if there is frequent coming and going as this necessitates car jockeying, which could involve backing onto a busy street. If there is a double-lane driveway, cars can be parallel parked along one side without greatly hindering movement of other vehicles. Off-driveway parking is sometimes preferable but it can take up a great amount of space. If this area is paved, it will require less maintenance than a similar area of grass and it can be used as a recreation space when not occupied by vehicles. A variety of aesthetically attractive hard-top materials and paving stones have been developed so that a large paved area appears attractive.

PARKING AND TURN-AROUND CONFIGURATIONS

Angular parking areas, which are easier to get into than parallel parking areas, can be at an angle of 45°, 60°, or 90°. Less space is required for vehicles to back up if the parking angle is sharp, but a greater width of space is needed to house each car *(see Figs. 4-30A, 4-30B, and 4-30C)* for minimum space requirements for the various parking patterns.

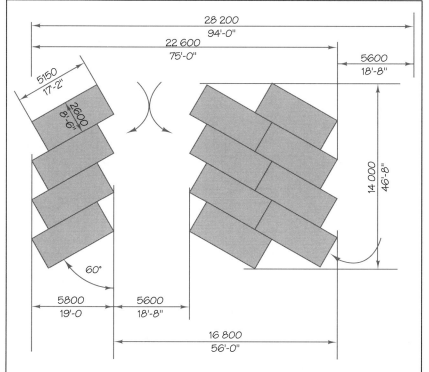

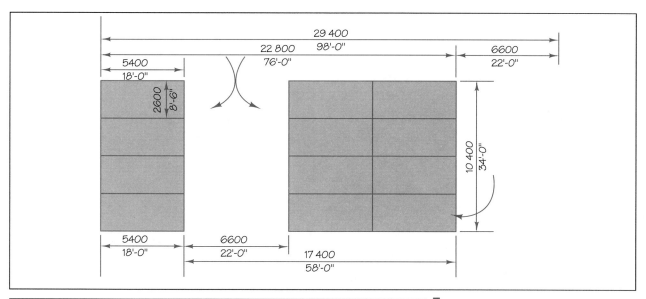

FIGURE 4-30A

Minimum space for 90° parking showing area for 12 cars

FIGURE 4-30B

Minimum space for 60° angle parking showing area for 12 cars

In order for a car to turn around, a hard-topped surface is a desirable safety feature, especially if the driveway opens onto a busy road. However, a turn-around space requires a very large area, as shown in *Fig. 4-31*.

When laying out a site plan, the location of the garage and driveway must be a primary consideration in order that access to roadways is as safe as possible.

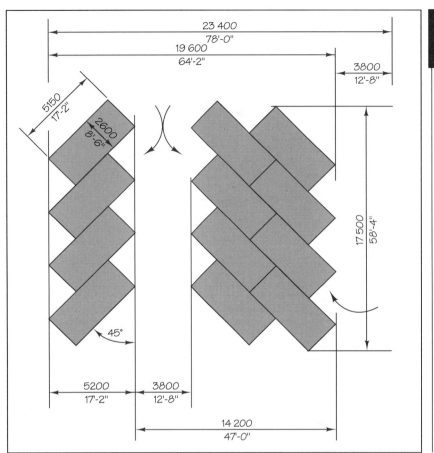

FIGURE 4-30C
Minimum space for 45° angle parking showing area for 12 cars

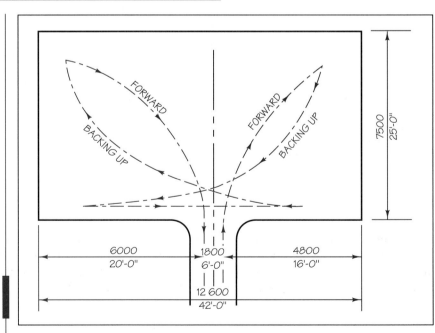

FIGURE 4-31
Typical turn-around space

REVIEW QUESTIONS

1. What size would you make an attached double-car garage if you do not intend to have a separate garden shed or other means of storing garden equipment?
2. What width of lot would be needed for a double-lane circular driveway and how much setback for the house would this driveway require?
3. How much back-up distance would you need for angle parking at 60°?

WHAT DO YOU THINK?

1. Which of the commercial parking lots in your area is difficult to drive into and which is the easiest to park in? State the reasons.
2. In your experience, does a difficult parking situation inhibit people from using that parking lot and the facilities it serves?
3. How can a residential two-car garage be accommodated on an average-sized urban lot?

ASSIGNMENTS

1. Add the garage, parking, and driveway facilities to the site plan that you have made of your own home, or a friend's home (Chapter 3, Unit 2, Assignment 1). Dimension these items. Measurements can be made by pacing the distances. Indicate how many cars can be parked on the lot at one time, including garage parking.
2. On a copy of the lot plan provided by your instructor for the orientation assignment (Chapter 3, Unit 2, Assignment 2), draw a garage as part of the structure. Add a double-lane driveway. Dimension all of these features.
3. Traverse III, which was drawn for Chapter 4, Unit 1, Assignment 9, is to be used as a parking lot for a baseball diamond on the grounds adjoining this lot. On the lot there is to be a clubhouse, consisting of a three-car garage at the front and a clubhouse at the rear which is 8000 mm (24' - 0") wide and runs the length of the structure. Locate the clubhouse on the lot, obeying the usual setback and side-yard constraints. Design the remainder of the property as a parking lot, making suitable allowances for back-up space both from the garage and the parking lot. Use a print of Traverse III to plan your work. Make a site plan on the original drawing.
   a. Dimension the following: the clubhouse and its location, an individual parking lot size, and back-up space.
   b. State the number of parking spaces.
   c. Indicate the traffic flow with arrows.

PREPARING SITE PLANS

THE PROJECT

At this point you will have selected a lot and have determined the maximum size of frontage for the type of house you are going to design.

Do Step 2, if this is appropriate to your course of study, then continue with Step 3.

Step 2

If you are studying the trigonometric construction method, draw the site plan as follows:

a. Redraw the survey plan using this method to fit an A3/B size sheet of paper. For an average-sized lot, a scale of 1:125 (1" = 10' - 0") will be suitable.

b. Make a closure for this survey plan on the form provided by your instructor.

c. Draw setbacks and side yards in construction lines and record the maximum frontage for the house at the bottom of the drawing.

Step 3

Using the original drawing of the lot made in Step 1 or the plan drawn in Step 2, prepare a site plan as follows:

a. Dimension the site plan fully, giving bearings and lengths for each side and include the lot identification, north symbol, and title block with all other relevant information. Keep all notes on the outside of the lot itself.

b. Draw the proposed size of the house you are going to design and give approximate overall dimensions. Note that this may be the maximum size allowable for the lot or less.

Do Step 4, if this is appropriate, and then continue with Step 5.

Step 4

Add the elevations for the corners of each lot and any other elevations that appear to be relevant to this site plan. If the lot is sloping, add the contours that may have to be adjusted to accommodate the house you have placed on the site plan. Also add any permanent landscape features such as an existing tree or pond.

Step 5

On the site plan, provide adequate garage, parking, and driveway facilities. The garage will usually be incorporated into the house design. Give the overall dimensions of the garage and driveway in order to complete the site plan.

Note: All the sizes given will be approximate and are meant for reference when designing the actual house plan.

CHAPTER **5**

Feasibility Study

SOONER OR LATER everyone currently in the school system will be faced with the task of finding living accommodation. This text was written in part to assist you in becoming an informed consumer and to increase your knowledge of the methods of financing, purchasing, designing, and constructing a standard house.

Most people who buy a house say that they own it. In reality, the greater part of the ownership usually belongs to a mortgage lender until the loan has been repaid in full. Legal ownership of a house is dependent on the purchaser's ability to maintain the payments over the life of the mortgage loan. This could be a 25-year period. Once a buyer is committed to the financial obligation that purchasing a home entails, that person gains an immediate sense of stability and a feeling of belonging to a specific community.

Pride of home ownership usually manifests itself by participation in local community affairs and in maintaining and improving the property. For these reasons, most government bodies support measures that will increase the number of homeowners.

When you are looking for new living accommodation, determine how much of your income you can afford to pay each month for accommodation and find out the standard of housing you can expect to obtain for that amount of money in a chosen location.

Your decision regarding how much you can afford for living accommodation should be made with great care as the amount of money you pay for rent or for mortgage payments will probably absorb a large part of your income for 20 years or more. Upkeep and maintenance costs are also ongoing and can absorb a large portion of an income.

Once you have made this financial decision, you can begin researching the availability of suitable housing. Some knowledge is required regarding the type of accommodation available in any chosen area and of the local house values, which can vary greatly from one area of a town to another.

You should conduct a substantial amount of research because your satisfaction with the dwelling will depend on many factors, ranging from good neighbours and local community amenities to the ease and cost of maintenance of the building. It is not always easy and is often costly to change a residence if it proves to be unsatisfactory.

UNIT 1 | Financing the Purchase

OBJECTIVES

- To assess affordability of accommodation with respect to income
- To appreciate the availability of various types of living accommodation
- To understand the responsibilities of buying or renting accommodation
- To understand how mortgages are applied
- To know the legal processes involved in purchasing a home

AFFORDABILITY

What a potential homeowner can afford to spend on housing is determined by gross income. **Gross income** is the total of all incomes before taxes including pensions, family allowances, and investment income. However, short-term income is not counted. If a member of a household intends to work only for a period of two years, this salary cannot be included since the expenses of the accommodation will continue after the person has stopped working. If a wage earner is subject to employment lay-offs, this must also be taken into account.

Normally, a household should not spend more than 25-30% of its gross income on housing. This amount of money should cover the mortgage and property taxes or the rental costs. An additional 5-10% of gross income will be put towards other expenses related to the accommodation, such as heating, electricity, water, maintenance, and insurance.

To determine the amount a household can afford to pay, use the chart below.

Gross Yearly Income
All Salaries $ _____
All Pensions $ _____
All Family Allowances $ _____
All Investment Income $ _____
                              Total Income $ _____
                              Divided by 12
                   Total Monthly Income $ _____

Housing Expenses
Monthly Mortgage (Principle, Interest, Taxes)/Rent $ _____
Monthly Expenses – Water/Electricity/Heating/Etc. $ _____
                   Total Housing Expenses $ _____

**Total Housing
Expenses** $ _____ Equals _____ % of **Total Monthly Income**

Affordability
15 to 25%   _____   Excellent
26 to 30%   _____   Good
31 to 39%   _____   Average
40% +   _____   Not Affordable

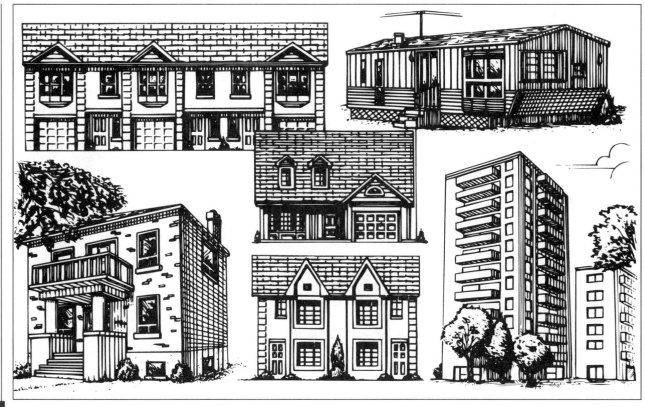

FIGURE 5-1 *Types of accommodation*

TYPES OF ACCOMMODATION

Once you have selected the community to live in, you must choose an appropriate type of accommodation. Listed below are several types of accommodation. However, not all of these options will be found in every community.

1. A **single-family detached dwelling** is one that stands on its own lot and has a private driveway. This type of house is usually one or two storeys high. This is probably the most costly type of accommodation related to the amount of living space.
2. A **semi-detached house** combines living accommodation for two families in one structure. The units are divided by a common central wall, and each unit has its own garden and private driveway.
3. A **duplex house** is a building in which the individual units are placed one above the other.

Usually there is a common entrance to both apartments and a shared driveway and garden.

4. **Row housing** includes a number of single dwellings that are separated from each other by common walls. Small garden plots are adjacent to each unit, and communal parking is generally available.
5. A **low-rise apartment block** will contain several units in a single structure. This type of multi-unit accommodation is not usually more than three storeys high. Shared garden and parking facilities are available. These are usually rental units.
6. A **medium-rise apartment building** has a greater number of units than a low-rise apartment block and is approximately six storeys high. Outdoor parking is available for these units, which are usually rental properties.
7. A **high-rise apartment building** contains a large number of units in a single structure that is more than six storeys high. Swimming pools, games

rooms, and outdoor facilities are frequently available, as well as indoor parking.

8. A **mobile home** is a factory-built house that has been designed to be transported along highways. Therefore, the width of the units is controlled. These units can be maintained as mobile homes or can be built into a site. This is the most inexpensive type of accommodation.

FINANCIAL INVOLVEMENT

The following options should be considered with regards to financial involvement.

RENTAL PROPERTY

Most rental units are **leased**. This is a signed agreement by the **tenant (lessee)** and the **landlord (lessor)** that the accommodation will be rented to a certain party for a set period of time at an established price. Most leases run for a year with the option of extensions. The lease will also set out a brief description of the premises, the condition of payment, and any other regulations concerning the management and maintenance of the accommodation. If the tenant must move before the prescribed date, it is usually possible to **sublet** the accommodation by getting someone to assume the remaining portion of the lease. However, it is advisable not to get involved with a lease if the lessees have reason to believe that they are not going to remain for the period of time covered by the lease.

Before signing any legal document such as a lease, read it very carefully to ensure that all of the clauses are understood. Sometimes additional payments must be paid by the lessee, such as local taxes and public utilities. Also the responsibility for the cost of redecoration and general maintenance should be clearly stated. Some of the advantages of renting accommodation are as follows:

1. The tenant has limited financial involvement – monthly payments.
2. It is quite easy to change accommodation.
3. The tenant has limited responsibility for maintenance.

4. No large initial payment is required, although the first and last months' rent are often paid in advance.

Some of the disadvantages of renting are:

1. The opportunity to capitalize on investment is non-existent. There is not a financial return when leaving and the tenant has no equity in the building.
2. Rents can be raised periodically.
3. An opportunity to make structural or extensive decorative changes is limited or non-existent.

CONDOMINIUM OWNERSHIP

Condominiums are most often units in an apartment or a row-house complex. This type of ownership is referred to as **strata titles** in British Columbia and as **co-ownership-immovables** in Quebec.

The owners of a condominium unit purchase the unit that they occupy, but the external spaces connected with the complex, such as walkways, parking areas, common halls, and stairways, are owned jointly by the collective owners of the building. The cost of upkeep of these spaces is covered by an additional monthly fee that is determined by a committee appointed by the owners and is liable to increase. In large condominiums, a corporation runs the site and employs a management firm to do the maintenance. Frequently, the monthly payments will include the mortgage, taxes, and maintenance costs. Sometimes the owners will be part of a co-operative that has the right to control the resale value.

Condominium ownership has become popular among families where the adult members of the family are employed full time and with persons who live alone, because this relieves them of the necessity of doing outside maintenance work themselves.

The advantages of condominium ownership are:

1. The buyer has the security of owning property.
2. There is the possibility of a capital gain on the investment.
3. There will be savings by group purchase of services and materials.

4. There is the convenience of home ownership with reduced liability for outside maintenance.

The disadvantages of this type of ownership are:

1. There is the necessity to comply with condominium regulations.
2. Improvements and maintenance are subject to the decisions of the board of directors.
3. Maintenance costs will probably increase.
4. There is less freedom to move elsewhere with short notice.
5. There is no private land.

SINGLE-FAMILY OWNERSHIP

If a person is able to make a long-term financial commitment, building a house or buying an existing house is a practical option.

To purchase a house, a potential buyer must make a sizable cash down payment and must be willing to pay off a mortgage in monthly installments that will usually be higher than those for comparable rental accommodation.

Most residential real-estate investments increase in value over the long term. However some properties do the opposite. A decrease in value may be caused by neighbourhood circum-

stances, such as by a municipal government action that causes a property to become less desirable. Examples of the latter would be construction of a nearby highway or a garbage dump.

The advantages of individual home ownership are:

1. The purchaser has independence of action.
2. The house is a capital asset that will probably increase in value.
3. The purchaser may recover the money invested when the property is sold.
4. Full legal title (ownership) to the house and land goes to the purchaser when the mortgage is paid off.
5. The purchaser has freedom to make structural or other changes to the interior and the exterior.
6. There is more incentive to improve a property.

Some disadvantages of home ownership are:

1. It is usually more expensive to maintain your own single-family dwelling than comparable rental property or a condominium.
2. A long-term financial commitment is involved.
3. A large cash down payment is required plus various fees and expenses, all payable *up front*.

FIGURE 5-2
Single-family ownership

4. There are ongoing maintenance costs and responsibilities.
5. There is less freedom to move elsewhere with short notice.
6. Selling a house usually takes time, and payment of legal fees is involved.

MORTGAGES AND FINANCING

Although a house or condominium unit can be bought outright, most people need to finance such a major transaction by means of a **mortgage loan**. A **mortgagor**, that is, the person or company lending the money, will advance approximately 75% of the appraised value of the house. The service of an approved appraiser will be required to determine the value of the property. Often the appraiser will be an employee of the lender. The selling price of an existing house is often higher than the appraised value so that the down payment required may be greater than 25% of the selling price.

The Canada Mortgage and Housing Corporation (CMHC), a federal agency that administers the National Housing Act, will guarantee the mortgage lender against financial loss for additional money if the buyer does not have 25% or more of the selling price required to close the deal. Accordingly, whether the house being purchased is new or a resale unit, a Canada Mortgage and Housing Corporation inspector will also appraise the property in these circumstances. He or she can oblige the buyer to make specific repairs or changes to the property, and until these are completed, the final loan will not be released by the lender. The buyer is responsible for insurance fees on the additional loan and for the inspection fee.

If a buyer is not able to obtain the additional loan through CMHC, he or she can often obtain money from other financial agencies, but the interest will be at a higher rate than that applied to the first mortgage and the loan will have to be supported by **collateral**; that is, the borrower must possess items that have a marketable value equal to the amount of the loan and that could be sold in case of default.

Requirements for obtaining mortgage loans vary from time to time and from place to place. However, it is unlikely that a house can be purchased through the usual lending channels without a substantial down payment.

A buyer may be in a position to make a down payment of more than the minimum amount. Naturally, the larger the down payment the smaller the mortgage payments will be. The total amount of interest paid also will be reduced.

In addition to the down payment, other expenses will be incurred during the purchase of the property. Inquiries should be made regarding these additional expenses before deciding on the amount that is affordable as a down payment. Listed below are the expenses usually associated with the purchase of a property.

1. appraisal fees
2. surveyor's certificate
3. lawyers' fees
4. cost of processing the loan (e.g., application fee)
5. mortgage insurance
6. municipal taxes and permits
7. down payment
8. essential major repairs to the house
9. moving expenses
10. new furnishings, window and floor coverings
11. new decorations

Allowance must also be made for ongoing maintenance such as exterior painting, roof repairs, etc. These will be minimal for a new house but could involve a large sum each year if the house is an older structure. An evaluation checklist similar to that shown below should be compiled to give a clear picture of the expenses and the conveniences of several houses in order to make a comparison.

Governments are keen to encourage home ownership so they will offer special concessions from time to time, such as income-tax rebates, to first-time home buyers. Sales tax on home purchases can be imposed by any level of government. Your lawyer will acquaint you with the current situation.

The availability of mortgages is not constant and varies with the economic climate. The period

HOME EVALUATION CHECKLIST

HOUSE NO. 1

Address _____
Asking price _____
Minimum down payment _____
Property taxes _____ Age of house _____

Style of House

Bungalow ❏   2 storey ❏   Split ❏

1 1/2 ❏   Detached ❏   Semi-detached ❏

Size of lot _____
No. of bedrooms/bathrooms _____
Garage/carport _____
Distance to:
elementary school _____ high school _____
shopping centre _____ church _____
Remarks _____

HOUSE NO. 2

Address _____
Asking price _____
Minimum down payment _____
Property taxes _____ Age of house _____

Style of House

Bungalow ❏   2 storey ❏   Split ❏

1 1/2 ❏   Detached ❏   Semi-detached ❏

Size of lot _____
No. of bedrooms/bathrooms _____
Garage/carport _____
Distance to:
elementary school _____ high school _____
shopping centre _____ church _____
Remarks _____

HOUSE NO. 3

Address _____
Asking price _____
Minimum down payment _____
Property taxes _____ Age of house _____

Style of House

Bungalow ❏   2 storey ❏   Split ❏

1 1/2 ❏   Detached ❏   Semi-detached ❏

Size of lot _____
No. of bedrooms/bathrooms _____
Garage/carport _____
Distance to:
elementary school _____ high school _____
shopping centre _____ church _____
Remarks _____

HOUSE NO. 4

Address _____
Asking price _____
Minimum down payment _____
Property taxes _____ Age of house _____

Style of House

Bungalow ❏   2 storey ❏   Split ❏

1 1/2 ❏   Detached ❏   Semi-detached ❏

Size of lot _____
No. of bedrooms/bathrooms _____
Garage/carport _____
Distance to:
elementary school _____ high school _____
shopping centre _____ church _____
Remarks _____

FIGURE 5-3
Professional assistance

over which the loan is to be paid back is usually from twenty to thirty years. This time is called the **amortization period**. The shorter the amortization period, the higher your mortgage payments will be *(see Table 12 in the Appendix)*. The payments are frequently calculated to include municipal taxes and insurance premiums and are usually paid monthly.

The interest to be paid on the loan also changes with the state of the economy. In recent years, interest rates on mortgages have varied from 9% to 20%. When a mortgage is arranged, a **term** is specified, which can vary from one to five years. This term establishes the rate of interest to be paid and for how long that rate will be guaranteed by the lender. At the end of this term, the mortgagor could legally demand repayment of the principal balance owing on the loan. This seldom happens as it is to the advantage of the mortgagor to maintain the loan. The new term will be at the current interest rate, which may be less or more than that paid during the first term, depending on the state of the economy at the time of renewal. Mortgage loans can be obtained from banks, trust companies, loan companies, and credit unions as well as from private individuals.

INSURANCE

To protect the lender from **default** (the mortgagee's failure to pay), most loans must also be insured. This cost may also be incorporated into the mortgage payments.

Fire insurance must be taken out at the time of purchase so that in the event of a fire, the full replacement value of the building is available to repay the mortgage balance.

Third-party insurance or civil liability can be obtained, which will cover the house owner's liability in the event that a visitor to the property sustains an injury.

Mortgage loan insurance is a form of life insurance; it ensures that in the event of the death of the owner or one of the owners, the balance owing on the mortgage is repaid. This type of insurance is recommended for families with young children so that if any of the wage earners die the survivors are protected against losing their home.

LEGAL PROCEDURES

When you buy a new or existing house, you will meet some necessary and quite complex legal procedures. You should hire a lawyer to oversee the purchase so that you can avoid errors or oversights that may cost money or result in the loss of the house.

The offer to purchase: To initiate the purchase, a written contract states that the vendor wishes to sell; that the purchaser agrees to buy; and that the price has been agreed upon. This document, the offer to purchase, is more than an offer; it commits both parties to the terms and conditions set down and should not be signed until the purchaser has made a decision and has consulted a lawyer. Usually the offer is conditional on the sale of previously owned property and the ability to obtain a mortage. A closing date is always given for these conditions to be fulfilled.

The transfer of title: A description of the property is contained in the deed, which must be scrutinized by a lawyer to ensure that the purchaser will have clear title to the property. If the purchaser and the lawyer are satisfied with the title, then the deal can be closed by the seller giving the purchaser a deed to the property and by the purchaser paying the balance of the price. Following the conclusion of this transfer, a copy of the deed should be filed with the local Registrar.

The mortgage agreement: This document states clearly the assumption of the debt by the purchaser and describes the financing conditions under which this loan will be paid off. If a borrower defaults in payment, the lender can take steps to acquire the property. If cash for the property can be paid, then a mortgage agreement is not necessary.

HOLDBACKS

Once the mortgage has been signed, work on a new structure can proceed. However, the money is not made immediately available to the builder, as the mortgagor has to establish that there is sufficient progress made at the site so that the money paid out can be redeemed in the case of default.

Building usually commences with funding from the down payment. A draw can be made on the mortgage money once the basement and footings are complete. This will usually be for 30% of the amount of the loan. A further draw of 30% is made when the framing is finished, the roof is on, and dry walling is complete. The remainder of the money will not be forthcoming until the house is completed according to the working drawings and the specifications.

REVIEW QUESTIONS

1. Approximately what percentage of income should be used for living accommodation?
2. What types of living accommodations are available?
3. What legal procedures are required to purchase a property?

WHAT DO YOU THINK?

1. Would you prefer to rent or purchase a property? Give reasons to support your decision.
2. Would you rather make a large or small down payment on a house?
3. What are the advantages of owning a condominium over an individual property?

ASSIGNMENTS

1. A couple are employed full-time. Their salaries are $35 000 and $30 000. A nephew is staying with them for three years while he is at college and contributes $3 500 annually for food and rent. The family receives family allowances for two children amounting to $65.50 per month. The family investments net them a further $6 500 per year. Calculate the maximum amount this family can afford to pay per month for living accommodation.
2. Collect information about the following types of properties from newspapers or obtain listing details from a real-estate office for:
   a. a rental property,
   b. the sale of an existing home,
   c. the sale of a new house.
   If possible, the properties should represent the same floor area. List reasons for any variations in cost price.

CHAPTER 6 | Design

THE **APPEARANCE** of a building, whether it is residential or commercial, is usually very important to the people occupying it. Our first impression of a building can make us feel comfortable, secure, excited, pleased, and satisfied, or it could make us feel uncomfortable, insecure, threatened, or dissatisfied. These impressions are often based on an individual's preference of style as well as the functional design of the building.

Our individual choices of style may be influenced by our culture, the type of home we grew up in, or social experiences such as travelling and visiting theatres, shopping malls, commercial buildings, art galleries, museums, etc. Even our personalities, size, general likes and dislikes can affect our choice of architectural style.

Designing includes the selection and arrangement of many components into a functional as well as an aesthetically pleasing design. Architects, designers, and draftspersons usually begin designing by making numerous rough sketches that show alternative ways of arranging the functional parts of the building. As the drawings proceed towards formal drafting plans, creative ideas to make the building unique and attractive are added. These are called the **aesthetics** of the design. Aesthetics means the beauty or *look* of the design. The designer must remember to harmonize both appearance and function.

A study and understanding of the fundamental theories of colour, design, and drawing are beneficial to the architectural student. Since today's society is constantly changing, an understanding and interest in social trends would also help in solving architectural design problems.

Almost everyone enjoys designing a dream home. As a residential design student, you have an ideal opportunity to do just that. In this chapter, several important areas in design are discussed that will help you understand how to create your own home.

The fundamentals of design, such as elements and principles, are explained in Unit 1. In Unit 2, more advanced approaches to design are clearly identified and explained. The third unit offers a brief historical overview of important architectural developments relating to residential building designs.

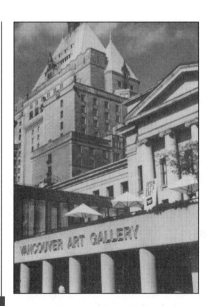

FIGURE 6-1 *Architectural style is an individual choice.*

The Province of British Columbia/Vancouver Art Gallery

UNIT 1 | Fundamentals of Design

OBJECTIVES

- To understand fundamental approaches to design
- To learn the elements of design
- To learn the principles of design

FUNDAMENTAL APPROACHES TO DESIGN

You will develop an understanding of design if you examine some basic concepts. There are *two* main approaches to take when beginning a design. The first approach is to consider the traditional styles of architecture usually called **period-style design**. This is the most commonly used approach to residential design in North America.

The second approach is to consider the **modern** or **contemporary styles**. This term is usually given to architectural designs that resemble the theories of one of the major schools of architecture called the Bauhaus school. This school began in Germany in 1919 under the direction of the architect Walter Gropius. The Bauhaus design theories stress the importance of function first; the style is typified by simple straight lines without unnecessary decoration or frills such as mouldings, carvings, or shutters.

The choice of approach by the designer may be governed by several factors such as the client's preference, the purpose of the building, surrounding structures, resale market, and building costs. Whichever style is chosen, the architect, designer, or draftsperson will use universally understood **elements** and **principles** of design.

ELEMENTS OF DESIGN

The elements of design consist of the six "tools" used by the architect to create the design, just as carpenters, bricklayers, or any trades people have

special tools that are used in their trade. It is very important to learn these elements and apply them to any architectural project in order to achieve a harmonious balance between function and aesthetics.

Line: The most familiar element to us is the line. We first learned to express an idea or picture by using a pencil or crayon to outline the shape of an object. Even as adults, we still sketch our ideas in line form first.

There are two basic kinds of lines: **straight** lines and **curved** lines. The design possibilities arising from using these two kinds of lines, however, are almost endless. Lines have several other important factors for the designer to consider. Our eye tends to move along a line, and because of this phenomenon, the line creates a sense of *direction* and *movement*.

There are four kinds of line movements:

1. **Static:** Horizontal lines and vertical lines suggest the least amount of motion because we expect things that are level or upright to be secure.
2. **Non-static:** Diagonal lines suggest movement of rising or falling, ascending or descending.
3. **Rhythmic:** Straight or curved lines that are repeated in a pattern create a rhythmic eye movement.
4. **Radiating:** When lines are drawn in a spiral or are arranged like the rays from the sun, the eye movement is directed towards the middle point or away from the middle point.

Form or Shape: The **shape** of an object is usually shown by outlining the edges. Shape has only two dimensions, width and height. In architectural design, it is more common to be working with **form** since it has three dimensions: width, length, and height. Unfortunately, the terms form and shape are commonly interchanged in daily use. There are four basic forms in architectural design. They are:

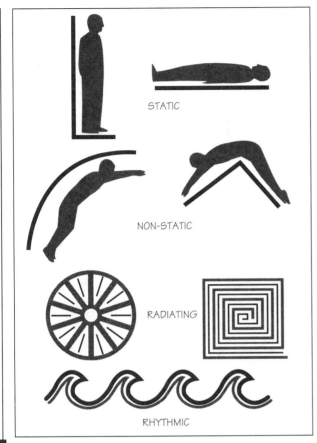

FIGURE 6-2 *Line movements*

FIGURE 6-3 *Shape and form*

1. the cube,
2. the sphere,
3. the cone or prism,
4. the cylinder.

Form creates **mass** and can be designed to look heavy or light. This effect depends on the size and type of materials used. The form of a building is usually determined by its function, materials, and costs.

Space: All forms occupy space, but in architectural design it is important to consider the space around the building as well as the space within

FIGURE 6-4
Visual spaces must be carefully designed in order to harmonize with solid areas.

W. McLennan, Museum of Anthropology, University of British Columbia

the building. The visual spaces must be carefully designed to harmonize with the solid areas so that both appear to function properly while remaining aesthetically pleasing.

Consider the space required by a common kitchen chair. We expect the chair seat to be 44 to 46 cm (17"-18") off the floor, the back to be 40 to 60 cm (16"-24") above the seat, and the seat to be approximately 38 cm (15") square. Further, if the chair is placed so that there is at least 38 cm (15") of space in front of the chair, we feel comfortable about using the chair to sit on because it looks right. Our spatial needs are usually judged by visually comparing space to our intended physical use. The space under, above, and around the seat area of the chair is both functionally and pleasingly designed.

FIGURE 6-5
Our spatial needs are usually judged by visually comparing space to our intended physical use.

You should consider how and by whom the building will be used, to allow proper use of space by people of all ages, including those who are disabled.

Light and Shadow: Human beings are very sensitive to the psychological effects created by the amount of light within a building. The proper use of light on forms and the consideration of cast shadows from forms can create dramatic depth to the building. Interesting patterns can also be created by use of light and shadow in the design.

Think also of the function of the building as it relates to the time of day. The architect usually considers the lighting needs for both functional use and artistic appeal and plans for both daytime

and night-time use of the building. Sometimes, because the lighting is wrong, expensive ornamentation such as carvings, mouldings, murals, or textured building materials are unnoticed.

Texture: The surface of building materials can range from very rough to very smooth and can have variations using both rough and smooth textures. This is called the **texture** of the material. Sometimes the texture is only visual, such as wallpapers, decorative laminates, or wood printed patterns.

If the designer uses an excessive amount of one texture, the design may look boring. It is better to have a variety of textures in your design so that it remains interesting to the eye and to the touch.

FIGURE 6-6 *An example of tactile design.*
Markham Suites Hotel Atrium Lobby — Courtesy of Markham Suites Hotel

This part of designing is often called **tactile** design and is used extensively in commercial buildings, particularly the lobbies, where water, plants, sculpture, or exotic materials are often used.

The designer will usually establish a major textural theme for the design and then add areas of other textures for contrast. Patterned materials can also be used to create the illusion of a change in texture. This is quite often seen in ceramic tile work.

Colour: The use of colour is an extremely important element. A general understanding of the language of colour can help the designer in applying it correctly to the design. Architects, designers, and artists work from a **colour wheel**, which is simply a chart that has 12 colours arranged equally around a circle. Three of the colours are called the **primary** colours. They are red, yellow, and blue and are considered first colours because they cannot be made by mixing any other colours together.

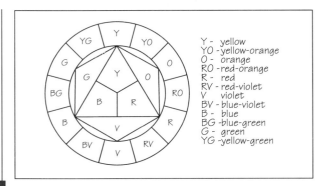

Y - yellow
YO - yellow-orange
O - orange
RO - red-orange
R - red
RV - red-violet
V - violet
BV - blue-violet
B - blue
BG - blue-green
G - green
YG - yellow-green

FIGURE 6-7 *Colour wheel*

The **secondary** colours are green, orange, and violet and are second because they are made by mixing two of the primary colours together in three combinations. Red and yellow will make orange; yellow and blue will make green; blue and red will make violet.

The **tertiary** colours are made by mixing a primary colour with a secondary colour. They have double names such as yellow-orange, red-orange, red-violet, blue-violet, blue-green, and yellow-green.

Colour has three main properties to consider: **hue**, **value**, and **chroma**. Hue is simply the name given to the colour such as red, blue, or brown. The second property, value, refers to the lightness or darkness of a colour. To lighten a colour, we would add white to it and to darken a colour we would add black or the colour directly opposite our colour on the colour wheel. When a colour is lightened, it is called a **tint** and when a colour is darkened, it is called a **shade**.

The third property of colour is called chroma or the intensity of the colour. This simply refers to how bright or dull the colour appears. A brighter colour means a higher chroma; the duller the colour looks, the lower the chroma. The intensity of a colour can be lowered by adding black or the opposite colour to it.

Here are some fundamental points to remember when using colour in design.

1. Warm colours such as red, yellow, and orange seem to advance or appear closer, while cool colours such as blue and blue-green seem to recede or appear farther away.
2. Bright colours advance while dull colours recede.
3. Tints of colour recede while shades of colour advance.
4. Tints make objects appear larger and lighter while shades make objects seem smaller and heavier.
5. Do not use too many colours in one design; use three at the most but use a variety of values.

There has been a tremendous increase in the desire for colour in the latter half of this century. People want designers to apply colour to most building materials. With the development of new plastics and lighting systems, it will be even more essential for the designer to understand the importance of colour. A current trend in modern home design is to design small areas of brighter colour as part of the exterior. This is done by taking the colour of the brick or siding and increasing the brightness of that colour as a wallpaper trim or flooring trim in the front entrance, or as the colour of the edging on the kitchen countertops.

PRINCIPLES OF DESIGN

Once the designer is familiar with the elements of design, he or she must learn the correct method of using them. This methodology is called the **principles** of design. There are six principles to use in an architectural design.

Balance: All humans have an innate sense of balance that is developed to a greater degree as they mature. You can probably recall learning to ride a bicycle or walking along a narrow edge, each time testing your balance. This aspect of feeling safe or secure is also present when we look at building structures.

People expect buildings to look perpendicular, level, or at least secure. Part of our judgement about how safe a building might be is whether it *looks balanced.* We are disturbed by things that are **imbalanced**, such as leaning walls, tilted stairs, or extreme **cantilevers**. The designer considers two kinds of balance. One is formal and is called **symmetrical balance**; the other is informal and is called **asymmetrical balance**.

FIGURE 6-8 *We expect buildings to look perpendicular.*

Symmetrical Balance: A teeter-totter is an example of something maintaining balance. A **fulcrum** is in the centre, and if two children of the

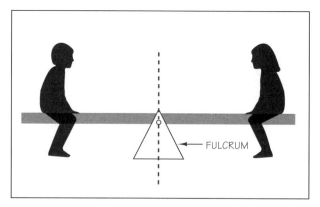

FIGURE 6-9 *Symmetrical balance*

same size and weight each get on an end of the teeter-totter, they are symmetrically balanced both physically and visually. As we look at the children, we tend to place an imaginary vertical line between them, and our senses tell us that they are equally balanced *(see Fig. 6-9).* When a building is designed so that the size and shape of the building parts are the same on both sides of an imaginary centre line, the building is in symmetrical or formal balance.

Symmetrical balance is usually used in the design of buildings and homes when a feeling of dignity, quietness, or historical importance is desired. The selection of exterior building materials is usually kept to one or two materials to create a formal, dignified look to the building.

Asymmetrical Balance: This type of balance occurs when the designer properly arranges parts of the building that are of different sizes, weights, or textures. Asymmetrical balance always relies on visual judgement since it cannot be measured or weighed.

Using the teeter-totter example, let us suppose that the two children are not the same size or weight. In order to make the two sides of the teeter-totter balance, we could place the larger or heavier child closer to the centre, or we could add another child to the smaller or lighter child's end of the teeter-totters. Our comparison of size and weight to the imaginary centre line in each case would cause us to feel that the teeter-totter now looks balanced *(see Fig. 6-10).*

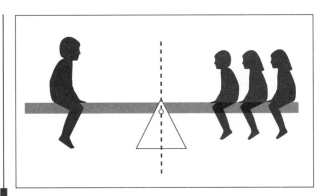

FIGURE 6-10   *Asymmetrical balance*

Asymmetrical design in architecture occurs when there are different sizes or numbers of building parts on each side of the imaginary centre line that are arranged so that they *appear to be balanced* in visual weight or importance. Asymmetrical balance is commonly used in architecture because the placement of doors, windows, chimneys, etc., is usually affected by the interior room requirements. Therefore, it is very important for you to study and practise asymmetrical design. It is considered to be informal because it creates more eye movement, excitement, and variation. The designer must consider the elements and principles of design very carefully when creating this type of design.

Repetition: Within a family, we see repeated characteristics such as hair colour, eye colour, height, weight, and build; these similarities tell us you belong together as a family. Architectural design uses the same principle to make all the parts of a building appear to belong together as one structure. Repeating the same forms (square, round, straight, and curved) inside as well as outside a building, and in the decorative parts as well as structural parts, unites the building, creating one design. This is called **repetition** of design.

Rhythm: The careful repetition of shapes, lines, or surfaces in a regular sequence helps to direct the eye throughout the structure, creating a sense of rhythm. Architects and designers learn to use subtle rhythmic designs with slight variations so that the design does not become too obvious or

boring. The design of the picket fence in *Fig. 6-11* shows the use of rhythm with repetition. Window treatments, colonnades, panelling, and brick work are areas where rhythm can be readily used in the design process.

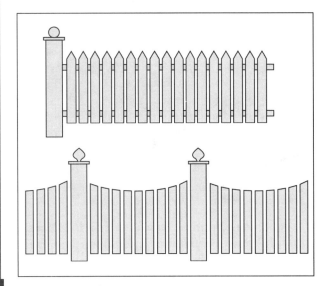

FIGURE 6-11   *Rhythm*

Variety: A building can soon become monotonous and boring if the designer has not added variety to the design. Two common mistakes in building design are a lack of variety in both the values (light and dark) and the textures of materials. Without some variety in these two areas, a building lacks depth and interest.

A foggy day appears to be boring because everything has the same value; speakers who never change their tone of voice sound boring. By contrast, a sunny day offers a variety of values and a singer a variety of sound. The designer must remember that the eye hears and feels as well as sees. Texture, light and shadow, and colour are elements that can add variety.

Emphasis: The face is usually the first part of a person that we notice. Throughout history, various methods, from masks to make-up, have been used to further attract attention to a person's face. For example, clowns emphasize parts of the face to create certain emotions.

FIGURE 6-12
Unity of design
Photo courtesy of Wolverine Technologies, Dearborn, Michigan

Architects emphasize parts of their buildings so that the viewer will notice those parts first, which will in turn create a certain emotion. Emphasis can be achieved by using contrast in size, texture, shape, colour, or balance. Emphasis, for example, is particularly used in designs for shopping malls to create a theme, a meeting place, or an unusual feature that distinguishes one mall from another.

Unity: Although designing a building requires the designer to consider special problems and functions of each part of the design, it is of prime importance that the finished building resemble *one complete structure.* There should not be any parts that look as if they are added on or out of harmony with the rest of the design.

For example, an orchestra sounds broken up as each instrument randomly tunes up. They become united into one beautiful sound by their conductor. The architect or designer adds unity to the design of a building by carefully arranging and using all the elements and principles of design.

Some suggestions for keeping unity in a design follow:

1. Keep visual lines such as roofs, windows, balconies, or mouldings at similar angles or parallel to each other.
2. Do not use too many different building material finishes on one building.
3. Use one style of architecture throughout the building.
4. If the design is an addition to an existing building, use the same style of architecture on the addition.
5. Keep one colour consistent throughout the design.
6. Make the proportions of the building visually pleasing.

REVIEW QUESTIONS

1. What does the term "aesthetics" mean in architectural design?
2. What are the four kinds of line movement in design?
3. What are the four basic forms used in design?
4. What is tactile design?
5. What are the six principles of design?

WHAT DO YOU THINK?

1. Why do you think most people like traditional house designs?
2. Describe how you would design your future home.
3. What do you think about the house designs in your neighbourhood?

ASSIGNMENTS

1. Using your t-square and set square, draw two simple line drawings of the front view (elevation) of a two-storey house that has five windows and one door. Make one view in symmetrical balance and the other in asymmetrical balance.
2. Using the outline of one of the fronts of the houses in Assignment 1 as a guide, sketch three designs — one that shows emphasis, one that shows texture, and one that shows repetition.
3. Draw a sketch of the front of a house in your neighbourhood and a sketch showing how you would improve the elevation using the principles of design.
4. Make your own colour wheel using coloured pencils or by pasting paint chips in the correct circular pattern.

UNIT 2 | Progressive Design

OBJECTIVES

- To understand human scale with reference to design
- To learn the design principle that form follows function
- To learn the fundamentals of straight-line versus curved-line design
- To learn transitional design
- To understand advanced design principles

HUMAN SCALE

Our feelings towards a structure are directly related to the proportions of a building— height, width, and length — as well as the proportions of all the rooms inside. We judge our feelings about the proportions as they relate to our human proportions; this is known as **human scale**.

When you go shopping for clothes, you subconsciously use human scale. You may try on several pieces of clothing before you choose the one that *feels and looks* just right for you. As an architectural designer, you will use the same approach in designing your house or building.

You feel most comfortable in a room when the width, height, and length allow you to move freely without having *wasted* space. You may feel detached from a building as it extends beyond your size. When a structure seems so large and out of your control, you can only look upon it in awe, without any sense of belonging. Some examples of buildings exhibiting this loss of control are cathedrals, the pyramids, or huge skyscrapers. This phenomenon also occurs when the proportions become much smaller than your human scale.

Designers consider that human scale proportions create dramatic effects for special areas such as family rooms, fireplaces, front entrances, or the overall exterior design. They can create the feeling of a massive area, a long or high area, an expansive space, or a private area. Human scale must be considered in the proportions of dining rooms, family rooms, kitchens, and bathrooms particularly, because they are actively used by various people. In order to establish human scale, a designer must consider *who* will be using the building and *what* the building is being used for.

FORM FOLLOWS FUNCTION

The design concept of **form follows function** came from the famous American architect of the late 1800s, Louis Sullivan *(see Fig. 6-13)*. He

FIGURE 6-13 *Sullivan's Wainwright Building*
Sadin/Karant Photography, Inc. 81318-F

believed that a designer should first consider the *function* or purpose of the building. If the functional plan is designed to do the job properly, the exterior shape or *form* will automatically be established. Further, if the designer uses the elements and principles of design on the exterior shape, it will be aesthetically pleasing as well. This form-follows-function style of architecture is also known as **functionalism.**

Louis Sullivan's form-follows-function theory was developed further by the Bauhaus school. This architectural style stresses simplicity of shapes, no frills or add-on decorations, minimum maintenance, and use of the then new technologically advanced materials. The expression commonly used to describe the Bauhaus theories is "less is more."

Although functionalism has been accepted in European design for decades, it is now becoming more popular in North American homes, primarily in kitchens and for appliances. The lifestyle of homeowners is vastly different than a century ago. The types of rooms needed in a house today are different. Today's faster, more mobile society with increased leisure time requires rooms such as recreation rooms, saunas, family rooms, as well as swimming pools, and these additions have demanded new ideas from designers.

Open-concept designing and multi-use rooms have developed because there is less concern about private areas in the home. The increase of radios, televisions, VCRs, etc., as well as more convenient appliances for cooking and cleaning has changed the function of some rooms in today's home. Individual style is created more through the interior design than the exterior design of the house; therefore it is common to see the same exterior house design repeated in one subdivision. Although functionalism is stressed inside the home, builders in North America still prefer traditional exterior designs because they are more popular for resale value.

As a designer, you must be able to blend traditional features such as columns, dormers, shutters, etc., with functional design. Individual style can still be maintained if you use the elements and principles of design wisely.

TRANSITIONAL DESIGN

Although most people have a preference for one style of house or building over another style, they usually combine several features into their own home. The mixing and blending of features taken from various styles is known as **eclectic** design, more commonly called **transitional** design. Extreme care should be taken when drawing transitional design since some features of one style do not harmonize with features of another style. A loss of proportions, unity, and aesthetics may result.

Some of the more common traditional features that people use in exterior design are columns, arches, shutters, dormers, and picture windows. Ornamental frills from past styles are also popular — stained glass, fancy mouldings, and intricate bricklaying.

Proportion is very important when combining these building features. Here are some points to consider about proportions.

1. Columns are proportioned by considering the height to the diameter. Try to keep a minimum height of seven times the diameter and a maximum height of ten times the diameter.
2. Shutters are designed to cover a window for protection; therefore, the width of a shutter should be one-half the width of the window and as tall as the window. Picture windows should not have shutters.
3. Dormers should be taller than they are wide.
4. Arches should be semi-circular or a segment of a circle and used in equal divisions so that there is not a part of an arch left over *(see Fig. 6-14).*
5. The proportions of a picture window should clearly make it either horizontal or vertical in design. Square is not pleasing.

If you are going to use transitional design, you should first decide whether your design will emphasize the classic style or the rococo style of design.

CLASSIC DESIGN

The main characteristic of classic design is the use of straight lines. The style was used during the Greek period, about 450 B.C., and used the principle of **post-and-lintel** construction *(see Fig.*

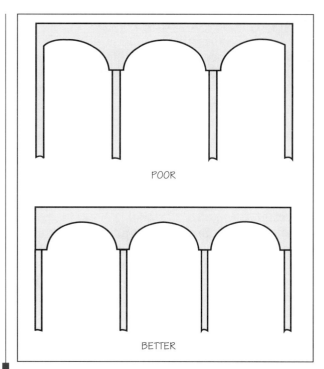

FIGURE 6-14 *Arch design*

6-15), more commonly known today as **post-and-beam** construction. The Romans continued to use the classic style and introduced the **arch** *(see Fig. 6-16)*. The arch allows greater spans because the wedge-shaped keystone in the centre transfers the weight of the load from the centre equally to both side support columns. Since the Roman arch is designed from a circle, the curved aspect of the design is also considered a classic. Classic or straight-line design can be found in many period styles of architecture but is especially apparent in modern architecture *(see Fig. 6-17)*.

Straight-line design is generally more economical to build and contains less material waste. You should be aware of proportions and contrast when using straight-line design to avoid monotony. Although circles or segments of circles harmonize with straight-line design, you should decide which of the two will be the dominating theme of your building; it should be either a circular structure with straight accents or a linear structure with curved accents.

FIGURE 6-15 *Post-and-lintel construction*

Courtesy of Greek National Tourist Organization

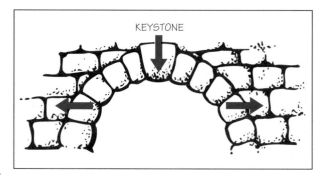

FIGURE 6-16 *The Roman Arch. A wall or another arch is needed to counter the outward force of the arch.*

FIGURE 6-17 *Straight-line design*

Cadillac Fairview Corporation Limited and Toronto-Dominion Bank.
Architectural Design: Mies Van der Rhoe. Opened: 1967

ROCOCO DESIGN

During the reign of Louis XV of France (1715-1774), there was an increase in **curved-line design**. This style was influenced by the discovery of Oriental textile patterns that stressed the sinuous, vine-like curves found in nature. **Rococo** or curved design is asymmetrical and uses informal balance. The graceful **ogee curve** (or S curve) became popular as corners for wall panels and wall brackets *(see Fig. 6-18)*. Floral carvings, curved ornamental mouldings, and curved staircases were commonly used in buildings exhibiting this style.

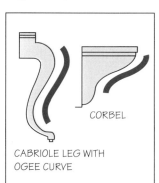

CABRIOLE LEG WITH OGEE CURVE

CORBEL

FIGURE 6-18
Curved-line design

Curved design is more difficult to build and creates more material waste. Curved design is used mostly in home landscaping or in swimming-pool designs, especially kidney-shaped pools. Commercial, industrial, or public buildings make use of curved design more often than residential housing, mainly because the added expense of construction is affordable for a large company.

If you choose to use rococo or curved lines for your house design, you should create contrast by using long curves and short curves together. The lines should flow smoothly from one direction to another as if they were growing from the stem of a plant.

ADVANCED DESIGN PRINCIPLES

As you become more skilled at applying the elements and principles of design to your work, you may wish to experiment with more challenging concepts. These advanced principles will help you to maintain unity in your design while allowing you more creative expression. Although there are numerous principles to learn, three of the most important principles are subordination, spatial proportions, and optical balance.

SUBORDINATION

Although every part of a building should be given careful design consideration, there should be one main focal point to the design. Designers rank parts of a building in importance from a visual viewpoint. This is one form of **subordination**. In most house designs, the most important part is the front entrance and other parts of the building should not detract from it. The entrance should look attractive and interesting and should welcome visitors. This visual effect can be created by careful use of proportions, materials, colour, and landscaping.

Subordination is also used in planning the room layouts of the house. If it is necessary to reduce the overall size of the house or to remove some rooms, the designer will refer to the subordinate list compiled with the client. The plan will be redesigned to leave in the most important rooms and to reduce or eliminate altogether the less important rooms. An example of this type of subordination is that the number of bedrooms or bathrooms to be in the home are often changed.

A third kind of subordination involves the building materials for the exterior. Your design will look better if you use only one or two building materials for the wall finishes, rather than a variety of materials. One material should dominate and the other should accent or complement the structure. As an example, the building could be primarily brick with some fieldstone for accent. The front elevation is usually given the priority in appearance, but you should also design all elevations to harmonize so that you do not create a false-front look to your design.

SPATIAL PROPORTIONS

The consideration of space in architectural design involves not only the building itself but its relationship to the lot and the neighbourhood. Local regulations will establish minimum and maximum boundaries, but the designer must consider the proportions of space within these restrictions. The most commonly built houses today are two-storey and split-entry. Because of the reduced size of suburban building lots *(see Fig. 6-19)*, these house designs can sometimes appear too large for the lot or too crowded in relation to the houses on each side.

As the designer, you should consider the proportions of the garage, front entrance, roof overhang, roof pitch, and area covered by certain materials, to maintain the aesthetic proportions of the house to the lot. You must also consider the space around the house in relation to the house. Sometimes the design may look better on the lot if the plan is reversed or flopped. For example, it would be better not to have two projecting garages side by side on two lots because they will appear to be too massive in proportion to either house, as well as the front yard of the houses *(see Fig. 6-20)*.

Excessive roof overhangs, particularly over the front entrance, can make the roof appear too dominant or the entrance door appear insignificant. If you wish to use a different material for the upper storey of the house, consider the proportions between the lower and upper structure. Avoid visually cutting the design in half. Your design will look better if one material appears in greater quantity than the other.

An interesting and important design principle of proportions is the use of three or odd numbers of segments. People prefer arrangements in groups of three or odd numbers as compared to groups of two or even numbers. This psychological phenomenon was discovered by the Greeks and is still used by designers today. The principle of three suggests that there should be one large item, one medium item, and one small item used in the arrangement. Ideally in a house design, the dominant item would be the house, the secondary item the front entrance, and the third item

FIGURE 6-19
Spatial proportions

Figure 6-20
*New houses with garages
side by side*

Figure 6-20
*New houses with garages
side by side*

the garage. This relationship is difficult to maintain because the garage is more massive than the entrance, but a designer can often correct the problem with landscaping and the careful use of optical balance.

OPTICAL BALANCE

Optical balance and interest are dependent upon one another. Whenever we look at a house, one part of it will attract our interest more than the rest. If the house is well designed, our attention will be directed to the entrance in such a way that the house, the landscaping, and the garage will all appear to be balanced. Simultaneously, our interest will be aroused in several ways.

The designer can arouse interest and achieve optical balance by the careful placement of shapes, textures, colour values, and space. As well, the designer can maintain balance through the use of eye direction. The following points will help you to maintain optical balance in your designs.

1. Place contrasting shapes near the entrance to the house or near the focal point of the building.
2. If there is more contrast of textures between materials, they will attract more interest.
3. Bright colours attract the eye more than dull colours. Use the following rule for chromatic colour distribution: the larger the area, the lower the chroma; the smaller the area, the higher the chroma. In other words, use dull colours in large areas and use brighter colours in small areas.
4. Keep natural building materials and painted materials similar in colour, while using contrast of values for interest. This will also help disguise unattractive necessities such as downspouts or service appliances.
5. Avoid having the space between objects equal to the object itself. Make the space greater or less than the object to increase interest and maintain balance.

REVIEW QUESTIONS

1. Explain the term "human scale", as it relates to architectural design.
2. Who was Louis Sullivan and what did he contribute to design?
3. What are some examples of traditional design features used with house design?
4. What is the main difference between classic design and rococo design?
5. What are the dominant, secondary, and third items you would see in an ideal house design?

WHAT DO YOU THINK?

1. If you were designing your own house, would you choose classic or rococo design? Give some reasons for your choice.
2. Should there be more individual house designs within a subdivision? Explain briefly.
3. Are new houses well designed? How might you improve them?

ASSIGNMENTS

1. Collect eight examples, from magazines or newspapers, of houses that clearly show transitional design, classic design, traditional design, and rococo design.
2. Sketch in pencil on notebook paper two designs for a front entrance to a house. Use straight-line design for one and curved design for the other.
3. Research the Roman orders of architecture to understand their relationship to proportions.

UNIT 3	Historical Design

OBJECTIVES

- To learn ancient building methods
- To learn important period-style housing
- To learn the development of modern design
- To become familiar with architectural leaders of various periods
- To learn architectural design terms

Throughout history, housing styles have been dictated mostly by the availability of local or imported materials and the culture of the people. Exploration of new countries brought new ideas back to old cultures, and consequently, architectural ideas from one culture began to influence the styles of other cultures.

Although it may seem that ancient architecture has little to do with today's residential housing, important structural fundamentals from the past are still used in housing construction.

ANCIENT BUILDING METHODS

EGYPTIAN

The Egyptians demonstrated their expert skills of building with stone in such famous works as the pyramids at Giza, the Great Sphinx at Giza, and their funerary temples such as Hatshepsut. One of the most common principles of construction, which is the use of post-and-lintel construction, was developed by the Egyptians. This method of support is shown in the ruins of the Court of Rameses II (1260 B.C.) and the Colonnade and Court of Amenhotep III (1390 B.C.) *(see Fig. 6-21)*.

The use of columns was prevalent in Egyptian architecture. Carvings were restricted to low-incised designs because of the hardness of the stone. The Egyptians' precision in fitting stones and laying out temples was possible through their understanding of geometry. Egyptian temples were designed to be used within the structure and

FIGURE 6-21
Court of Amenhotep III
Royal Ontario Museum, Toronto

the use of a **colonnade** to enter the temple was later copied by the Greeks and the Romans. A colonnade is a row of columns supporting a row of arches across the entrance to a building. The use of post-and-lintel construction, combined with a colonnade of attractive columns, is often used in today's homes to beautify patios or swimming-pool areas.

GREEK

Greek architecture copied much from the Egyptians. The Greeks maintained the use of post-and-lintel construction, with stone being the prime building material. Since the stone was not as hard as that found in Egypt, the Greeks were able to carve the stone more easily and therefore the columns could be fluted. The structure of the columns became significant to the Greek design and, during the classical phase of Greek architecture, three orders of column design were established.

The Greek orders were **Doric**, **Ionic**, and **Corinthian**; the Greek orders dictated the number of columns that could be used on a building. Therefore, all Doric-designed temples, for example, are similar. *Fig. 6-22* illustrates the three orders and shows the design of the top of the column.

FIGURE 6-22 *The Greek Orders*

Greek temples were not designed to be used from within, possibly because of the mild climate, and therefore the exterior of the building was more important. Altars were usually placed in front of the building for ceremonies, leaving the

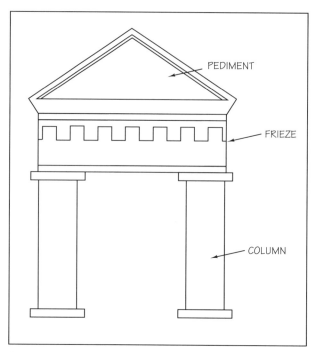

FIGURE 6-23 *Greek temple architecture*

façade of the temple to act more as a backdrop. To enhance the exterior design, the Greeks developed a **pediment** at the ends of the gabled roof *(see Fig. 6-23)*. The triangular shape of the pediment was heavily framed with a stone moulding. A wide band of stone called a **frieze** encircled the building just below the pediment. Both the frieze and the pediment became important sections for carved design even in later architectural styles. Two major features of Greek classic are the rectangle and the straight line. Many new homes today have returned to using classic Greek panels around dining-room walls or in the entrance foyer. Deep borders of intricate mouldings combined with decorative corbels are being used under the eaves of two-storey houses. These are called cornices and are imitations of the stone frieze used by the Greeks.

ROMAN

Many structural ideas have come from the Romans. There are strong similarities between Greek and Roman architecture but a number of important developments must be noted.

Roman architecture introduced the use of the circle and curved design. Since stone would have been too difficult to shape for large curved walls, the Romans redeveloped a concrete mixture. Concrete became their main building material. To hide the imperfections of concrete, they covered the building with a facing of brick, marble, or plaster. Columns were used extensively for both support and aesthetic appeal. The Roman Orders of Architecture were soon established and incorporated the three Greek styles and another style known as **Tuscan**.

A revolutionary system of span and support was developed by the Romans. The Roman arch is designed around a semi-circle. The Romans discovered that an arch constructed with a keystone design allowed greater spans between the columns. The keystone is the last stone to be laid in place, therefore a wooden structure must be built first to support the stones on the curve of the arch during construction. This is called **centring**. The principle of the arch is that the load above the centre is transported by the tapered keystone to the support columns. This allows greater loads over a wider span to be built. Adjoining walls supported the outward thrust of the columns.

Another structural idea was an expansion of the arch principle. By placing arches behind one another, the **vaulted ceiling** was formed. This type of ceiling is called a **barrel vault** *(see Fig. 6-24).* The principle of the barrel vault was used further by

the Romans to build aqueducts, bridges, and even sewer systems. Combining arches and vaults and the flexibility of concrete construction allowed the Romans to create buildings with vast interior spaces *(see Fig. 6-25).* The Pantheon, for example, has a ceiling height of 357 m (143') and a circular inside diameter of 357 m (143') for exact balance.

FIGURE 6-25 *The Pantheon*

The Interior of the Pantheon; Giovanni Paolo PANNINI; National Gallery of Art, Washington; Samuel H. Kress Collection (Date: c. 1740; oil on canvas; 1.28 x 0.99 cm [50 1/2 x 39 in])

The **groin vault**, which is formed by placing two barrel vaults at right angles to each other as seen in *Fig. 6-26,* became important later during the Gothic period. Groin vaults were used by the Romans in larger structures. The vaulted ceilings are significant because this approach to construction led to the idea of a domed ceiling. An example of this is the Pantheon. Buildings with domed ceilings have retained their aesthetic appeal throughout history.

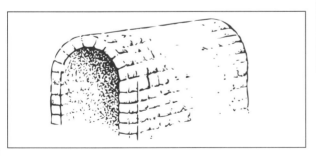

FIGURE 6-24 *A barrel vault is a half-round stone ceiling that is made by placing a series of round arches from front to back.*

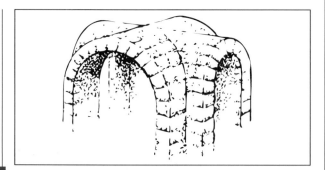

FIGURE 6-26 *A groined vault is formed when two barrel vaults meet at right angles.*

Mittler, Gene A. "Features of Roman Architecture." *Art in Focus*, 2nd ed.
Copyright © 1989 by Dr. Gene A. Mittler, published by Glencoe Publishing Company,
a division of Macmillan Inc. Used by permission of Glencoe/McGraw-Hill,
a Macmillan/McGraw-Hill Company.

Roman houses introduced new ideas that are still being used in housing developments. The single-family Roman house, called a **domus**, often had an **atrium**, a room lighted by an opening in the roof. A garden atmosphere could be created within the atrium and sometimes a colonnade would be built around the garden as well. A unique housing system was developed by the Romans for accommodating many families. The **insula**, or city block, was a housing complex that had stores on the ground floor and apartment dwellings on the upper floors. Modern housing construction owes a great deal to the Romans' ingenuity in architecture. The vaulted ceiling is widely used in entrance halls, living rooms, and family rooms of two-storey homes today. Often this dramatic ceiling is accented by carefully arranged skylights, some using stained glass.

GOTHIC

The Gothic period of architecture, which began about the middle of the twelfth century, introduced three major changes in construction. The **Gothic arch form** was altered from the Roman circle to a taller, narrower, pointed arch *(see Fig. 6-27)*. A Gothic arch directs the thrusts downward, with less lateral strain on the columns. This allows less horizontal support of the columns. Bricks, stone, or concrete were usually used for column support and these forms were called **buttresses**.

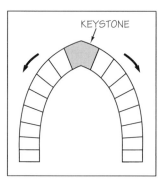

FIGURE 6-27
A Gothic arch

Since the Gothic arch did not require massive buttress forms, buttresses were made thinner and often arched themselves. Many Gothic cathedrals had one buttress built on top of another, in various sizes and these were called **flying buttresses**

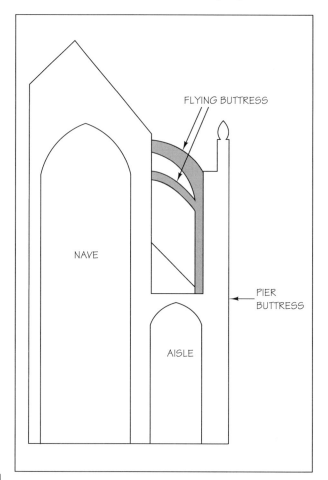

FIGURE 6-28 *Gothic Cathedral with flying buttress*

FIGURE 6-29
A contemporary Tudor house

(see Fig. 6-28). The Gothic arch was enhanced by the newly created Gothic stained glass windows.

The aesthetic charm of stained glass eventually became a decorative feature in the entrances of different period-style homes. In the latter part of the twentieth century, stained-glass windows are once again becoming popular as part of the front entrance to large single-family homes.

PERIOD-STYLE HOMES

Although the Renaissance period of the sixteenth century brought forth such master architects as Bramante and Michelangelo, their work was directed to churches and public buildings. However, a new class of merchants was developing. These wealthy merchants built their own residences and therefore a style of housing developed that was copied many times in later centuries. Some of the features of that style are even used in present-day houses. This house style was known as the Elizabethan-style house. Many of its features were adapted from the English Tudor house of the fifteenth century.

Each period style had individual characteristics that fulfilled the demands of the culture from that period. There are nine predominant period styles with which you should become familiar. The following is a brief description of the main features that distinguish each style.

TUDOR

The Tudor home was the first of the period-style homes that influenced architecture in North America. It was an English style of the fifteenth century that was popular briefly during the late nineteenth century. Although this house style is not very popular today, several of its features are often mixed with other styles. The Tudor house had a rambling, added-on room plan that was asymmetrical in design. It was a two- or more storey house with many high-pitched gables. Shallow **dormers** were used on some of the slopes. The walls were made of brick or masonry at the first-floor level and of stucco between exposed timbered sections on the upper floors. Tudor chimneys were very high with decorative pots at the top. Windows were the narrow casement type with small panes of glass. Exposed beams and lintels as well as thick panelling were used inside the house. One of the main features of the Tudor design was the distinctive flattened Gothic arch that was used over doorways and fireplace openings *(see Fig. 6-29)*.

FIGURE **6-30**
A contemporary Elizabethan house

ELIZABETHAN

This style evolved from the Tudor in the late sixteenth century and was named for the reign of Elizabeth I of England. The rooms of the house were also randomly added, causing an asymmetrical design. The Elizabethan house was two storeys in plan, with the first floor having a masonry exterior. The second storey was enclosed with exposed vertical half-timbers set in stucco or mortar. A unique feature of the Elizabethan style is the **cantilevered** second storey. Exposed beams or decorative **corbels** were used to support the overhanging walls.

The windows were also a narrow casement style, with small panes, similar to the Tudor style. Since the rooms were added as needed, windows were also randomly placed with little thought to exterior appearance. The roof was steeply pitched with many gables and dormers *(see Fig. 6-30).*

GEORGIAN

Two discoveries in the mid-eighteenth century had dramatic effects on residential housing: the rediscovery of Greek art as the original classic style; and the excavations of Pompeii that revealed the daily life of the Romans. A return to

FIGURE **6-31**
A contemporary Georgian house

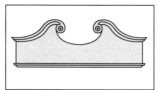

FIGURE 6-32
Chippendale pediment

formal, classic design using Greek and Roman characteristics followed. Even the interiors of houses were designed in this manner. The leading architect of this period was Robert Adam, who was from England. Adam incorporated Greek motifs into his furniture designs for homes and copied from the Pompeii excavations decorative borders or geometric forms for ceilings and walls.

The Georgian-style house became the most popular of all period-style designs *(see Fig. 6-31)*. When introduced to the southern colonies of America, a classic Roman **portico** was often added across the front. This style is usually called **Georgian Colonial**. The porticoes used Roman Doric, columns which gave the house a noble look. Eventually, the more ornate Ionic columns became popular because of the fluted column and carved volutes on the capitals. Another term used to describe the period of Georgian architecture is **Neo-Classic**.

Georgian-style houses had a formal floor plan. They were symmetrical in design both inside and outside. A centre hall was the dominant inside feature. The house was a two-storey rectangular plan with a large fireplace at each end. Although the roof was quite steeply pitched, dormers were seldom used. A large classic pediment, Greek in

design, was built above the main entrance. To complement the pediment, a classic, ornate **cornice** was used under the roof overhang. Sometimes a smaller glassed pediment, or **broken pediment**, was built immediately above the front door. The most popular design for a broken pediment was Chippendale *(see Fig. 6-32)*, which was designed to represent the letter C (reversed) identifying the designs of Chippendale, the famous furniture maker.

The exteriors of Georgian homes were constructed of masonry for both storeys. The windows were planned for exterior appearance and arranged symmetrically on the façade. Window designs were wider but still used small panes. Small, classic pediments were often placed over the top of each window.

ENGLISH REGENCY

A few details distinguished the style of the Regency. It was a formal, early nineteenth-century two-storey plan that used brick as an exterior finish. The bricked front had low projecting walls extending to the sides. Greek and Roman details were used on the cornice and entry. A curved roof on the porch, with wrought-iron railings, was common. Small wrought-iron balconies adorned upper storey windows. The double-hung windows had small panes and a unique Regency design of long shutters used on the first-storey windows. Another window treatment that typified Regency style was an octagonal window in the front of the house *(see Fig. 6-33)*.

FIGURE 6-33
A contemporary English Regency house

FIGURE 6-34
A contemporary French Regency house with mansard roof

FRENCH REGENCY

This style was very similar to the English Regency but it had two important features. The first was the roof line. The famous French architect François Mansart designed a roof that had steep slopes on the sides and a relatively flat centre section. Dormers, with rounded windows, were usually placed on the sides of the roof. Ornamental iron railings encircled the flat section for decoration. This style of roof is called a **mansard roof** *(see Fig. 6-34).*

The second feature of French Regency was the use of curved design. The extending side walls were curved concavely and sometimes accented by a column. The windows and doors had curved pediments, and a round or oval window was used in the front. Delicately panelled glass doors were introduced to divide interior rooms or to provide an entrance onto porches. Shutters were installed similar to the English Regency style.

ITALIANATE

This late nineteenth-century style two-storey house used either symmetrical or asymmetrical design. The roof was low pitched and made of tiles. A wide overhang was braced by the generous use of large ornate corbels. Exterior finishing featured decorative bricklaying to accent the classic lines. For example, two or three rows of brick were corbelled near the cornice, which gave the illusion of a heavy frieze around the top of the walls. The corners of the house use **quoined bricks** *(see Fig. 6-35)* to simulate the classic use of stones on the corners.

A revival of Romanesque design was seen in Roman arched windows, doors, and columned porches. Concrete window sills and concrete framed bays were often part of the design. Windows were tall, narrow, and casement in style. Three distinct features were usually found in Italianate design: a large tower section as part of the house; a balcony with a **balustrade**; and a **loggia** that opened onto a garden *(see Fig. 6-36).*

FIGURE 6-35 *Quoined brick*

FIGURE 6-36 *A contemporary Italianate house*

SPANISH

The Spanish-style house had a low-pitched, tiled roof. The wall finish was white stucco, rather than brick, which created a dramatic contrast to the reddish roof tiles. A typical Spanish design used casement windows that opened onto balconies of gracefully curved wrought iron. Entranceways were floored in decorative tiles, and a new area was introduced that has become a standard feature today. It was the patio. The Spanish style is often referred to as the Mediterranean style, which is really a mixture of Southern Italian and Spanish design *(see Fig. 6-37)*.

VICTORIAN

Victorian houses were large, two-storey, and asymmetrical in design *(see Fig. 6-38)*. The designers ignored the principles of unity, balance, and proportion. The house incorporated numerous ornate designs such as angled porches, stained-glass windows, balustrades, and slate gable roof tiles.

The revolutionary machines for woodworking, such as the lathe, bandsaw, and sanders, allowed mass production of wood trim patterns. A new era of fancy scrolls, spindles, **newell posts**, and **finials** began. These wood designs were used to decorate the cornices, pediments, and archways of Victorian houses. Several styles were used on one house. This architectural approach became known as **bandsaw architecture** or **gingerbread architecture**. The latter term was used because often the fancy trim was painted in accent colours and looked like the wavy icing that outlines gingerbread houses. The interiors were also very ornate with wide trim and cornices.

FIGURE 6-37
A contemporary Spanish house
Courtesy of the Tourist Office of Spain

FIGURE **6-38**
A contemporary Victorian house

CAPE COD

Early settlers along the eastern coast of North America developed this quaint single-family house. The traditional Cape Cod design is one and a half storeys high, with a livable attic area. This was made possible by using a high-pitched roof that allowed space for tall dormers that could have a double-hung window. Usually, there were several identical dormers arranged symmetrically across the front roof pitch. Later development introduced a full-width **shed dormer** across the rear roof.

The basic floor plan was generally a formal, centre-hall plan. A large fireplace was placed in the centre of the house for equal distribution of heat. Another feature of the Cape Cod is the **clapboard** exterior. The principle of the overlapping boards is that the winter moisture would cause them to swell and seal themselves against the winter winds. In the hot dry summers, they would shrink and allow cool air to move in and out of the house.

Since brick or stone was not readily available but lumber was plentiful, Cape Cod houses were

FIGURE **6-39**
A contemporary Cape Cod house

almost entirely made of wood, including the thick shake shingles. The windows were double hung with small panes of glass. A simple, straight-line classic trim was used because the settlers did not have time to add fancy ornamental trim. **Fascia** boards and cornices required little work because there was only a small overhang to the roof. The unique Cape Cod style is considered by many to be the true Colonial home, and this design is still very popular today although brick is usually used in place of clapboard for durability *(see Fig. 6-39)*.

MODERN HOUSING

The term **modern** is generally applied to designs that have been produced since the Industrial Revolution period of the late nineteenth century, excluding those that imitated the period styles previously discussed. Modern architecture is directed by new materials and engineering skills and by philosophies of design from architectural schools or individual architects.

In the twentieth century, architectural advancements are being applied quickly to the residential field. However, the advances in new materials and construction are more readily accepted by the public compared to the advances in housing design. This conflict betwen progress and nostalgia in design began about the turn of the century.

Cast iron was the first metal substitute for wooden or concrete posts. It has great strength even when reduced in size, is easily fastened together, and can be formed in intricate shapes. During the Industrial Revolution, cast iron was first used architecturally by Joseph Paxton, for his magnificent Crystal Palace, built for the Great Exhibition in 1851 *(see Fig. 6-40)*. After demonstrating its versatility in this structure, cast iron started being used in bridges, public buildings, railroad sheds, and numerous other designs. For residential use, however, it was confined to ornamental columns, banisters, canopies, or gates. The usual designs for these ornaments were copies of stone carvings or wood turnings from past period styles.

A new improved iron was soon developed, called **rolled iron** or **wrought iron**. Rolled iron made possible the design of high-rise buildings, with as many as fifteen floors. The invention of steel, with much greater tensile strength, allowed high-rise structures that were almost limitless. Sheet-formed steel, some with textured patterns, began being used in commercial buildings but was not accepted in residential design.

The material that was incorporated into most architecture, including residential, was glass. The continuous improvement in clarity, size, and strength of glass made it a major component in modern architecture. During the 1920s, Walter Gropius, an architect in Germany, started a school

FIGURE 6-40
The Crystal Palace

of design that revolutionized the world of architecture. Numerous artists, craftspeople, and architects attended or taught at the school called the Bauhaus. They adopted the philosophy of the American architect Louis Sullivan, who believed the theory of "form follows function."

Many of the major design concepts conceived by the Bauhaus school were directed towards residential living. Furniture, cooking utensils, and accessories were streamlined into simple, uncluttered, functional designs. Their housing designs were totally new. Glass and steel were the dominant materials. Structural members were often left exposed as part of the design aesthetics. Full walls of glass were commonly used to unite outside views with inside living quarters. Wood panelling remained smooth without the use of ornamental mouldings.

The leading architect of steel and glass construction was Mies van der Rohe, an instructor at the school. Upon coming to North America, he led the movement to modern steel and glass skyscrapers in the major cities. The rapid expansion of glass design was a direct influence on today's homes. The large picture windows, floor-to-ceiling glass, and wide sliding glass doors are all Bauhaus ideas. Regions in the south and on the west coast of the United States were more appropriate to the Bauhaus style house because of the moderate climate.

Probably the most influential architect of residential housing in North America was Frank Lloyd Wright. By the first half of the twentieth century, he was revered as the foremost architect. His philosophy on housing design was that the house should appear to be part of the landscape, as if it had *grown* on the lot. He called his style **organic architecture.**

To accomplish this harmony between house and lot, he used stone, wood, glass, and concrete. Wright was one of the leaders in developing **reinforced concrete** and successfully used it in house design. Mass and space dominated his designs, and the low horizontal lines of the houses soon caused them to become known as prairie houses. Wright introduced multi-level terraces, balconies, and rooms in order to create a unity between the

house interior and the outdoors. These multilevel, offset floor plans led to the popular split-level houses of the 1960s.

The flat or very low-pitched roofs had extreme overhangs to protect the glass wall areas from the sun. The balconies, too, had expansive overhangs to create blocks of space within the design. To visually balance the space, large chimneys of ledge rock and walls of smooth concrete were built.

Wright was also the first architect to use the **cantilever.** Rooms and balconies, supported on large reinforced concrete columns, seemed to float in space because of the extreme cantilevered design. Straight-line design, rectangular forms, and natural earth-toned materials also typified his house designs.

One of Frank Lloyd Wright's most famous houses, called Falling Water, clearly shows the genius of his designs. This visual example illustrates that, although it was built in the early twentieth century, it is still as modern as the houses of today *(see Fig. 6-41)*. Numerous architects who trained under Frank Lloyd Wright have expanded his theories in contemporary house designs throughout the world.

FUTURE CONCEPTS

Architectural designs continue to change as new materials are developed and new demands are made by the general public. The greatest progress in new materials and construction techniques has taken place in the twentieth century. Consequently, we are witnessing exciting architectural designs throughout the world.

Manufacturers are experimenting with new ideas and products that will improve building standards without being harmful to the environment. Revolutionary plastics, glass, stainless steel, concrete, reclaimed wood products, synthetic fabrics, aluminum alloys, and synthetic aggregates are being used in the design of buildings in new ways. Structural methods have greatly improved through the use of stronger fastening devices, glues, and materials. The computer has

FIGURE 6-41
Falling Water House
The Bettmann Archive

helped to overcome complex design concepts and has given architects more freedom of expression. Several new ideas to create large buildings with vast open spaces have become possible with shell construction. Buckminster Fuller's geodesic dome principles are being applied to housing, allowing open-concept designs *(see Fig. 6-42)*. The famous Japanese architect Kenzo Tange proved the validity of another shell system with the huge sports hall in Tokyo. This building has a welded steel net roof suspended like a tent on large reinforced concrete masts *(see Fig. 6-43)*. Perhaps a similar system may be used in housing design in the future.

In Canada, many of the leading architects such as Arthur Erickson, Geoffrey Massey, and Raymond Moriyama have greatly contributed to the advancement of contemporary residential and commercial architecture *(see Fig. 6-44)*. Although the majority of home builders today still cling to the traditional styles of the past, the future is unknown. Perhaps a dramatic change in residential design is already on the drafting board or maybe it is still an idea developing in the mind of a residential design student reading this text. It could be yours!

FIGURE 6-42 *Geodesic dome*
Photo: Ville de Montreal

FIGURE 6-43 *Tokyo Sports Hall*

The Bettmann Archive
Architect: Kenzo Tange

FIGURE 6-44 *Simon Fraser University, Instructional Media Centre, Burnaby, B.C.*

Architect: Geoffrey Massey and Arthur Erickson
Photo number: 87096-19   Photographer: Chris Hildred

REVIEW QUESTIONS

1. What civilizations used post-and-lintel construction?
2. Who developed the keystone arch?
3. What is meant by the Greek orders?
4. What is the difference between Greek and Roman orders?
5. How does the Roman arch differ in design from the Gothic arch?
6. What is gingerbread architecture and what period style used it?
7. What famous building first used cast-iron construction? Who designed it?

WHAT DO YOU THINK?

1. Should the design ideas of the Bauhaus school and the architects of today be used to a greater degree in house design? Explain.
2. Why do you think the flat-roofed, glass-walled house designs have not become very popular in Canada?

ASSIGNMENTS

1. Research the meaning of the following words: aqueduct, dormer, cantilever, portico, cornice, broken pediment, balustrade, loggia, newell post, finial, and reinforced concrete.
2. Collect pictures and material information folders that show details of construction for the house style that you like best.

CHAPTER **7** | # Landscaping

PLANTING SHRUBS AROUND the foundation of a house is different from properly landscaping the site. Many new homeowners fail to take the time to plan their landscaping wisely, resulting in costly mistakes. Landscaping the property to a functional plan will increase the value of the house considerably.

As a general guideline, the total cost of landscaping should be about 10% of the cost of the house. Landscaping, of course, does not have to be completed all at once, but is usually designed to be finished in stages. This approach makes the costs easier to handle and also allows growth patterns to fit the plan. For example, large shade trees could be planted first, since they are slow growing, and expensive ornamental shrubs or a swimming pool added later when affordable.

Large residential projects may use the services of a landscape architect who is trained to design complex, multi-purpose living areas. Individual homeowners can get professional help from landscape nurseries. These businesses offer planning advice as well as a wide variety of nursery stock to suit most landscape plans.

Landscaping includes more than just planting. The lot should first be designed into functional areas of *service*, *recreation*, and *beautification*.

FIGURE 7-1
A poorly landscaped house

In order to design these areas, two important considerations must be examined. First, the legal restrictions imposed by local building codes and zoning must be adhered to. Second, the designer should consider climate orientation for all four seasons of the year. The residential design student should have a good understanding of these fundamental landscaping procedures.

UNIT 1

Legal Restrictions and Climate Orientation

OBJECTIVES

- To learn about landscaping by-laws
- To learn about climate control in landscaping
- To learn the importance of proper landscape planning

All communities have by-laws and zoning restrictions that affect landscaping plans. The distances that the house, garage, storage buildings, fences, hedges, and septic tank beds must be from the lot boundary lines are determined by municipal by-laws. These are referred to as **setbacks**. Often the heights of auxiliary buildings, fences, and hedges are also determined from the by-laws. In some communities, even the design of the auxiliary buildings is controlled to maintain architectural harmony in the neighbourhood.

Fences are usually restricted to a maximum height. Any fence built above the maximum could be considered a "spite fence" by the neighbour and ordered removed. Fences must also be installed so that the decorative side is directed towards the adjoining property. For safety reasons, most communities require a fence around all sides of a swimming pool, as well as a locked gate.

Legal restrictions may also apply to control water drainage from one lot to adjoining lots. Altering the lot elevations or the building of retaining walls, etc., should be carefully planned with regard to drainage. Any plantings or structures along the lot perimeters should be placed to allow access by the owner for maintenance, without intruding on neighbouring properties.

CLIMATE ORIENTATION

Regional and climatic conditions play a major role in landscape design. The direction in which the lot faces will determine the seasonal amount of sun each area of the lot receives. The lot direction also has a bearing on the effects of seasonal winds and snow deposits. When designing a landscape plan, consider landscaping the lot into **microclimates**, to control the advantages and disadvantages of local climate. A microclimate is the localized climate of a given site which is different from surrounding general climatic conditions because of topography, vegetation, and orientation of the site to the sun. This controlling of the sun, wind, snow, or rain within the site allows the maximum function of each part of the lot. Refer also to Chapter 3, Unit 2.

Areas such as lawns, gardens, and swimming pools should be placed to receive maximum sun. Use canopies, shade trees, or privacy fencing to control sun zones in lounging or outdoor eating areas. Create fully shaded areas with shade trees and accessory buildings. These shaded areas are well suited for storage sheds or car parking.

Seasonal winds can be controlled through microclimate design by the careful placement of trees, shrubs, fences, and buildings. Ground textures can also be used to control heat and wind. Changing the contours of the lot by the addition of **berms** will alter wind direction through deflection. A berm is a mound of earth, usually elongated, built to alter the land contours for functional or aesthetic reasons. It may be sodded or planted with vegetation. The size of the berm should be in scale with surrounding forms and should have smooth, gentle slopes.

Hard materials such as paving stones, concrete, asphalt, and wood decking absorb heat as well as reflecting the sun's rays and heat after the sun has set. Soft materials act as cooling agents. Grass or living ground covers are excellent soft materials to use near lounging patios and pools *(see Fig. 7-2)*.

Trees and shrubs are the major components used in landscaping, but choose them carefully for the site. Coniferous or evergreen trees are excellent as a year-round windbreak and therefore should be used on the north or northwest sides of

FIGURE 7-2

Landscaped patio

Courtesy of Aardvark Landscape Design &
Build Ltd., Toronto.

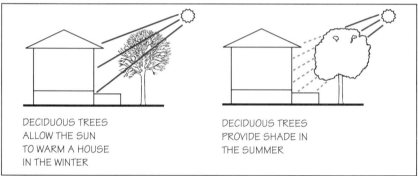

DECIDUOUS TREES
ALLOW THE SUN
TO WARM A HOUSE
IN THE WINTER

DECIDUOUS TREES
PROVIDE SHADE IN
THE SUMMER

FIGURE 7-3

*Deciduous trees help to
conserve energy.*

the lot. In order to create shade in the summer and yet allow the sun to warm the house in the winter, deciduous trees should be planted on the south or southwest sides of the lot *(see Fig. 7-3).*

A common error in planting trees and shrubs is placing them too close to the house. It is important to know the full height and width that the tree or shrub will attain at maturity to avoid overcrowding. The general shape of the mature tree should be in visual harmony with the house. Trees are either tall and conical or wide and spherical. Conical trees are better suited as a windbreak because they can be planted more closely together. A spreading, ball-shaped tree is ideal for shade.

In snow regions, fences and hedges are used to control drifting snow. The snow fence or hedge is placed to alter the wind force so that the snow will drop on the opposite side of the fence or hedge from the wind direction *(see Fig. 7-4).* It is impor-

tant therefore to allow enough room for the snow to accumulate at the fencing without infringing on driveways or walkways.

A well-planned landscape design using microclimates will enhance any residential property while greatly increasing the overall value *(see Fig. 7-5).*

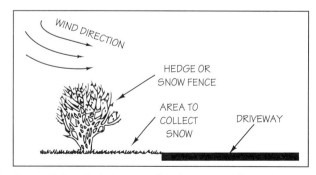

WIND DIRECTION

HEDGE OR
SNOW FENCE

AREA TO
COLLECT
SNOW

DRIVEWAY

FIGURE 7-4   *Placing a snow break next to a driveway*

FIGURE 7-5

Microclimate landscaping plan. This house is landscaped for microclimates. The patio provides controlled shade zones; the trees and house provide a full shade zone; the wall provides protection for a morning and mid-day sun zone; the wall and surrounding trees also provide a partial sun zone for the late afternoon; the pool provides a full sun area; open areas provide full sun zones for plants and vegetables; and the greenhouse provides absolute climate control.

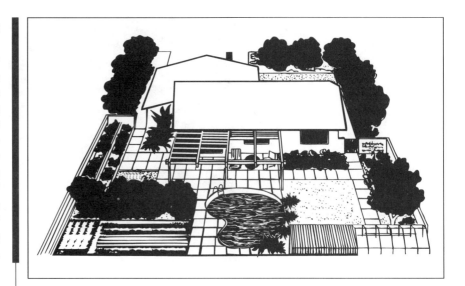

REVIEW QUESTIONS

1. What is the general guideline for the percentage costs of landscaping compared to the cost of the house?
2. List the three functional areas a lot should be designed for. List some examples of each area.
3. What is meant by the term "setbacks"?
4. What is a spite fence?
5. List three areas that should be located to receive maximum sun.
6. What is a microclimate?
7. What type of tree should be planted on the south side of the lot? Explain why.

WHAT DO YOU THINK?

1. Should individual communities develop stronger controls on local environmental pollution to protect trees and green areas? Explain your opinions.
2. Noise pollution is becoming a problem in larger urban centres. How could you reduce noise when landscaping your lot?
3. What factors would you consider when choosing a building lot to landscape?

ASSIGNMENTS

1. Using a print of your Traverse I drawing from Chapter 4, Unit 1 using property line AB as the road side, indicate the placement of trees, berms, fences, or accessory buildings to form the lot into a microclimate plan.
2. Using a print of your Traverse I drawing from Chapter 4, Unit 1 using property line CD as the road side, indicate a garage and a driveway from the south side of the lot. Draw in a proposed northwest wind break of trees and a snow fence. Label the type of trees you chose and show the dimensions between the fencing and driveway in scale.
3. Obtain from a local engineer's office or from the civic records a copy of the by-laws that relate to property setbacks, fencing, auxiliary buildings, and swimming pools. File them for reference in your notebook.

UNIT 2 | Designing a Functional Plan

OBJECTIVES

- To learn the purpose of landscaping
- To learn the service areas of a lot
- To learn the recreation areas of a lot
- To learn the beautification of a lot
- To learn how to draft a landscape plan

New homeowners spend a great deal of time planning the layout of a house, but they seldom give much thought to the layout of the rest of the property. A residential building lot is used for three main purposes: service, recreation, and beautification. These three areas can be planned by using "bubbles" *(see Fig. 7-6)* to locate each area on preliminary sketches. When the most appropriate arrangement is decided upon, a scale drawing of the lot should be made and each area drawn in detail to scale. The order in which each area will be landscaped can be keyed on the plan, using numbers or letters, or by the use of a colour chart. Materials and plantings should also be charted on the plan.

SERVICE AREAS

The driveway is a prime example of a service area. It should be located in such a way that it is easy to drive into or back out of the garage or carport. The north side or shady side of the lot is the best location.

Two common storage service areas are required: a storage shed for garden tools and bicycles, and a shed or area for the storing of garbage containers. The storage shed for garden tools should be located so that it is convenient to the backyard as well as to the driveway. This will allow machinery to be transported for repairs. The garden shed design should also blend aesthetically with the design of the home. If a compost is to be part of the landscaping service areas, it should be placed so that it is concealed from view from the patio. Wind direction should also be considered to lessen compost odours.

Garbage container storage should be inconspicuous and secure against animals. Although it is convenient to have the garbage storage within reasonable distance from the house, care should be taken not to place it too close to an outdoor eating patio. Wind direction should also be considered when choosing a garbage storage location to avoid unwanted odours entering the house. Decorative screening or planting can help make this service area more attractive.

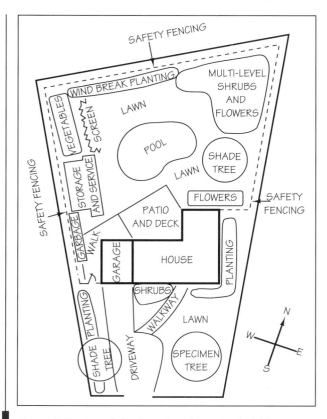

FIGURE 7-6 *Rough landscaping plan using bubbles*

Although most houses are designed with a laundry room to have a washer and dryer, many people still prefer to hang clothes in the fresh air to dry. Clotheslines should be planned for a sunny location and away from busy pedestrian walkways or children's play areas.

A swimming pool requires its own service area to store pumps and pool equipment. Since a change area is also required, a well-designed building may be used to service both needs.

RECREATION AREAS

The backyard is usually the location for a recreation area. It is quite common to have several recreation areas because of the various interests of family members. An area for a sandbox, swings, or slide is preferred by families with young children. Such an area should be located in partial shade and within sight of the kitchen or family room of the house. If the patio is designed at ground level and constructed of a hard surface material, such as interlocking brick, it can be used for riding tricycles or playing basketball.

The patio is designed primarily as an outdoor eating area and lounge where family members or guests can be entertained. The patio should be located in an area with partial sun. Incorporating a barbecue area on the downwind side of the patio and convenient access to the house for serving refreshments further enhance the patio. Recently, patios have been designed with multi-level wood decks. This trend offers opportunities for raised planter boxes and built-in saunas, as well. When designing patios or decks, give consideration to privacy. Attractive fencing and ornamental shrubs or hedges are some methods used to create a privacy area within the patio.

An above-ground or in-ground swimming pool is the most expensive recreation area to add to a residential home. The designer should carefully consider the location of the pool. A full sunny spot will help maintain the water's temperature. Large trees should not be planted near the pool in order to avoid falling leaves or root damage to the pool's structure. An easy-to-clean, firm, and slip-proof material should be used as a walkway around the pool. An open area of grass creates a soft, cooling contrast to the hard materials of the pool, as well as providing an ideal area for sunbathing *(see Fig. 7-8)*.

Sufficient room is needed both to fence the entire yard or pool for safety reasons and to move freely around the pool. Legally pools must be enclosed with a 1600 mm (5'-4") high fence. Wind breaks should also be part of the pool design. A proper drainage system should be pre-planned in case the pool has to be drained for maintenance.

FIGURE 7-7
A multi-level wood deck

Courtesy of Aardvark Landscape Design & Build Ltd., Toronto

BEAUTIFICATION

The pride of owning a house is usually reflected in the design and care of the landscaping. The amount of lawn or planting areas surrounding the house is an individual preference. Maintenance becomes an important factor when deciding what to plant. Although flower gardens are beautiful and vegetables gardens are very practical, not everyone enjoys the work involved to maintain them. A landscape plan should therefore be designed to bring maximum pleasure to the homeowner, with minimum maintenance.

The first area of the lot to be landscaped is usually around the perimeter of the house. This is called **foundation planting**, for which a mixture of evergreen shrubs is most commonly used. Foundation planting should be planned using the elements and principles of design outlined in Chapter 6. The architectural style of the house must be considered so that the foundation planting enhances and complements the design. Shrubs should be chosen so that their sizes are in proportion to one another, ensuring that the visual mass of each grouping remains proportionately constant throughout their growing period.

A variety of sizes, shapes, textures, and colours should be used to create a natural appearance to the planting. Large and tall shrubs should be placed near the outer corners of the house to soften the angle and visually extend the length of the house. A wide, undulating, curved planting bed that arcs away from the corners of the house creates an aesthetically pleasing foundation planting *(see Fig. 7-9)*.

Medium height and low spreading shrubs are suitable under windows or near the entrance. Flowering deciduous shrubs tend to grow quite large and should be placed well out from the foundation, towards the corners of the house. By using coarse- and fine-leafed shrubs, interesting textural changes can be achieved. Colour variations are achieved by mixing dark, light, or variegated shrubs within the same planting bed. A main focal point is sometimes created near the entrance by the use of a statue, water fountain, or an interesting specimen plant. Foundation planting should never appear to overpower the house, but should act as a picture frame to unite the house and lot.

Trees help to beautify a lot. Large trees in the backyard act as a frame for the front of the house. Ornamental trees are commonly used on front lawns. Coniferous varieties such as spruce or pine are selected for their yearly display of texture. Trees such as the blue spruce may also be used for their colour. Many people enjoy the appearance

FIGURE 7-9

Curved foundation planting with the corner of the house

Photo compliments of Parklane Nurseries Ltd.

FIGURE 7-10

Blue spruce in the back yard

Sheridan Nurseries Limited, Georgetown, Ontario

of the snow-covered boughs of evergreens in winter and decorate them with Christmas lights.

Ornamental deciduous trees are usually chosen for their blossoms, although there are many, such as the Golden Raintree, that have interesting foliage. Some deciduous trees are selected because of their fruit and ability to attract birds to the region. The placement of ornamental trees should be planned so that they beautify the lot externally but can be seen and appreciated from within the house as well.

Flowers bring instant beauty to any lot. Planter boxes for flowers make it easier to control weeds and allow the designer to group flowers in masses of colour. Areas with full sun or partial shade are the most appropriate locations for floral beds. Flower beds soften the hard appearance of a driveway, but remember to allow room for snow removal.

Driveways and walkways can be made more attractive through careful proportioning and selection of materials. The most common mistake in positioning sidewalks is placing them too close to the house. They should be wide enough to allow two people to walk side by side. By extending the front walkway away from the house towards the centre of the driveway's

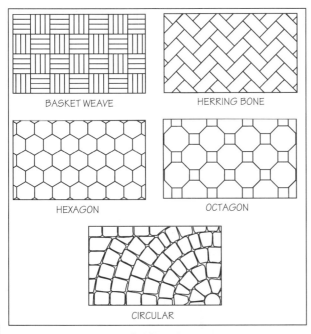

FIGURE 7-11 *Common brick paving patterns*

FIGURE 7-12 *Night beautification with lights*

Photo courtesy of Noma Inc., Scarborough, Ontario.

length, a more functional path is created. Sidewalk materials should be strong, attractive, and easy to clean. Concrete, interlocking brick, and flagstone laid in concrete are all suitable to create an attractive walkway.

Although concrete and asphalt have been used as traditional driveway materials, the new interlocking paving stones are becoming very popular. The stones allow more design patterns and colour possibilities in order to harmonize with the house design. Traditional design patterns for laying interlocking stones are hexagon, octagon, circular, herring bone, and basketweave *(see Fig. 7-11)*. Paving stones can also be laid in free-form mosaic patterns that can create striking designs for patios or swimming-pool decks.

Decorative fence designs, garden gates, trellises, and arbours are other features that can be used in beautification. Night beautification is usually achieved through lighting, with emphasis on the most dramatic areas.

DRAWING THE PLAN

A scale drawing of the lot showing the location of the house and garage should be made and several copies printed to use for preliminary planning. Outline bubbles are used on the rough sketches to indicate the various areas. When the desired layout has been selected, a detailed scale pencil drawing is started. The location of the house is indicated with a broad outline or the entire house area may be filled in solid.

Step one: Draw the location of the driveway and walkways in outline only *(see Fig. 7-13)*.

Step two: Draw the location of auxiliary buildings in outline, showing the entrance to the buildings as well *(see Fig. 7-14)*.

Step three: Indicate the position of all large trees using circles to show the total spread of each tree at maturity *(see Fig. 7-14)*.

Step four: Draw the shape of any patios or decks in their proposed locations. If a swimming pool is to be included, indicate its size and shape also *(see Fig. 7-15)*.

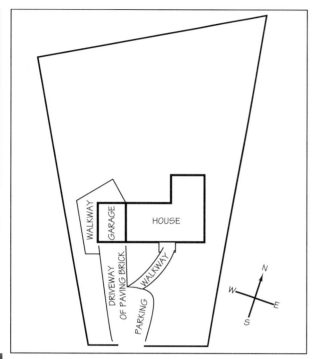

FIGURE 7-13 *Landscaping plan of driveway and walkway*

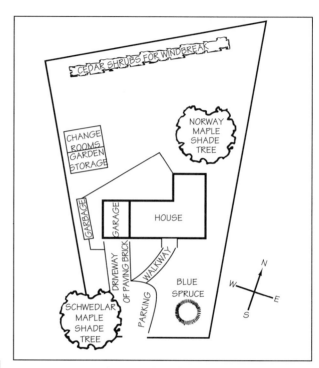

FIGURE 7-14 *Landscaping plan of trees and service buildings*

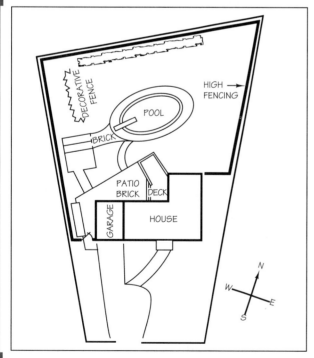

FIGURE 7-15 *Landscaping plan of patio, deck, pool, and fencing*

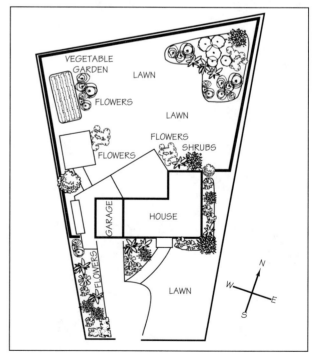

FIGURE 7-16 *Landscaping plan of planting beds for shrubs, flowers, and vegetables*

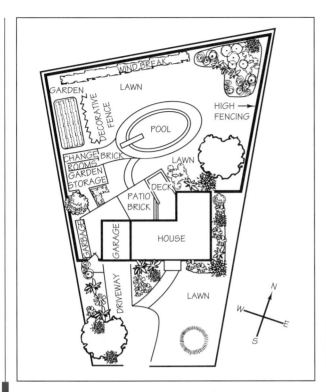

FIGURE 7-17 *Complete landscaping plan*

Step five: Complete the outline by indicating planting beds and fence lines *(see Fig 7-16)*.

Step six: The drawing can be completed in pencil by indicating the textures of all vegetation and materials in darker tones *(see Fig. 7-17)*.

You may wish to render the outlines in ink and then colour code the plan from the reverse side of the paper using coloured pencils. The size of paper you select for the landscape plan should allow you to make a chart to list plants by number and name.

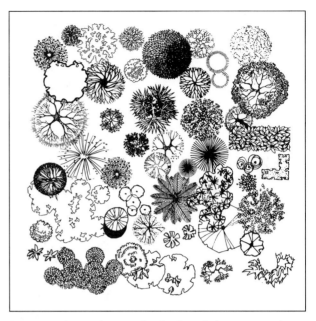

FIGURE 7-18 *Various methods of rendering trees and shrubs on a plan.*

To indicate trees in a plan, two types of views are generally used: an overhead view that shows the texture of foliage in an opaque style, and a sectional overhead that suggests a slice of the tree, showing the centre trunk and an outline of the total spread of the tree. The latter is more transparent and is used when information that is under the tree must be shown. You should develop your own style of rendering trees and shrubs, working around a circular guideline. *Fig. 7-18* shows some methods of indicating trees, shrubs, and hedges. If the landscaping plan is to be executed in stages over a number of years, the large trees or slow-growing plants are usually included in the early stages. A title block and a border give the landscape plan a finished professional appearance.

REVIEW QUESTIONS

1. Where should the garden storage shed be located and why?
2. Where should the play area for young children be located on the lot?
3. What is the purpose of a patio?
4. List three design features that should be used when locating a swimming pool.
5. What is foundation planting?
6. Where should tall and large shrubs be placed in foundation planting?
7. What is a common mistake made in locating sidewalks on a lot?

WHAT DO YOU THINK?

1. Do you think people will make more use of their backyards in the next 20 years or less use of the backyard? Give your reasons.
2. What changes might you expect in the future in landscaping of residential lots?
3. Why do you think lawn service companies are so successful?
4. Describe what you would have as the main attraction of your landscaped lot.

ASSIGNMENTS

1. Using the assigned elevation sheet, indicate a front foundation planting scheme using your B pencil.
2. On an A3/B size sheet of paper, draw a complete landscape plan for the assigned two-storey house. The lot size is to be 20 m x 40 m (60' x 120'). The house setback from the street is 10 m (30').
3. On an A3/B size sheet of paper, draw a landscape plan for a backyard that is 20 m wide x 15 m deep (60' x 50').

CHAPTER 8

Technical Design

A **GREAT DEAL OF** technical knowledge has been assembled over the centuries that has enabled present-day architects to create more attractive and functional buildings and to make the best use of the available materials by a thorough understanding of structural design.

In previous times, buildings were constructed to be stronger than was necessary, and materials were used wastefully because of a lack of knowledge about the properties of various materials. Today, architectural engineers have access to a great deal of data about natural and synthetic materials.

In the past, materials had to be cut by hand because the machinery that is available today did not exist. For instance, the dimensions of a piece of lumber were more often related to the size of the tree that had been cut down than the size required to do the job.

The population explosion in this century has made it imperative that we conserve materials carefully so that more of the people of the world can be adequately housed.

Prefabrication of items such as windows and doors and the standardization of material sizes, such as in lumber and panelling, allow buildings to be erected more quickly and with less waste.

Many designers use a modular scheme, whereby each element of a building is related to the others in size. Most factory products are now designed with modular planning in mind.

Energy that is used to heat our homes must also be conserved, particularly if fossil fuels such as gas, oil, or coal, which cannot be replaced, are used. Therefore, consideration must be given to the orientation and effective insulation of contemporary housing.

All these factors have an impact on construction techniques and must be taken into account when planning the functional and aesthetic design of a building.

UNIT 1 | Structural Design

OBJECTIVES

- To understand the effects of stress on materials
- To differentiate between a dead and a live load
- To determine the tributary area for a structural component
- To calculate the load on a joist or rafter
- To understand the significance of structural tables
- To appreciate the effects of soil conditions on a building
- To understand the importance of foundations

From earliest times, architects have striven to produce greater achievements in architecture than those of previous periods. The great Romanesque and Gothic churches of Europe built during the Middle Ages, the skyscrapers of North America, and the more recent CN Tower of Toronto (currently the tallest free-standing structure in the world) are all examples of the urge to build taller structures. The Pantheon of ancient Rome, the Crystal Palace of Victorian England, the SkyDome Stadium of Toronto all met the challenge of enclosing unprecedented amounts of space.

FIGURE 8-1
Robson Square, Vancouver
The Province of British Columbia/
Robson Square/Vancouver

FIGURE 8-2
SkyDome
Photography by Lenscape Incorporated

STRENGTH OF MATERIALS

Architectural engineering required the development of technology regarding the use of materials to construct these structures. The study of the properties of materials has resulted in improved design for modern housing, which is much more flexible and functional than in previous times.

The study of the loads that various materials can carry is called the **strength of materials**. Structural designers use a variety of formulas to determine the correct size a component made of a certain material must be so that it will be strong enough to support a particular part of a building. Designers and draftspersons should also be aware of the various factors that relate to the ability of a material to carry the required load.

STRESS

Stress is the result when a load is placed on materials. Stress is the internal reaction to an external force. For example, when a weightlifter holds a heavy load overhead, his or her muscles will shake after a period of time and the person will eventually be forced to drop the load. A building will have a similar reaction if too much weight is applied for the size and strength of the components.

This type of stress is known as **compressive stress**, which means that the particles in the material are being forced together and if the load becomes excessive, the material will eventually collapse. For example, a piece of styrofoam will break up if it is pounded with a mallet. Foundations of buildings are subject to this type of stress between the load of the structure and the resistance of the ground on which the foundation stands *(see Fig. 8-3A)*.

Another type of stress is that caused by **tensile stress**. This means that the particles of the material are being pulled apart. We apply tension when we stretch an elastic band. If we apply too much force, the band will break. It is this type of stress that the bottom chord of a triangular roof truss must resist during a heavy snow storm *(see Fig. 8-3B)*.

A third type of stress is **shear stress**, which is caused when one set of particles is forced in the opposite direction from others that adjoin them. Tearing a piece of paper is an example of shearing force. This type of stress occurs to a cantilevered balcony when someone sits on it *(see Fig. 8-3C)*.

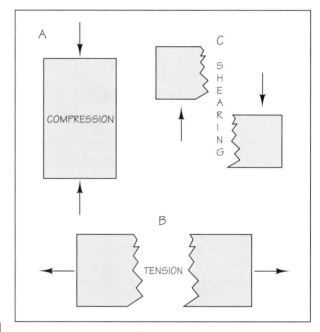

FIGURE 8-3A *Compressive stress;*
B *Tensile stress;*
C *Shear stress*

Every material reacts differently to each type of stress. These reactions are formulated in charts. An example of one of these charts, in metric and imperial measurement, is shown in *Fig. 8-4*.

Note that concrete reacts well under compression, is weak under shearing conditions, and is very poor under tension. Timber reacts best to tension and is weaker under compression and shearing. Wood has the advantage of being very light and therefore contributes less to the dead load of a building. Steel is unsurpassed in resistance to stress but it is a heavy material to use. When selecting material for a component, study the type of stress to which that part will be subjected.

Materials	Ultimate Stress					
	Metric MPa (megapascals)			Imperial p.s.i. (pounds per square inch)		
	Tension	Compression	Shear	Tension	Compression	Shear
Concrete		170			2 500	
Brick masonry		140			2 000	
Stone masonry		170			2 500	
Wrought iron	330	330	275	48 000	48 000	40 000
Steel structural	425	425	425	60 000	60 000	45 000
Timber, parallel to grain	66	53	3	10 000	68 000	500
perpendicular to grain			20			3 000

FIGURE 8-4   *Stress loads in various building materials*

DEAD AND LIVE LOADS

Two different types of loads that a building can be subjected to that will cause stress are a dead load and a live load.

A **dead load** is the weight of the materials and equipment that form the permanent structure of the building. A **live load** is a variable load. A considerable load can be exerted on a building by a wind force or by the weight of snow on a roof. Some buildings, because of their special function, from time to time are subject to considerable additional loads, such as the weight of cars in a parking garage, people in an auditorium, or goods in a warehouse. Such factors must be taken into account when assessing the ultimate load that a building will eventually exert on the land.

Loads are applied in two ways:

1. as a concentrated load that bears down on a limited area, such as a furnace, and
2. as a uniformly distributed load that is applied over an extended area such as the weight of a length of the exterior wall on the foundations.

TRIBUTARY SUPPORT AREAS

The tributary support areas can be best understood from a foundation plan. A beam running the length of the house will normally support an area equal to one-quarter of the width of the house on each side, or an area equal to half the width of the house in total minus half the distance to a support at each end.

A column or pier will support not only a concentrated weight directly above it but will support a proportion of the total weight of the house which surrounds that column. This tributary support area will extend half the distance from the column to the adjacent support on each of the sides.

A joist or rafter will have to support a uniformly distributed load equal to half the space between the members on both sides, which in effect is the same distance as the *on centre spacing* (o.c.) of the joists or rafters. For residential houses, the distance is usually 400 mm (16") o.c. The area that the joist or rafter will support will be the width of the spacing times the length of the member.

For example, a joist that supports a living room in a two-storey house is 3 m (10' - 0") long spaced at 0.4 m (1 1/3') o.c. and will therefore have a tributary support area of 3 m × 0.4 m (10' - 0" × 1 1/3') = 1.2 m² (13.33 sq. ft.) *(see Figs. 8-5A and 8-5B)*.

Once the area to be supported is known, it is simple to calculate the load that the support beam, pier, joist, or rafter will carry. Multiply the area by the known load per square metre (per square foot)

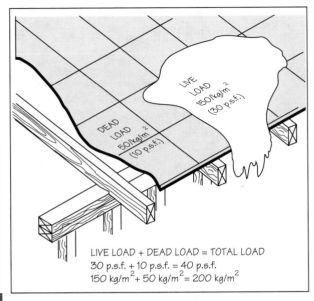

LIVE LOAD + DEAD LOAD = TOTAL LOAD
30 p.s.f. + 10 p.s.f. = 40 p.s.f.
150 kg/m² + 50 kg/m² = 200 kg/m²

FIGURE 8-5A *Determining the roof load*

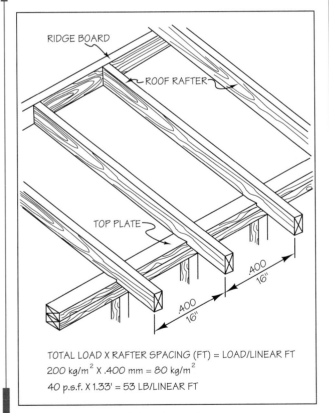

TOTAL LOAD X RAFTER SPACING (FT) = LOAD/LINEAR FT
200 kg/m² X .400 mm = 80 kg/m²
40 p.s.f. X 1.33' = 53 LB/LINEAR FT

FIGURE 8-5B *Determining the load on the rafters*

Construction Area	**Live**		**Dead**	
	kg/m²	p.s.f	kg/m²	p.s.f.
Roof	150	30	100	20
Ceiling joist, attic floor	75	15	100	20
Floor of living room	200	40	100	20
Floor of bedroom	150	30	100	20
Partitions	0	0	100	20

FIGURE 8-6 *Typical loads for a two-storey house*
Note: p.s.f. means pounds per square foot

for that area. A chart giving approximate loads for various parts of the house is shown in *Fig. 8-6.*

For example, the ceiling joist tributary support area has been calculated to be 1.2 m² (13.33 sq. ft.). The ceiling load for the living room of a two-storey house is 150 kg/m² (30 p.s.f.). The total load is 1.2 m² × 150 kg/m² = 180 kg (13.33 sq. ft. × 30 p.s.f. = 399.9 lbs.).

The larger the load to be carried, the larger the individual member must be in section. Greater strength can be attained by placing members closer together. However, when building a house it is preferable to keep all the components at the standard spacing of 400 mm (16") o.c.

TABLES FOR DETERMINING THE SIZE OF COMPONENTS

The loads supported by the various components of a house can be calculated by using Strength of Material formulas. The scope of this book does not permit dealing with these types of calculations, which would be the responsibility of an architectural engineer.

However tables related to house construction can provide the solutions to strength of material problems regarding the size of joists, rafters, beams, etc. because the materials used and distances spanned in most residential houses are similar. These tables can be found in the National and Provincial Building Codes and in the book *Canadian Wood-Frame House Construction* published by the CMHC. Selected tables to be used in the choice of joists and beams for the working drawings are reprinted in the Appendix of this book. Their use will be explained in detail in Chapter 14, Unit 4. When you use any of these tables, choose a distance slightly larger than the spanning distances required by the drawings.

THE NECESSITY FOR FOUNDATIONS

Because the entire load of the structure rests upon the soil, it is important that the resistance of the ground is sufficient to carry that load over a period of time.

The technical knowledge that has been accumulated by architects and construction engineers over the years ensures that buildings are stable and roads are durable. Various types of soil differ according to their respective load-bearing capacities. Care has been taken to ensure that the soil of a building lot is able to resist the weight of the structure placed upon it.

The great pyramids of Giza in Egypt are among the oldest surviving structures in the world. They are certainly the heaviest as they consist of some 2 000 000 stones, each weighing approximately 2.5 t (2 1/2 tons), yet the pyramids have remained stable because they were built on solid rock. By contrast, the smaller pyramid at Meidum, which was built in the same era but on a sand base, has collapsed.

To ensure the stability of a structure, soil conditions must be tested. *Fig. 8-8* gives approximate loads that various types of soil conditions will sup-

FIGURE 8-7 *Pyramids at Giza*
Photo courtesy of Museum of Fine Arts, Boston.

port. However, **soil borings** are usually made throughout the lot, and these samples are tested to determine the load that particular site will support.

As well, care must be taken to ensure that the footings, which are the lowest part of the foundation on which a structure is constructed, are taken below the frost line. Ground that freezes and is subject to thawing will be unstable as heaving will occur that will eventually cause cracks in the

Soil Type	Safe Load	Safe load
	kg/m2	p.s.f.
Soft clay, sandy loam	5 000	1 000
Firm clay, fine loose sand	10 000	2 000
Hard clay, fine compacted sand	15 000	3 000
Coarse sand, compacted	19 500	4 000
Gravel and sand, compacted	29 500	6 000
Soft rock	39 000	8 000
Hard shale, sandstone	52 500	15 000
Medium hard rock	120 000	25 000
Bedrock, granite	500 000	100 000

FIGURE 8-8
Safe soil loads

building. Therefore the footing of the building must be below the frost line (1200 mm [4'-0"] below the grade in Ontario). Ground that is permanently frozen and therefore not subject to thawing is called permafrost and is stable. In areas where the ground is not subject to freezing, houses can be constructed on a concrete pad set directly on the ground.

REVIEW QUESTIONS

1. Differentiate between three types of stress.
2. Explain how a tributary support area is calculated.
3. How can the load-bearing capabilities of soil be determined?

WHAT DO YOU THINK?

1. Why is it important to make the best use of materials?
2. How would you determine the sizes of joists and rafters for a house?
3. Why are foundations important?

ASSIGNMENTS

1. Calculate the total load on a rafter 38 mm x 140 mm (2" x 6") which is 3150 mm (10' - 6") long and spaced at 400 mm (16") o.c. The live load is 200 kg/m² (40 p.s.f.) and the dead load is 100 kg/m² (20 p.s.f.). Remember that the answers will be in kilograms per square metre (pounds per square foot). Therefore appropriate units must be used throughout.
2. Work out the tributary area for the beam shown in *Fig. 8-9*. If the load is 250 kg/m² (50 p.s.f.), how much is the total load on the beam?

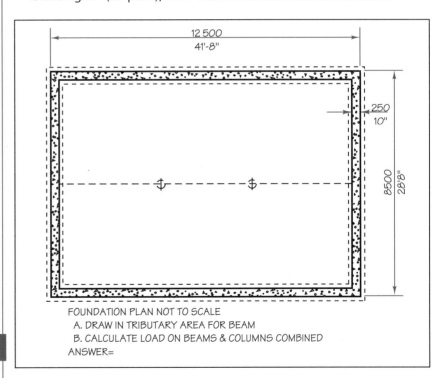

FOUNDATION PLAN NOT TO SCALE
   A. DRAW IN TRIBUTARY AREA FOR BEAM
   B. CALCULATE LOAD ON BEAMS & COLUMNS COMBINED
ANSWER=

FIGURE 8-9

UNIT 2 | Modular Design

OBJECTIVES

- To learn the historical development of modular design
- To learn the principle of modular design
- To learn the application of modular design

HISTORICAL DEVELOPMENT

The term **modular** refers to the use of standard proportions as a unit of measurement. This module is then used in determining all dimensions of the structure. The modular method of standard proportions was used by the early Greeks. Their module was the diameter of a column, and a set number of diameters determined the height of the column. The length and width of a building was also made equal to multiples of the column height.

The Romans maintained the Greek module and refined it to standardize the height of various types of columns. These columns were known as Ionic, Tuscan, Corinthian, and Doric *(see Fig. 8-10)*.

Leonardo Fibonacci found another system with which to proportion buildings, as well as other things. This Italian mathematician used an arithmetic progression of numbers, whereby, when the third number is equal to the sum of the previous two numbers, a "pleasing" proportion results. For example, the numbers 1, 2, 3, 5, 8, 13 create pleasing proportions between any two sequential numbers such as 2 to 3 or 5 to 8. These numerical proportions produce a rectangle that is pleasing to the eye.

Euclid first used these rectangular proportions during the third century B.C., and they have been found in numerous natural forms, such as seashells and leaves. It is often considered to be the key to formal beauty and is called the Golden Rectangle *(see Fig. 8-11)*. Designers in many fields of design use the golden rectangle for the division and proportioning of space *(see Fig. 8-12)*. Modular systems have even been used to record the human form in paintings and sculpture.

These examples of early modular proportions in various cultures were directed towards achieving aesthetically pleasing proportions. However, the Industrial Revolution brought about different needs for modular design. The invention of machines to produce goods faster resulted in the

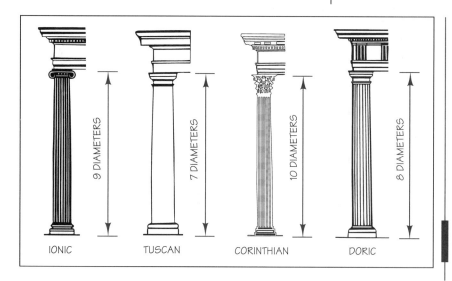

IONIC — 9 DIAMETERS
TUSCAN — 7 DIAMETERS
CORINTHIAN — 10 DIAMETERS
DORIC — 8 DIAMETERS

FIGURE 8-10
The Roman Orders of Architecture

FIGURE 8-11
Constructing a golden rectangle

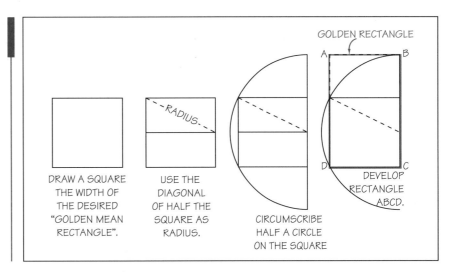

GOLDEN RECTANGLE

DRAW A SQUARE THE WIDTH OF THE DESIRED "GOLDEN MEAN RECTANGLE".

USE THE DIAGONAL OF HALF THE SQUARE AS RADIUS.

CIRCUMSCRIBE HALF A CIRCLE ON THE SQUARE

DEVELOP RECTANGLE ABCD.

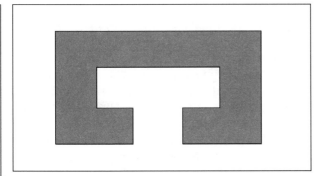

FIGURE 8-12 *Canada Trust trademark using golden rectangle*

beginning of mass production. People were willing to accept products of repetitive design, and perhaps lower quality, in favour of rapid production.

Machines can mass produce, however, only if everything remains standardized. Modular design soon became beneficial to mass production. One of the most famous examples of using modular design for speed and flexibility was constructed during the Industrial Revolution. In 1850 a world exhibition was planned for London, England, to display the newest inventions in the fields of science and industry. The leading architects' designs for the main exhibit building were unacceptable to the committee in charge. An engineer by the name of Joseph Paxton undertook the design problem. Through the use of modular design, the major components of wrought- and cast-iron units and glass panes could be manufactured throughout England. These units were then assembled on the site. The building was called the Crystal Palace and was the largest building in the world at that time. Seventeen acres (6.9 ha) were enclosed under one roof. The main building was 1851 feet long (564.5 m) to match the year in which it was built. It was erected in only six months because Paxton used a form of modular construction. Following the Exposition, it was dismantled and erected again at another site, where it stood until destroyed by fire in 1935.

The Crystal Palace displayed the advantages of modular design and prefabrication for speed and flexibility. The prefabrication construction method is used today in the building of huge skyscrapers. It was inevitable that the principles of modular design would be directed towards multiple housing as a means of lowering residential building costs.

In the 1940s, Charles Jeanneret, a Swiss architect, introduced a major influence of modular design on residential construction. He preferred to call himself Le Corbusier and is known in the world of architecture by that name. Le Corbusier contributed two important facets to modular design. Although he agreed with Fibonacci's golden rectangle and numerical proportions, he maintained that it is easier to work with modules of even numbers rather than odd and even numbers

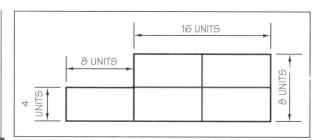

FIGURE 8-13 *An example of a modular system using even numbers*

(see Fig. 8-13). He developed a system he called *le modular,* which uses only even numbers. This concept was accepted by building material manufacturers, and the standard units of four-by-eight sheets or equal divisions of them became prominent. As we shall see later, the use of even-numbered modules became the base for modular construction.

The second contribution of Le Corbusier was his direct application in 1947 of modular design in planning apartment buildings for rejuvenating the areas of Marseilles, France, that had been bombed. Since each apartment plan was the same, components could be prefabricated and erected on the site. This modular design approach also made it possible to quickly erect apartment buildings of great height.

A common complaint about modular design is that the buildings can appear boring and monotonous. Architects have struggled with this problem and tried many ideas to create more interesting buildings while still using modular design. One of the best solutions to the problem was designed by architect Moshe Safdie from Israel. Habitat, his housing complex at the Montreal Expo '67 *(see Fig. 8-14),* used prefabricated modular designed units that could be arranged like children's blocks in a zigzag pattern.

Although the result looks confusing but interesting from the outside, the inside is a unique design of openness. Each apartment offers a different view, a private entrance, and a feeling of individual design. The ideas from Habitat have been used in many more modular housing projects.

The use of prefabrication soon became popular for single-family homes. The development of truss designs for roofs, new plastics, better insulating, stronger glues, and more efficient fastening systems brought a rapid increase in prefabricated housing. A co-ordinated system of modular dimensioning of components was established in the lumber trades. Millions of houses have now been built using modular construction.

FIGURE 8-14
Habitat

Photo: Ville de Montreal

THE PRINCIPLE OF MODULAR DESIGN

Using the theory of proportions with even numbers, a module of 4" was selected as the standard unit of measurement for modular design. The designer must make all components of the plan fit multiples of this standard unit. To do this, blueprints are usually first drafted on a 4" grid when planning room layouts. The grid is divided into 4", 16", 24", and 48" spaces (*see Fig. 8-15*). Wall studs, windows, and door panels use the 16" unit to allow flexibility in design. Overall house dimensions use increments of 24" and 48". The 24" module is called the *minor module* and the 48" module is called the *major module*. Modular dimensions are used in planning length, width and height. Window and door manufacturers as well as makers of other housing components have standardized sizes to conform with modular design principles.

The 16" module used for wall studs, joists, and rafters allows modular sheathing materials to be applied quickly as nailing positions are easy to

locate. When designing a modular house, you must draw all parts of the plan to fit the 4" module dimension minimum, or multiples of it.

The metric system of modular design uses the same principle of grid design as the imperial system, but the basic modular unit is slightly different in size. A basic module of 100 mm is used in multiples to establish a horizontal and vertical modular grid design. These multiples are known as **multimodules** and are used as follows:

- To control horizontal dimensions, the multimodule is 600 mm.
- To control vertical dimensions, the multimodule is 300 mm and 600 mm.

The metric modular grids use both a rectangular grid and a three-dimensional grid (*see Fig. 8-16*). This three-dimensional grid allows a variety of components, all of related modular size, to be arranged in horizontal and vertical designs. Any components that are to be smaller than the 300 mm and 600 mm multimodules are designed using the 100 mm basic module.

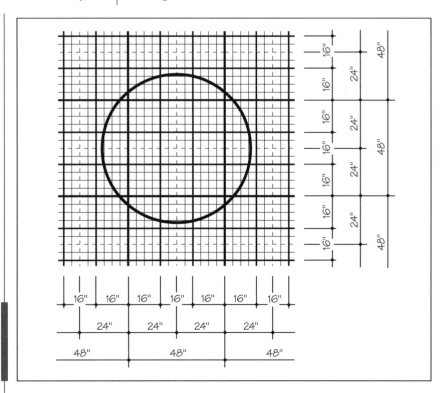

FIGURE 8-15

Modular-component grid

Hepler/Wallach: *Architecture: Drafting and Design*, 5e, © 1987. Reprinted by permission of Glencoe/McGraw-Hill Educational Division.

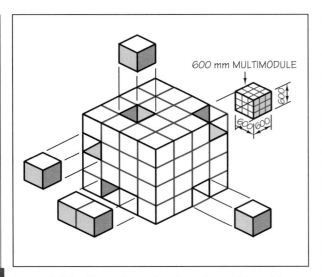

FIGURE 8-16 *Three-dimensional metric modular grid*

Jensen, C. *Architectural Drawing and Design for Residential Construction*, McGraw-Hill Ryerson Ltd.

APPLYING MODULAR DESIGN

The outside shape of the floor plan is first drawn to scale using the minor and major modules. These dimensions are taken from the outside of one wall to the outside of the opposite wall *(see Fig. 8-17)*. Any recessed areas or extensions must also be drawn to the minor or major module.

All interior partitions are then drawn on the plan to fit the modular grid. One side of the partition is always aligned to a module on the grid. To obtain the actual interior dimension, the wall thickness must be subtracted from the overall modular dimension *(see Fig. 8-18)*. Doors into rooms are plotted on the grid by modules.

Exterior doors and windows can then be located using the modular grid. The basic floor plan is now complete and has been formed into components that fit the modular grid *(see Fig. 8-19)*.

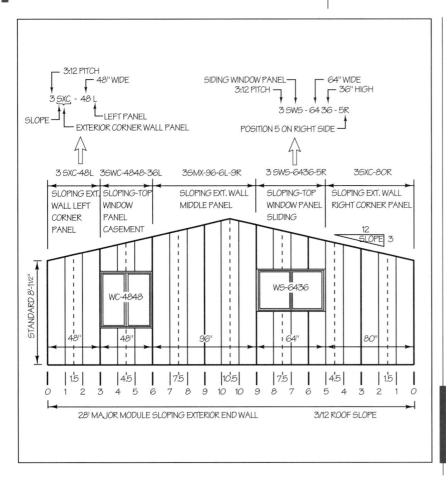

FIGURE 8-17

Modular wall dimensioning

Hepler/Wallach: *Architecture: Drafting and Design*, 5e, © 1987. Reprinted by permission of Glencoe/McGraw-Hill Educational Division.

FIGURE 8-18

Modular room dimensioning — metric

Jensen, C. *Architectural Drawing and Design for Residential Construction*, published by McGraw-Hill Ryerson.

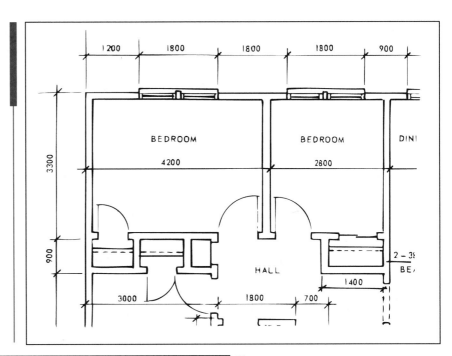

FIGURE 8-19

Modular dimensioning plan — metric

Jensen, C. *Architectural Drawing and Design for Residential Construction*, published by McGraw-Hill Ryerson.

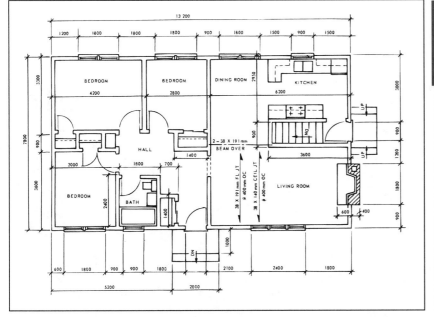

A system of short-form identification for fabricated components creates a simple, practical method of applying modular design *(see Fig. 8-20)*. Major components are identified by a letter and/or number code that tells the erection crew what the component is. To make installation easier, an erection sequence is included on the final detailed blueprints. For example, ER1 is erection component one; ER2 is erection component two, etc. This code clearly shows where to start erecting the house, through to completion.

X	Exterior-wall panels
XC	Full-corner exterior-wall panels
XCBM	Cantilever-beam exterior-wall corner panels
XCA	Cut-back corner exterior-wall panels
RP	Roof panels
FP	Floor panels
P	Interior partition panel
WC	Casement window panels
WD	Double-hung window panels
WS	Sliding window panels
WAF	Fixed-awning window panels
WP	Fixed picture-window panels
WPP	Full-height, fixed, picture-window panels
GG	Glass gable panels
D	Door panels with one door
2D	Door panels with two doors
DS	Door panels with one side light
2DS2	Door panels with two doors and two side lights
DS2	Door panels with two side lights
DSL	Sliding door panels
DA	Garage door panels

FIGURE 8-20 *Abbreviations for modular components*

Hepler/Wallach: *Architecture: Drafting and Design*, 2/e © 1971.
Material is reproduced with permission of McGraw-Hill, Inc.

The basic modular floor plan is redrawn into a detailed component plan that includes dimensions and codes for fabrication and erection. Elevation component plans are also drafted using the modular grid and coded for construction. The complete set of house plans are drawn to the modular grid, including any detailed drawings for special areas of the house.

Modular, prefabricated housing is increasing in popularity for several reasons: less waste material; factory-produced components; quality-controlled assembly; technologically advanced materials and assembly; less building time; less on-site finishing; competitive pricing; and flexibility of designs.

FIGURE 8-21 *Modular home — ranch style*

Viceroy Homes is a major Canadian manufacturer of both modular and pre-cut engineered houses. All Viceroy house designs are under registered copyright and no reproduction or use of these designs is permitted without prior approval of the company

REVIEW QUESTIONS

1. What is the Golden Rectangle?
2. Who was Joseph Paxton and what building is he famous for? What materials were used in the building?
3. How did Le Corbusier's theory of numerical proportions differ from that of Fibonacci's?
4. What are the standard module, the minor module, and the major module used for in today's modular designed houses?

WHAT DO YOU THINK?

1. Explain why you would or would not buy a prefabricated modular house.
2. What are five advantages to modular designed houses?
3. Do you think housing construction techniques will change greatly in the next 20 years? Explain your answer.

ASSIGNMENTS

1. Redraw the floor plan assigned by your instructor into a modular grid plan.
2. From the assigned floor plan, draw a front elevation for a house that fits the modular grid. Make sure the window and door locations are drawn with the correct module.

UNIT 3

Energy-Efficient Design

OBJECTIVES

- To learn about low-energy home design
- To learn about heating systems
- To learn about heat pumps

Every new home requires a heating system. Standard heating systems are either electricity, natural gas, oil, or wood. Heat is also added to a home by lights, appliances, people, and solar energy. A great deal of heat is lost from a conventional house through the walls, the roof, the windows, the basement areas and cracks in the structure. The construction methods of a conventional house do not allow sufficient space for enough insulation to increase the insulating factor to maximum efficiency.

During the 1980s, a growing concern developed about energy resources and costs. A new concept in the construction methods of a house resulted in a design known as the R-2000 house. The R stands for residence and the 2000 for the year 2000, by which time it is hoped that most new houses will be using the new ideas. The R-2000 house is called a **low-energy** house.

There are four key elements upon which the program is based: control of air leakage; high levels of insulation; efficient heating systems; and continuous mechanical ventilation. A major difference in the design of a low-energy house is the use of 2' × 6' wall studs, to allow for more insulation, and an increase of insulation in the basement level. Basement walls are insulated on the outside or the inside depending on the individual house design *(see Fig. 8-22)*. The R-2000 house has an increased insulating rating (R factor, RSI for metric) throughout the house *(see Fig. 8-23)*. There is also a continuous vapour barrier of plastic sheeting from the basement to the first- or second-storey ceiling. Window and door openings are also sealed against air leaks.

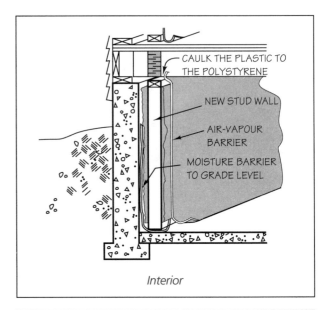

Interior

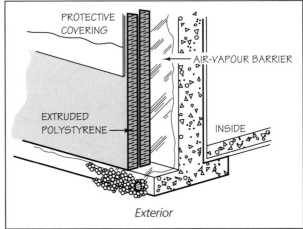

Exterior

FIGURE 8-22 *Interior and exterior basement insulation*

A great deal of consideration must be given to controlling moisture build-up within a house. This problem is controlled in an R-2000 house by the **heat recovery ventilation system (HRV)**. The HRV is installed in the basement and controls the flow of air within the house as well as the

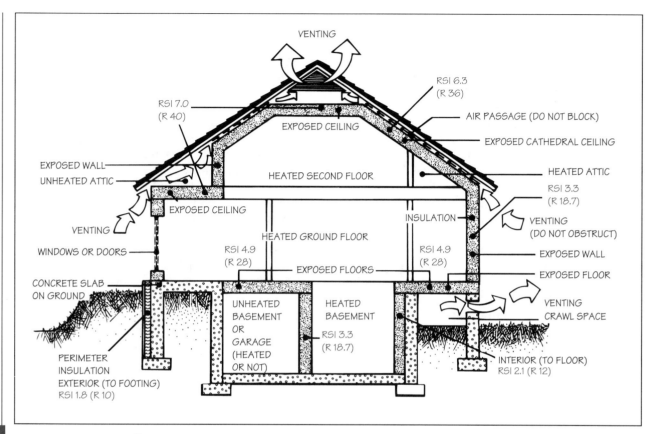

VENTING

RSI 6.3
(R 36)

RSI 7.0
(R 40)

AIR PASSAGE (DO NOT BLOCK)

EXPOSED CEILING

EXPOSED CATHEDRAL CEILING

EXPOSED WALL

HEATED ATTIC

UNHEATED ATTIC

HEATED SECOND FLOOR

RSI 3.3
(R 18.7)

EXPOSED CEILING

INSULATION

VENTING
(DO NOT OBSTRUCT)

VENTING

HEATED GROUND FLOOR

EXPOSED WALL

WINDOWS OR DOORS

RSI 4.9
(R 28)

RSI 4.9
(R 28)

EXPOSED FLOOR

EXPOSED FLOORS

CONCRETE SLAB
ON GROUND

VENTING

UNHEATED
BASEMENT
OR
GARAGE
(HEATED
OR NOT)

HEATED
BASEMENT

CRAWL SPACE

RSI 3.3
(R 18.7)

INTERIOR (TO FLOOR)
RSI 2.1 (R 12)

PERIMETER
INSULATION
EXTERIOR (TO FOOTING)
RSI 1.8 (R 10)

Figure 8-23 *Energy-efficient insulation standards*

Courtesy of Ontario Hydro

amount of air entering or leaving the house. To further conserve energy, the HRV recovers the heat from the air leaving the house, controls dust, and removes stagnant air.

Attic areas are more heavily insulated and air ventilation in the roof framing helps to increase the R factor from the standard RSI 5.64 (R-32) to RSI 10-5 (R-60) rating. Caulking all service holes, plastic vapour barrier seams, doors, windows, and vents adds the finishing touch to the R-2000 low-energy house. Because it is more expensive to build than the energy savings over a reasonable span of years, the R-2000 home is not as cost-efficient as originally projected.

A major public concern is the increase of pollution and acid rain in our environment. Since the burning of fossil fuels is one of the prime causes of air pollution, heating system manufacturers have improved their products dramatically. New high-efficiency furnaces are smaller, produce more heat, yet are clean burning.

Many models do not even require a conventional brick chimney to remove exhaust fumes, but can be exhausted through stainless steel ducts either through the roof of the house or through an exterior wall. Most high-efficiency furnaces are 90% efficient and therefore very few exhaust pollutants are expelled into the environment.

The two fuel systems of heating with a furnace are gas and oil. Both gas and oil furnaces supply heat throughout the house by forcing heated air through a system of metal ducts. The ducts are usually placed between the floor joists and wall studs and are arranged to heat every room in the house by the use of a vent. Heating vents are generally placed on the floor near an exterior wall, often under the windows of a room. The use of ducts for carrying the heating system also allows easier installation of central air-conditioning systems because the same ducts can transfer the cooled air throughout the house.

Electric heating systems offer a clean, efficient method of heating, although it can be more expensive to operate. The electrical heating units may be installed in the ceilings of each room or may be designed as baseboard units installed along the exterior walls of a room. Each room can have a separate thermostat heat control, allowing setting of individual room temperatures.

Improved technology and engineering design have made hot-water heating systems more attractive. Hot-water systems are now designed to fit along baseboards and, like the electric heating systems, can be installed to allow individual heat control within each room of the house. Although the forced hot-water systems require a gas, oil, or solar furnace to heat the water, it is a cleaner system since it does not blow dust or pollutants around the room. A hot-water furnace system does not require a large water-storage tank because the water is recirculated with minimal loss of volume.

The heat pump is a heating system that also provides air conditioning in the summer. A heat pump works in a similar fashion to a refrigerator, since a unit circulates liquid refrigerant through the system to collect any heat that is in the air. A compressor raises the temperature of the collected air heat to the desired temperature and the warm air is blown into the duct work of the house. The heat pump is so efficient that even on cold winter days, heat is still removed from the outside air, heated, and pumped into the house. In the summer, the system is reversed and the heat pump now acts as an air conditioner, removing the heat from inside air and replacing it with cooler air. Although the heat pump is more costly than a conventional furnace, the savings in fuel costs and its efficiency in heating and cooling are making it more popular today.

REVIEW QUESTIONS

1. What are the four key elements concerning the design of an R-2000 house?
2. How is moisture build-up controlled in an R-2000 house?
3. What is a heat pump?

WHAT DO YOU THINK?

1. Would you build an R-2000 house for yourself? Explain why or why not.
2. Do you think that nuclear-powered furnaces could be a feasible means of heating a house? Explain your thoughts.

ASSIGNMENTS

1. Collect literature on the latest designs for high-efficiency furnaces and heat pumps.
2. Use the literature collected in Assignment 1 to determine the most suitable type of heating in terms of the preservation of the environment.

PART 3

PRESENTATION DRAWINGS

Part Three explains, in a step-by-step method, how to design a house. You will learn about the stages from the preliminary planning to the presentation made to the client. The presentation drawings comprise a floor plan, a perspective drawing, and sometimes a model. Layouts for the design of kitchens, stairs, and bathrooms are discussed and the importance of good traffic patterns is emphasized.

This part of the text will be of particular interest to students taking interior design or technical illustrating courses, as well as architectural drafting and construction.

CHAPTER 9

Presentation
Floor Plans

A SET OF PRESENTATION DRAWINGS enables clients to confidently make decisions regarding the selection of a set of house plans when they decide to build a house.

A set of presentation drawings consists of:

1. an easily understandable floor plan showing the arrangement of the individual rooms and their respective sizes together with the overall size of the house. Since most contractors estimate on a per-square-metre or a per-square-foot basis, the overall sizes will enable clients to determine the approximate cost of building the house.
2. a perspective drawing showing the house situated on an imaginary lot. To give a realistic impression of the completed house, the exterior building materials and the landscaping are shown.

Other optional items include:

3. details of exceptional features such as a fireplace or a solarium.
4. a scale model. However, because models are expensive and time consuming to build, they are usually commissioned only for large or unusual structures.

The CAD system of designing a house allows you to store several variations of floor plans in the computer for later viewing or allows you to print a copy for client selection.

UNIT 1 | Preliminary Design and Traffic Flow

OBJECTIVES

- To become familiar with different types of house design
- To understand the purpose of making presentation drawings
- To understand the necessity of good traffic patterns
- To make a preliminary design for a house

Once you have decided on and purchased a lot, you must determine:

1. the size and area of house you like and can afford to build;
2. the orientation and maximum size of frontage for a house that is suitable for the lot determined by the site plan.

TYPES OF HOUSE DESIGN

There are several different types of house designs you can choose from, for example, the single-storey house, 1 1/2-storey house, bi-level house, two-storey house, and the split-level house. Options in single-family dwellings are semi-detached or row-house construction. Before making any decisions about the type of house you would like to design, study the comments beside the diagrams for houses designed for level lots *(see Fig. 9-1A)* and for houses designed for sloping lots *(see Fig. 9-1B)*.

Also available to house designers are *home magazines,* which publish examples of sets of presentation drawings *(see Fig. 9-2)*. Most home magazines offer plans for all styles and sizes of houses. Full sets of plans are available for purchase so that the house can be completed. They are readily available in supermarkets, variety stores, bookstores, newsstands, and libraries.

A set of presentation drawings should provide a client with a house plan that suits his or her needs and budget. The house plan should also be designed to fit the site plans for a particular lot.

It is important that the drawings be as attractive as possible since most clients are not experienced at reading technical drawings. The information provided must be easy to understand and yet be sufficiently detailed that a client can confidently assess the suitability of the design.

ESTABLISHING THE COST

The size of the house is the major factor in establishing the cost. The price of most houses is estimated on a cost per-square-metre or per-square-foot. The area of the house is calculated on the living space and does not usually include the basement.

Comparative House Areas

Small	75 - 125 m^2	(800 - 1400 sq. ft.)
Medium	135 - 200 m^2	(1500 - 2200 sq. ft.)
Large	220 - 365 m^2	(2500 - 4000 sq. ft.)

The cost per-square-metre or per-square-foot will vary with the type of house and also with the economic conditions of the area at a particular time. Inquiries regarding up-to-date costs must be made yearly.

DESIGNING THE PRELIMINARY FLOOR PLAN

The first step in preparing to make a presentation floor plan is to begin designing the layout of the house. Start by relating the rooms to the overall orientation of the house on the lot. This is best achieved by using bubbles that are proportionate to the amount of space required for each major activity such as living, eating, and sleeping. Make small sketches of the way the rooms might be

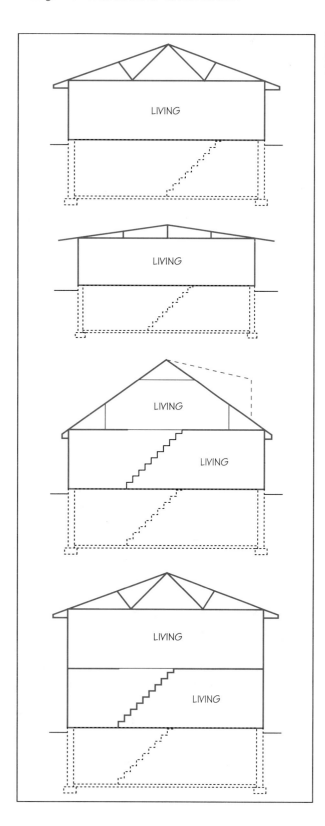

FIGURE **9-1A** *House designs for level lots*

Courtesy Canadian Wood Council

One-Storey Pitched Roof and Flat Ceiling

There are more size, shape, and design variations in one-storey houses than in any other type. Despite these variables, the construction simplicity of most one-storey designs provides an excellent basis for studies of construction methods which may result in important cost savings.

From a livability standpoint, one-level houses are advantageous. Families of all ages, including the retirement group, favour the convenience of one-storey houses. Many multi-level houses are designed with a variety of one-storey additions as a basic feature of the composite architectural design.

One-Storey Pitched Roof and Sloping Ceiling - Flat Roof

The roof design and load-bearing elements of houses with flat roofs and those with continuous sloping roofs and ceilings are similar. Both types are significantly different, in structural design, from houses with trusses or with rafters and ceiling joists. Good architectural detail, in the functional design of these basic house types, will result in exciting examples of contemporary living. These same roof construction details are often used in multi-level houses.

1 1/2-Storey Two Living Levels - Varying Second Floor Area and Ceiling

The most familiar 1 1/2-storey house is the "Cape Cod." The basic simplicity of the Cape Cod design should be retained, in proportion and detail, if an approach to historical authenticity is desired. The 1 1/2-storey basic shape permits a wide design variety other than traditional. The steep, sloping roof can be the basis for many outstanding contemporary designs. The second-floor living area, which varies in size with the house dimensions and use of dormers, provides for flexible planning.

Two-Storey Two Living Levels - Varying Roof and Ceiling Types

Like 1 1/2-storey houses, two-storey house types should be designed with great respect for proportion and detail, regardless of their architectural style. The box-like, two-storey form provides maximum living area at the least cost. A wide range of roof types can be used to vary the design characteristics of the two-storey house. Lower- and upper-level walls can be in the same plane or, in some cases, the upper-level walls may be projected to gain more floor area and break the high wall appearance. Various types of additions to the two-storey box often enhance overall design composition.

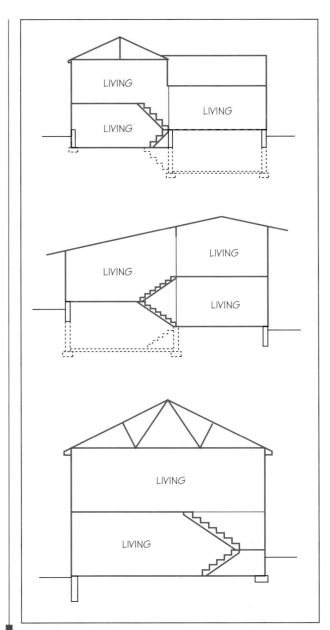

Split-Level A: Three or More Living Levels - Varying Roof and Ceiling Types

Split-level house types have three living levels and an optional fourth-level basement. All levels are connected by segments of stairs that combine in pairs to make one full-stair flight. The multi-levels provide distinct separation for different living functions which can be planned with unlimited variety. Split-levels function and look better on rolling sites where lower-level living areas can have full-storey height exposure to outdoor living. Split-level exteriors may also vary with unlimited design variety. However, they are complicated and, without sufficient design study, can result in awkward proportions. Split-level living areas can have full-storey height exposure to outdoor living.

Split-Level B: Three or More Living Levels - Continuous Sloping Roof and Ceiling

Split-level B is characterized by a sloping roof which is continuous over two or more floor levels. The roof extension over the middle level establishes certain dimensional limitations that control the width of the middle level and the floor-to-floor relationship. The exterior simplicity of split-level B houses usually results in a functional design of pleasant proportions. Interiors, too, can have many interesting characteristics through the use of different roof and ceiling materials on the continuous slope. In terms of livability, both split-level types are similar.

Bi-Level Two Living Levels - Varying Roof and Ceiling Types - Split-Level Foyer

The bi-level may also be identified as a sunken two-storey house without a basement, or a raised one-storey house with optional finished basement. The split-level foyer, between two full living levels, is a predominating characteristic of the bi-level design. Functional arrangement of the living areas, in the bi-level, varies widely. Some have complete living facilities on the upper level, with flexible use of space on the lower level. Other designs split the living facilities between the two floors in various combinations. Control of construction costs, combined with maximum living areas, have established the bi-level as a good value in the housing market.

arranged, then mark in the position of the front and rear entrances with large arrows *(see Fig. 9-3A)*.

Next, determine the approximate size that you would like the individual rooms to be and develop your plan by using simple rectangular shapes.

Sketch them, on graph paper, as they will be located on the plan *(see Fig. 9-3B)*. Do not be concerned if the rooms do not fit together exactly; you can make adjustments later. This task can be easily accomplished with a CAD program.

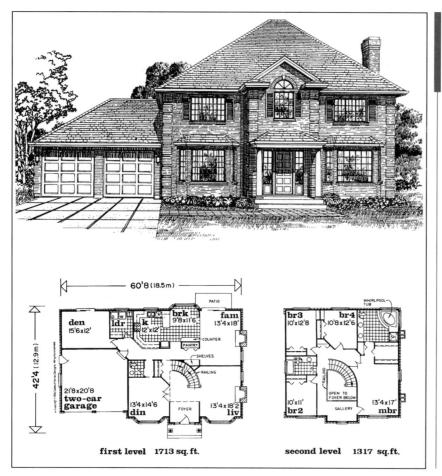

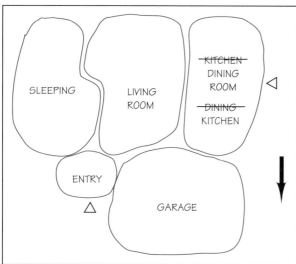

FIGURE 9-3A *Bubble diagram – stage "A" in planning*

TRAFFIC FLOW

There must be easy access to each room by means of doors and passageways. The location of stairways, which are really inclined passageways, should also be considered.

Occupants of a house generally will find movement through the house much easier when the designer has made provision for good traffic flow. A well-designed house should enable occupants of various ages and with different activities to move around the house with the least amount of interruption *(see Figs. 9-4A and 9-4B)*.

Certain rooms in a house will generally be located next to each other, such as the kitchen and dining room; the bedrooms and bathrooms; the main foyer and living room. Ideally, the kitchen should be located near the driveway for

FIGURE 9-3B

Sketch showing approximate room sizes and locations – stage "B" in planning

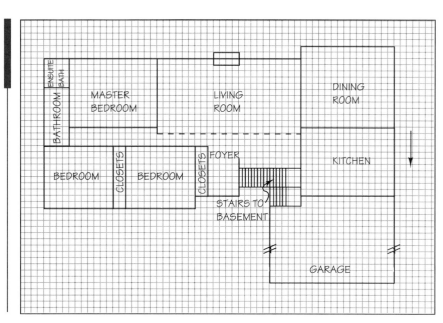

FIGURE 9-4A

Poor traffic flow

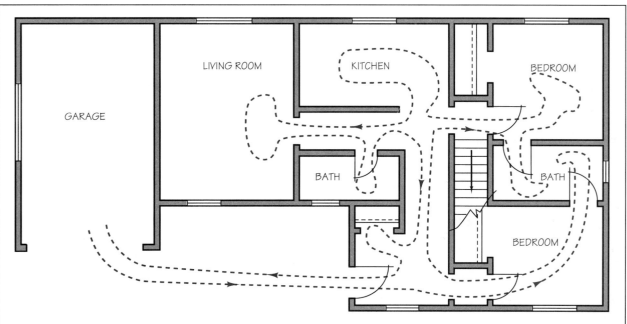

unloading groceries and taking out the garbage. The stairs should be in a location that maximizes efficient traffic flow to the rest of the house.

A variety of factors may have to be considered for other areas. As an example, consider the factors in deciding the placement of a laundry room. Should it be located upstairs where most of the laundry originates; in the basement, so that less living space will be used up for a utility area; in the kitchen, so that housekeeping chores can be integrated with each other; or near an exit door for proximity to a clothesline? Will the location selected be close to other plumbing in the house?

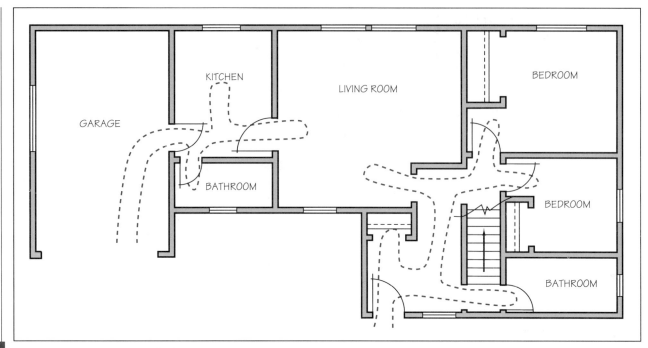

FIGURE 9-4B *Improved traffic flow*

PASSAGEWAYS

The pathway a person takes when moving from one area of the house to another is controlled by passageways, stairs, and doors. The minimum width of a passageway should be 860 mm (2'-10") from face to face of walls. Try to avoid long passageways. They are unattractive and do not provide usable living space yet cost the same amount per unit area to build and maintain. Passageways should not exceed 15% of the area of the house. By using the dead-end space between rooms as closets or as storage, passageways can often be shortened. This has the advantage of forming an effective sound barrier between rooms because the clothes in the closet absorb sound *(see Figs. 9-5A and 9-5B).*

DOORS

The side on which a door is hung will determine the direction a person takes after going through that door *(see Figs. 9-6A and 9-6B).* A door can provide a form of privacy if it is hinged on the room side. However, if the door is hinged on the wall side, there will be more usable space avail-

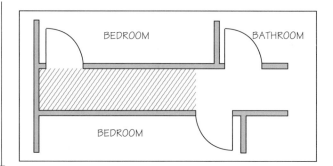

FIGURE 9-5A *Minimal use of passageway*

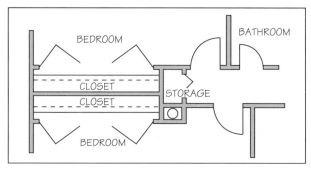

FIGURE 9-5B *Improved use of space to create an effective sound barrier*

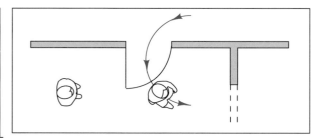

FIGURE 9-6A *Door hinged on right directs traffic pattern*

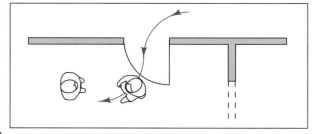

FIGURE 9-6B *Door hinged on left directs traffic pattern*

able. This would be a consideration in a small room *(see Figs. 9-7A and 9-7B)*.

FURNITURE

Traffic patterns are also influenced by the placement of furniture. When a room has diagonally placed entrances, a large couch, chair, or table carefully placed will cause a person walking between the doors to follow a path. It will be a less direct path but will not interrupt any activity that is taking place in the room *(see Figs. 9-8A and 9-8B)*.

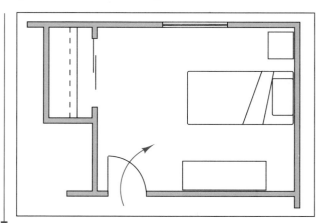

FIGURE 9-7A *Door hinged on wall side – less privacy, more apparent space*

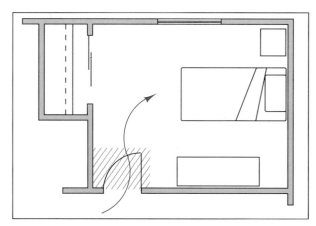

FIGURE 9-7B *Door hinged on room side – more privacy, less apparent space*

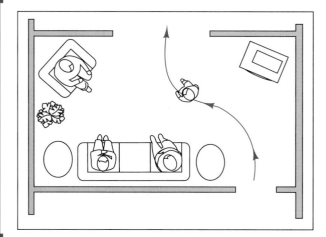

FIGURE 9-8A *Entrances controlling traffic flow*

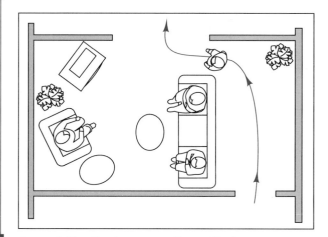

FIGURE 9-8B *Furniture controlling traffic flow*

ASSESSING THE TRAFFIC FLOW

On a copy of your floor plan, assess the traffic-flow pattern by tracing, in coloured pencils, the probable movements of different occupants of the house during times of major activity, such as early morning or early evening. Review the results, and decide whether you could improve upon the traffic flow of the floor plan you have designed *(see Figs. 9-9A and 9-9B).*

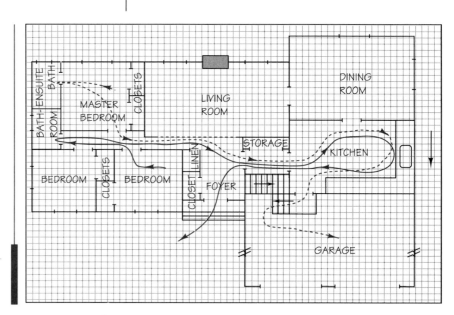

FIGURE 9-9A
Traffic flow of household from 7 A.M. to 9 A.M.

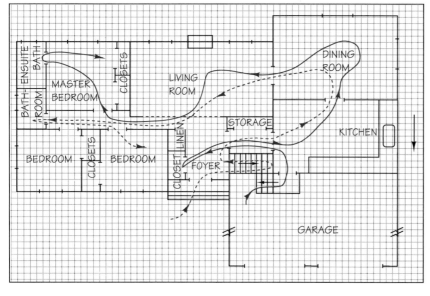

FIGURE 9-9B
Traffic flow of household from 5 P.M. to 11 P.M.

REVIEW QUESTIONS

1. What decisions must be made about the house before you can begin to design it?
2. Describe how the traffic patterns in a house can be influenced by the placement of doors and furniture.
3. Describe how to avoid dead-ended passageways.

WHAT DO YOU THINK?

1. In your opinion, what are the advantages and disadvantages of each type of house design?
2. Which type of house has the most practical traffic patterns? Explain your answer.
3. Study the traffic flow in your own home and outline what improvements could be made. If there are none, explain why it is ideal.

ASSIGNMENTS

1. Sketch the floor plan of your own home or a friend's home on graph paper using a scale of 4 squares = 1 m or 1 square = 1'-0".
   a. Show the traffic pattern made by three members of your household during a particular time of the day. Use different coloured pencils for each member's pattern.
   b. Comment on how the traffic pattern could be improved.
2. Using two copies of a floor plan, supplied by your instructor:
   a. indicate the morning traffic pattern, using a coloured pencil on one plan;
   b. make minor structural changes that will improve the traffic pattern on the second plan;
   c. using another coloured pencil, indicate the revised traffic-flow pattern.
3. On the upper floor plan, supplied by your instructor, rearrange the closets to make the best use of space and sound-proofing for bedrooms. Make your changes by tracing over the drawing on vellum.

UNIT 2 | Kitchen and Bathroom Design

OBJECTIVES

- To appreciate the significance of the work triangle
- To explore the historical and sociological development of kitchen design
- To design a workable kitchen and bathroom plan
- To appreciate why plumbing should be concentrated in one area of the house

KITCHEN DESIGN SEQUENCE

The layout of a kitchen can influence home buyers more than any other feature of a house. In a well-designed kitchen, the work areas are divided into three stations to accommodate the sequence of activities *(see Fig. 9-10)*. However, allowances must be made for alternative sequences.

THE WORK TRIANGLE

A person working in a kitchen will move between the sink, refrigerator, and cooking unit. Locate a point at the centre front of each of these locations, then join these points to form a triangle. This triangle is called the **work triangle** and is the basis for all kitchen design *(see Fig. 9-11A-F)*. It indicates the pattern of movement most followed in a kitchen. For a comfortable and practical work space, the perimeter of the work triangle should not measure more than 6 m (20'-0") or less than 3.5 m (11'-6"). Care should be taken to ensure that other traffic patterns do not intercept the work triangle.

COMMON KITCHEN LAYOUTS

A change in lifestyle over the last 50 years has caused an inevitable change in the organization of the North American kitchen. The most common kitchen layouts used during this period are shown below with the approximate years of their popularity.

1930-1940: One-Wall Kitchen *(see Fig. 9-11A)*
This type of layout was suitable so that several people from the large extended family could assist with food preparation. A large table was placed along the opposite wall and everyone could eat together. Today, a one-wall kitchen would be too long for all the modern equipment to comfortably fit. This type of kitchen is rarely found in contemporary homes.

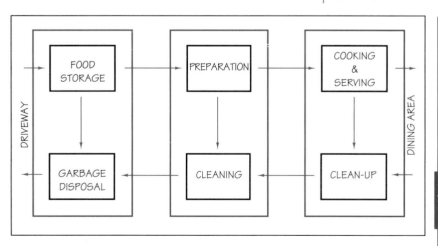

FIGURE 9-10
Schematic sequence of kitchen activities

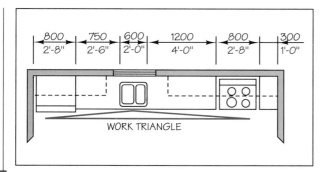

FIGURE 9-11A *One-wall kitchen*

Courtesy of CMHC: The Use and Design of Space in the Home

1940-1955: L-Shaped Kitchen *(see Fig. 9-11B)*

This layout fits well into a rectangular space with an eating area in the opposite corner of the room. Several people are able to work together in this kitchen. It is still found in some modern houses.

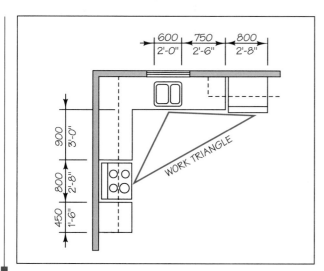

FIGURE 9-11B *L-shaped kitchen*

Courtesy of CMHC: The Use and Design of Space in the Home

1955-1965: U-Shaped Kitchen *(see Fig. 9-11C)*

This is a very popular design for a kitchen and is still used today. Only two people can work in this area comfortably together since the width of the U is usually only 1-2 m (3'-3" - 6'-6"). The main advantage of this layout is that traffic cannot pass through the work triangle and interrupt the movement. An eating area can be conveniently placed in an adjacent and separate area.

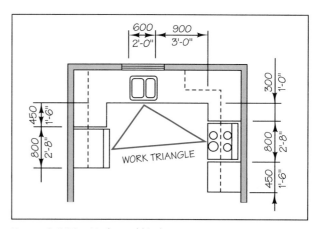

FIGURE 9-11C *U-shaped kitchen*

Courtesy of CMHC: The Use and Design of Space in the Home

1965: Corridor Kitchen *(see Fig. 9-11D)*

This is a practical kitchen for an apartment or a small house because everything is within reach. Only one person can comfortably use this kitchen at a time as the space between counters can be as narrow as 1.2 m (4'-0"). Take care to see that no traffic patterns run through this kitchen.

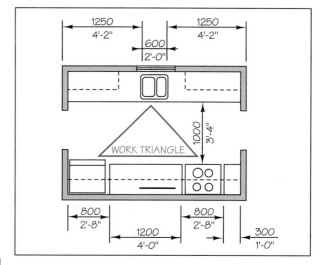

FIGURE 9-11D *Corridor kitchen*

Courtesy of CMHC: The Use and Design of Space in the Home

1975: Island Kitchen *(see Fig. 9-11E)*

The island configuration is most convenient if it incorporates one of the major appliances or a sink. Quite often, the island includes a snack counter.

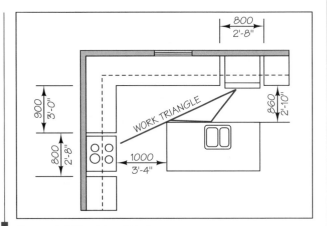

FIGURE 9-11E   *Island kitchen*

Courtesy of CMHC: The Use and Design of Space in the Home

The island should have an 860 mm (2'-10") wide passageway on all sides. Therefore, the space for an island kitchen must be large. It is possible to put the island on castors so that it is movable.

1991: Dual Work Triangles *(see Fig. 9-11F)* Busy working couples often share cooking responsibilities. If two people are to work together in a kitchen, the layout of the kitchen should be designed with this in mind. A kitchen can be designed with two adjacent work triangles. A bar sink and microwave oven, placed at the opposite side of the kitchen from the main sink and cooking centre, will form a convenient subsidiary work triangle using the refrigerator as the third apex of both triangles.

If the kitchen is not large enough for this arrangement, then two separate working areas should be incorporated into the plan. A vegetable preparation area can be placed adjacent to the sink, and a meat preparation area can be planned near the stove.

SAFETY DESIGN CONSIDERATIONS

The kitchen is the area in a home where most accidents happen. Care must be taken in the design to eliminate as many safety hazards as possible.

Plan the placement of kitchen doors carefully. Doors leading directly into the kitchen take up space and can create a safety hazard. For example, doors opening into the working area could collide with someone handling sharp knives or hot dishes. For this reason, all cooking units should be well clear of doors and the traffic coming into the area from entrances to the kitchen.

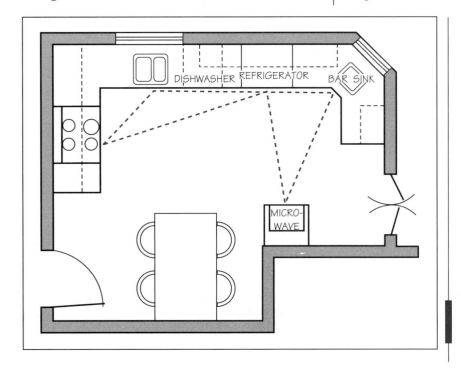

FIGURE 9-11F
Dual work triangles

Kitchen windows, whether they are covered or openable, should not be placed directly over cooking or heating surfaces.

All electrical wiring must comply with safety regulations in accordance with the provincial electrical codes.

KITCHEN COUNTERS AND CABINETS

Once the initial kitchen plan has been developed, the specific arrangement of counters, cupboards, and drawers can be considered.

There should always be approximately 600 mm (2'-0") of counter space either side of the sink for receiving dirty dishes and placing clean dishes in an easy sequence. Also, a clear counter space 900 mm (3'-0") long should be available for the major work area in the kitchen.

Doors on appliances and cabinets should open towards the sink (that is, the hinge side should be furthest from the sink) as often as possible. At least six drawers should be incorporated into the design of the cabinets for utensils, table mats, and so on.

Stoves and refrigerators should always have a counter at least 450 mm (18") long placed between them so that temperatures generated by one will not affect the other.

Cabinets can be custom built on-site by a carpenter or can be selected from a brochure of ready-built cabinets. Most kitchen cabinet manufacturers will assist you in determining the correct units for your kitchen layout and will install the cabinets. Since prefabricated units are factory made, they are quality controlled, which is important because drawers and cabinet doors are an integral part of the kitchen cupboards and must continue to fit well for the life of the units. In selecting factory-made kitchen cabinets, quality is usually relative to cost.

APPLIANCES AND MATERIALS

Manufacturers are constantly improving the design, quality, and selection of modern kitchen equipment and materials. Local building suppliers can show you current brochures and provide advice regarding the practicality and relative costs of the latest materials.

Maintenance and safety factors, such as slipperiness of surfaces or flammability, should be the main consideration in selecting equipment and materials for this heavily used work area.

DRAFTING THE KITCHEN

Symbols for drawing kitchen plans and the minimal space required between various appliances have been shown in the kitchen layout diagrams. *Fig. 9-12* shows the standard sizes for cabinet work. It is unwise to deviate from these sizes to suit the immediate users because of the possible depreciation effect on the resale value of the house.

Base cabinets are generally 600 mm (2'-0") deep and are indicated by a solid line on the floor plan. Wall cupboards or upper cabinets are only 330 mm (13") deep and are shown with a dashed line. Wall cupboards may extend over the refrigerator and stove, in which case the bottom of these cupboards should be raised to accommodate the height required for the appliances. Initial plans can be approximated using graph paper. A plan drawn at a scale of 1:20 (3/4" = 1'-0") will provide enough space to allocate areas for specific tasks and storage facilities. The usual scale for a finished plan as part of a set of working drawings is 1:50 (1/4" = 1'-0").

LAUNDRY FACILITIES

Some people prefer a separate laundry room or utility room that is placed between the kitchen and an exterior door. A laundry room that is close to the bedroom and bathrooms might also be considered, as this is where the majority of clothes will be discarded for washing and where most of the clean clothes will eventually be stored. If space is unavailable on the main floor, laundry rooms are often located in the basement. Also you should consider that a laundry room with a concrete floor is advisable in case of water spills.

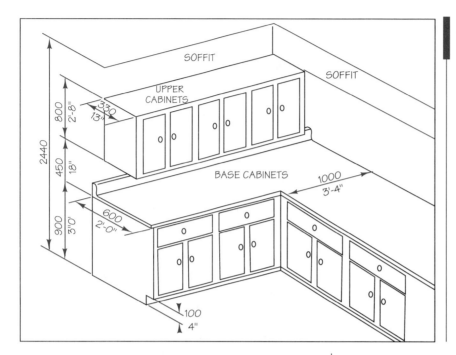

FIGURE 9-12
Cabinet and counter sizes

Other than the washer and dryer, the laundry room should be equipped with double tubs and indoor overhead drying lines. A storage bin of some sort could be included in the laundry design, as well as a counter for sorting and folding laundry. If the laundry is in the basement, a laundry chute from the upper floors can easily be incorporated into the structure between the studs. Space for an ironing board should also be part of the plan.

STORAGE

Most households have a lot of items that have to be stored. A good house plan provides storage spaces for seldom used items.

THE LOCATION OF BATHROOM FACILITIES

All houses must have at least one full bathroom and could include another small washroom with only a toilet and sink. Washrooms, apart from those that are ensuite, should be readily accessible to all occupants of the house and to visitors. The best location for the full bathroom is central to the bedroom area.

A good location for a general use washroom is close to a rear door, with easy access from the kitchen, or in the main foyer for the convenience of guests. There should be a toilet facility on each floor level of a house.

PLUMBING LOCATIONS

When planning the location of the bathrooms, laundry room, and kitchen, be aware that it is best to locate all of the plumbing in one area of the house. It will be much less expensive to install plumbing lines that service facilities located directly above or below each other on different floors. Also, a hot-water supply will be much more efficient and economical if all the sinks in the house are close to the hot-water tank. A soil pipe, which should descend vertically to the foundation and sewer pipe, must be installed from each toilet. Care must be taken to locate each of the toilets so that the path of the soil pipes will not pass through the centre of any rooms.

When building a house, it is practical to have washroom plumbing roughed-in for the basement even if this level is not to be finished off immediately. This will make it much cheaper to install plumbing connections and fixtures later.

BATHROOM SIZES

When designing a bathroom, make allowances for the amount of space needed for uninterrupted human movement when the bathroom equipment is being used. Also, there should be enough space between the bath (or shower) and other fixtures in the room to allow a person to dry off and dress in comfort.

Infants and small children require special equipment in the bathroom. This equipment, although temporary, takes up space. Elderly or disabled people may also need particular facilities even if they are only occasional visitors. Therefore, it is wise to allow additional room in a bathroom than might otherwise appear adequate for general use.

The size of contemporary bathroom equipment varies considerably. Consult current brochures or retail order catalogues for detailed information on specific items.

	Metric	Imperial
Bathroom Sizes		
Small	2400 mm x 1800 mm	8'-0" x 6'-0"
Medium	3300 mm x 2100 mm	11'-0" x 7'-0"
Large	4200 mm x 2700 mm	14'-0" x 9'-0"
Washroom Sizes		
Small	2000 mm x 900 mm	6'-6" x 3'-0"
Medium	2100 mm x 1500 mm	7'-0" x 5'-0"
Large	2700 mm x 1800 mm	9'-0" x 6'-0"
Bathroom Equipment		
Bathtubs	1500 mm-1800 mm x 850 mm	(5'-0")-(6'-0") x (2'-10")
Shower Cabinets	900 mm square	3'-0" square
Toilets	500 mm wide	20" wide
Vanities	425-550 mm deep	17"-22" deep
Space Allowances (Minimum)		
Edge of Bath and Other Fixtures	850 mm	2'-10"
Centre of Sink or Mirror to Sidewall	450 mm	18"
Centre of Toilet to Sidewall	375 mm	15"

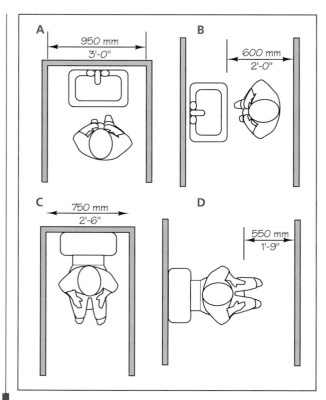

FIGURE 9-13A *Space for wash basin between walls;*
B *Alternative space for wash basin between walls;*
C *Space for toilet between wallls;*
D *Alternative space for toilet between wallls*

Courtesy of CMHC: The Use and Design of Space in the Home

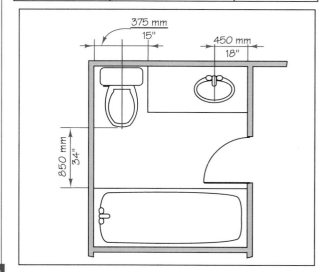

FIGURE 9-14 *Minimum distances for bathroom fixtures*

DOORWAYS

Use discretion when positioning the bathroom doors. An open door should not reveal the toilet facilities even to a hallway. Since a bathroom is not usually intended to house furniture, a door 600 mm (2'-0") wide will be enough.

REVIEW QUESTIONS

1. What is the normal sequence of activities in a kitchen?
2. Why should all the plumbing be located in one area?

WHAT DO YOU THINK?

1. Sketch a kitchen design for the future. Consider changes in lifestyle and eating habits. Use your imagination.
2. Which kitchen layout described in this chapter do you like best and why?
3. Bathroom facilities have become more luxurious in the last few years. Describe your ideas for a contemporary bathroom.

ASSIGNMENTS

1. Draw a layout of your kitchen or a friend's kitchen on graph paper using a scale of 4 squares = 500 mm (2 squares = 1'-0").
   a. Discuss the layout of the kitchen with your family and report on good and poor facilities in a written report.
   b. Plan one change that might be made to improve the efficiency of the kitchen. Draw it in on the plan with a coloured pencil and write up this change.
   c. Rate your kitchen at home using the assessment sheets supplied by your instructor. Record the score on your drawing.
2. a. Plan a kitchen layout for a given area plan supplied by the instructor. Do not include an eating area in your design but do indicate where all doors and entrances lead. Use the scale of 1:20 (3/4" = 1'-0") and record this on your drawing.
   b. Rate your kitchen design using the assessment sheet supplied by your instructor. Record results on your drawing.
3. Correct major design errors in the kitchen layout supplied by the instructor.
   a. On a sheet of vellum, superimposed on the supplied drawing, redesign the kitchen. Only minimal structural alterations should be made.
   b. Rate your design using the assessment sheet supplied by your instructor and make your own appraisal of the changes that you have suggested.
4. Research the development of a major kitchen appliance from the 1900s to contemporary times and write a consumers' report giving ideas for further improvements in the foreseeable future.
5. On graph paper using 4 squares = 500 mm (2 squares = 1'-0"), sketch a plan of the bathroom and washroom facilities in your own home or in a friend's. Give the overall dimensions and show the distances between corner and wall; toilet and wall; tub and counter or wall; and so on.

UNIT 3 | Stairway Design

OBJECTIVES

- To appreciate safety concerns in stairway design
- To understand the significance of the placement of stairways
- To calculate the size of risers/treads and rise/run
- To determine the size of the stairwell opening
- To appreciate different types of stairways

REGULATIONS FOR STAIRWAYS

Stairways are a potential hazard in a house and are the cause of many serious accidents. Therefore, it takes careful planning to ensure that they are convenient to use and that potential safety hazards are minimized. Government building codes are precise regarding many aspects of stairway

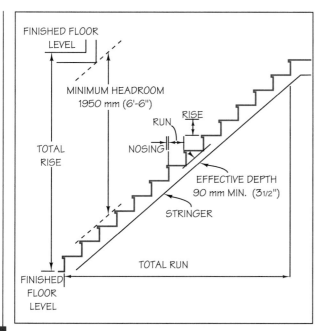

FINISHED FLOOR
LEVEL

MINIMUM HEADROOM
1950 mm (6'-6")

RISE

RUN

NOSING

TOTAL
RISE

EFFECTIVE DEPTH
90 mm MIN. (3½")

STRINGER

TOTAL RUN

FINISHED
FLOOR
LEVEL

FIGURE 9-15 *Stairway terminology*
Courtesy of CMHC: The Use and Design of Space in the Home.

design. Students should familiarize themselves with these regulations. The Canada Mortgage and Housing Corporation book *Canadian Wood Frame House Construction* provides an overview of the regulations.

TRAFFIC FLOW

Since a stairway is really an inclined passage, it forms part of the traffic pattern in a house. The minimal width for a passageway is 860 mm (2'-10"), when measured from face to face of the enclosing walls. A width of 1000 mm (3'-4") is preferable for most stairways but should not exceed 1350 mm (4'-6") in the average house. Most residential stairs have a solid wall on one side and a handrail on the open side. Totally enclosed stairs, that is, with a wall on each side, are less attractive and make a hallway appear narrow.

Since stairs are used often by all members of a household, which may include the elderly and the very young, they must be easy to use. The activity of ascending stairs involves lifting one's weight over a distance that is greater than one's height, so a designer must consider the proportions and the mechanical ability of the human frame. The study of the mechanical ability of the human frame is called **ergonomics**, and many different professionals such as architects, product designers, and engineers use it in their work.

PASSAGEWAY FOR FURNITURE

Furniture has to be transported to other levels in a house by way of the stairs. When the stairs must change direction, the most common method of design is to use a landing before the change of direction. These designs are called **non-winder** stairs, and several types are shown in *Fig. 9-16*.

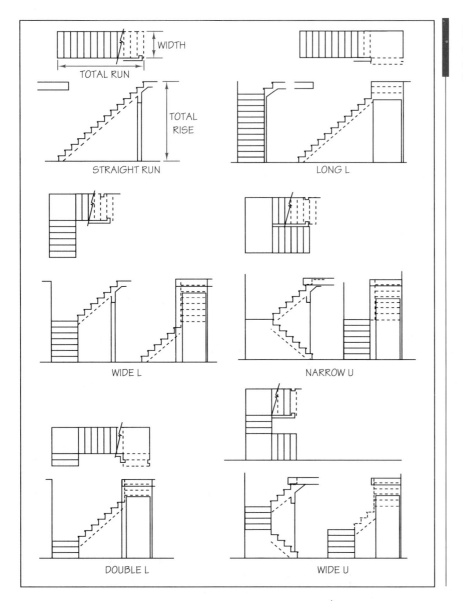

FIGURE 9-16

Different types of non-winder stairs

Courtesy of CMHC: The Use and Design of Space
in the Home

Another method of changing the direction of the stairs without using a landing is to use a set of **winders**. Winders are wedge-shaped stairs, and only one set is allowed between floor levels *(see Fig. 9-17)*. Either of these alternatives is almost certain to result in difficulty when large pieces of furniture are moved up stairs. Therefore, if stairs must change direction, they should be wider than the minimal width for stairs.

Sometimes stairs are constructed to curve between two walls that are at right angles to one another. This makes the movement of furniture easier but takes up more space and is more expensive to build than the two designs mentioned above. Curving stairs should be restricted to the plans for larger houses *(see Fig. 9-18)*.

In contemporary houses, the main staircase tends to be a feature of the entrance hall. As a result, it takes up a lot of space. By contrast, stairs that lead to the basement tend to be much smaller. Since basement stairs are service stairways with heavy traffic flow, making them steep and narrow

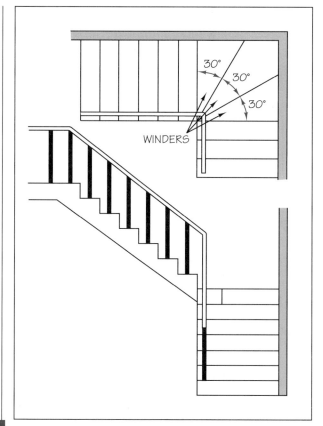

FIGURE 9-17 *Winders – one set only between levels.*

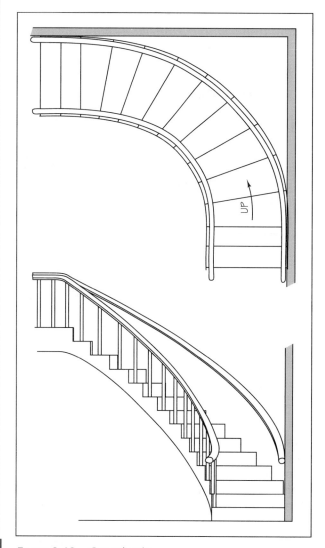

FIGURE 9-18 *Curved stairs*

can make them dangerous. Usually there is enough room in the basement to accommodate wider and more spacious stairways than those often built.

STAIR LOCATION

Stairways take up a lot of space. Each stairway must have a landing at each end and the pattern must funnel traffic towards it. To place **runs** for different levels of stairways at two different locations on your floor plan wastes usable space. To economize on space, put the main and the basement stairs directly above one another in a two-storey house *(see Fig. 9-19)*. Short runs of stairs, such as those found in split-level houses, should be placed adjacent to one another for the same reason.

SAFETY

Stairways should be well lit by windows for the daylight hours and by overhead lighting when natural light is not available. It is illegal to have any type of window or glass partition at the foot of a stairway unless the glass is fracture-proof or reinforced.

All stairways require three-way electrical switches at the top and the bottom of the stairs so that lighting can be controlled from both locations.

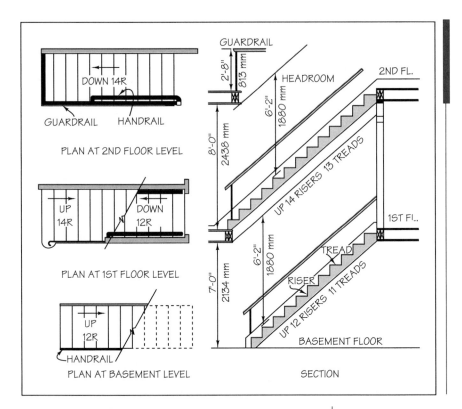

FIGURE 9-19

*Typical plan views and section
through a stairway*

Courtesy of CMHC: The Use and Design of Space
in the Home

If a door is located at the top of a stairway and swings towards it, the door must open over a landing that must be square and the same width as the stairs. When space for a landing is limited, a door can be hinged to swing outwards from the stairs. This practice is not recommended as such a door can block the passageway or can strike a person approaching the door.

All stairs must have handrails and guardrails to ensure safety. A **newel post** and **balusters** are part of the support system for the handrails. Stairs are supported by **stringers** which are the boards that are cut out to support the treads, risers, and weight of the total load applied on the stairs when the stairs are being used *(see Fig. 9-20)*.

EXTERIOR AND SHORT RUNS OF STEPS

Exterior and short runs of steps should receive the same amount of design and safety consideration as a full flight of stairs. The same relationship between **riser** (the height of each stair) and **tread** (the depth of each stair) and the maximum and minimum allowable sizes for stairways should be maintained *(see Fig. 9-21)*. Exterior ramps to accommodate wheel chairs should often be considered. A gradient of 1:12 is the most suitable.

STAIRWAY CALCULATIONS

Once the location of the stairs has been decided upon, the specific sizes and number of the risers and the total run of the stairs must be calculated. Make the following calculations for each stairway you design:

1. Total Rise – Calculate the total rise from finished floor to finished floor. Include the room height plus joist size and floor finish.

	Metric	**Imperial**
Total Height	2440 mm	8'-0"
Joist Size	184 mm	9 3/8" (variable)
Floor Finish	10 mm	3/8"
Total Rise	2634 mm	8'-9 3/4"

FIGURE 9-20
Stairrail terminology

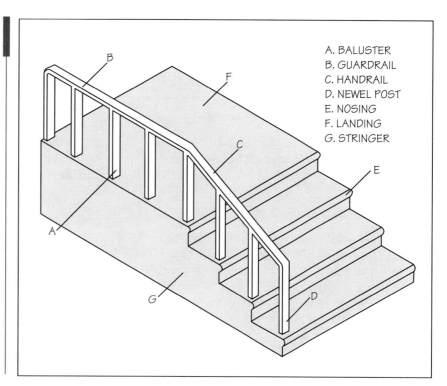

A. BALUSTER
B. GUARDRAIL
C. HANDRAIL
D. NEWEL POST
E. NOSING
F. LANDING
G. STRINGER

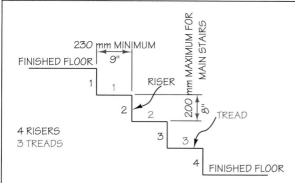

FIGURE 9-21 *Comparison between the number of risers and treads*

2. Number of Risers – To calculate the number of risers, the total rise is divided by the maximum size of the riser.

$$\frac{2634 \text{ mm}}{200 \text{ mm (maximum)}} \qquad \frac{8\text{'-}9\ 3/4\text{"}}{8\text{" (maximum)}}$$
$$= 13 + 34 \text{ mm remainder} \qquad = 13 + 1\ 3/4\text{" remainder}$$

Note: All risers must be equal in size and must not exceed the maximum size. When the number of

risers does not work out to be a whole number, your answer must be rounded off to the next highest whole number.

Adjusted Answer = 14

3. Size of Risers – To calculate the size of risers, the total rise is divided by the number of risers calculated above.

$$\frac{2634 \text{ mm}}{14} \qquad \frac{8\text{'-}9\ 3/4\text{"}}{14}$$
$$= 188.15 \text{ mm} \qquad = 7.55\text{"}$$

4. Number of Treads – The number of treads required is always one less than the number of risers; therefore the answer is 13.

5. Size of Treads – The comfort and ease of use of a stairway depends on the proportional relationship between the rise and run in a stair. This is worked out by an empirical formula. An **empirical formula** is one that does not depend on a provable theory but has been arrived at by trial over an extended period of time.

The calculations for metric and imperial measurements have different empirical formulas.

The metric formula for stairs states that the size of riser multiplied by the size of tread must equal between 45 000 and 48 500.

To find the size of tread, divide 45 000 by the size of riser.

$$\frac{45\ 000}{188\ mm} = 239.36\ mm$$

This figure may be rounded up but must not then exceed 48 500 when multiplied by the size of the riser.

188 mm x 240 mm = 45 120

The imperial formula for stairs states that two risers plus one tread must equal 24" or 25". Alternatively, 24" or 25" minus two risers equals one tread. Therefore 24 - 2(7.55) = 24" - 15.10" = 8.90" which can be rounded up to 9" and stays within the formula

2 risers + 1 tread = 24" or 25"

6. Total Run – To determine the total run, multiply the size of tread by the number of treads.

250 mm x 13 = 3250 mm   9" x 13 = 9'-9"

7. Length Requirements – All stairways require square landings at the top and the bottom of the stairs.

If the stairway is 1000 mm (3'-6") wide, the length requirements for that stairway will be:

Total run + 2 landings
3250 mm + 2(1000 mm)   9'-9" + 2(3'-6")
= 5250 mm   = 16'-9"

STAIRWAY LAYOUT

The size of the **stairwell opening** that will allow adequate headroom for anyone ascending or descending the stairs is determined by completing a layout.

A **layout** differs from a drawing in its purpose and accuracy. The purpose of a drawing is to give the dimensions of an object to those who are going to make the item from the information on the drawing. Dimensions should always be read

off the drawing and should not be scaled from the drawing directly. However, the function of a layout is to determine, for the designer, an unknown dimension that is difficult to establish by calculation. A layout must be highly accurate because a dimension will be scaled from it and should be drawn at the largest convenient scale.

To draw a layout using the data from the stairway calculations in this unit, follow the steps outlined in *Figs. 9-22A-J*. Do not add labels or dimensions until the drawing is complete.

a. At a scale of 1:20 (3/4"=1'-0"), draw two horizontal construction lines, the total rise apart, across an A3/B sized sheet. Immediately under the top line, draw in two more construction lines to scale representing the floor finish and the depth of the ceiling joist (see Fig. 9-22A).

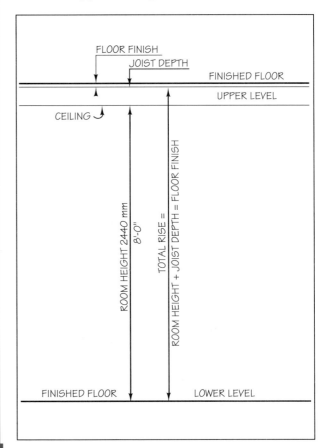

FIGURE 9-22A   *Total rise of stairway*

b. Locate the height of each riser by dividing the total height into 14 equal parts (the number of risers determined by the calculations).

The most accurate method of doing this is to set a scale at an angle across the two lines representing the total height. Place the zero of the scale on one line and any multiple of 14 on the other line. For example, you may select 28 and make 14 equal divisions by marking every second unit. But if you select 42 (14 × 3), you will mark every third unit to get 14 equal divisions. Draw these horizontal divisions in construction lines completely across the paper *(see Fig. 9-22B)*. The spaces you have created represent the height of the risers. The lines you have drawn indicate the level of each tread.

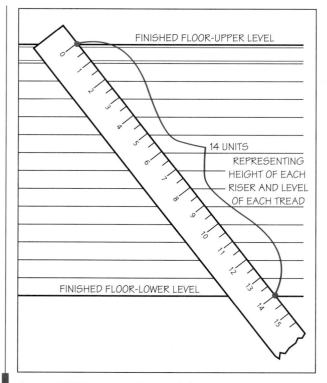

FIGURE 9-22B *Layout for equal riser spaces*

c. At a scale of 1:20 (3/4"=1'-0"), draw two vertical construction lines from the top to the bottom line of the drawing the total run apart *(see Fig. 9-22C)*.

d. Divide this distance into 13 equal parts, which will represent the length of each tread and the front surface of each riser. The most accurate way

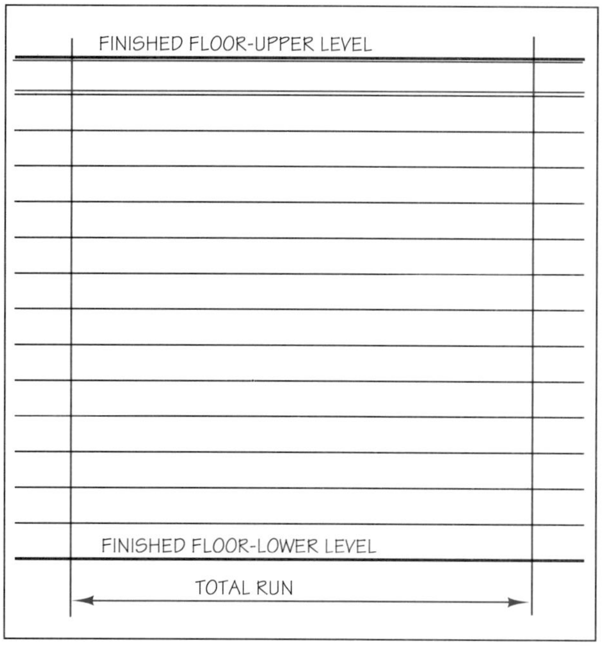

FINISHED FLOOR-UPPER LEVEL

FINISHED FLOOR-LOWER LEVEL

TOTAL RUN

FIGURE 9-22C *Layout of total run*

of doing this is to draw in the stair slope line. Join the point where the top horizontal line of the drawing intersects one of the vertical lines to a point at the opposite and lower end of the stairs where the horizontal line representing the first tread intersects the line at the other end of the total run *(see Fig. 9-22D)*. (*Note:* Do not use the bottom horizontal line.)

e. Draw in the risers by dropping perpendicular lines from the point where the horizontal lines intersect the stair slope line to the horizontal line immediately below. This will clearly form the outline of the stairs. The stairs should start and end with a riser *(see Fig. 9-22E)*.

f. Darken in the treads and risers and draw in the stringer, which is the board that is cut out to support the treads and risers. The board must be a minimum width of 150 mm (6") below the cutouts *(see Fig. 9-22F)*.

g. To establish the minimum headroom, draw a line parallel to the stair slope line at a vertical distance of 1950 mm (6'-6") from it. Measure the headroom vertically from the stair slope line. Then draw the parallel line by using two set squares. Set one set square along the stair slope line. Maintain the set

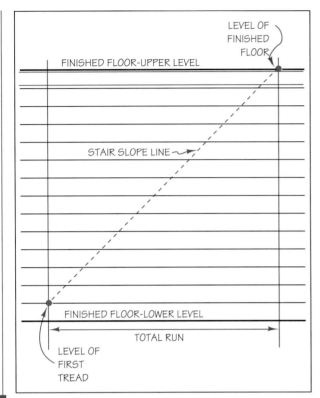

FIGURE 9-22D   *Draw in stair slope line*

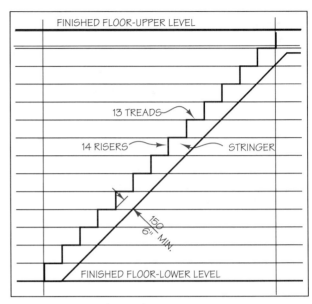

FIGURE 9-22F   *Darken stairway*

square at that angle by supporting it firmly along the lower edge with the other set square. Run the top-most set square along the edge of the set square supporting it until you reach the point of minimum headroom. Draw in the parallel line *(see Fig. 9-22G)*.

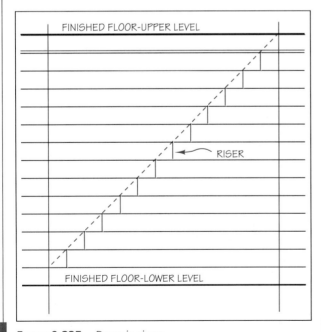

FIGURE 9-22E   *Draw in risers*

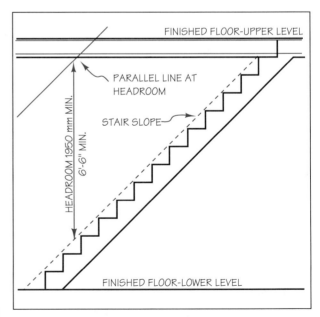

FIGURE 9-22G   *Establish headroom*

h. The minimum stairwell opening will extend from the face of the riser at the top end of the stairs to where the parallel line indicating the minimum headroom cuts the bottom of the ceiling joist at the other end. Draw extension lines from each end of the stairwell opening. Measure the distance and record the dimension on the drawing *(see Fig. 9-22H).*

i. Add the landing distances required at each end of the stair and dimension the total length required for the stairway *(see Fig. 9-22I).*

j. Label all the lines and add the necessary dimensions. Do not erase any construction lines *(see Fig. 9-22J).*

The construction layout you have made will be similar for the design of the stairs on any working drawings or floor plans you are making. An adjustment must be made so that the size of the joist and the height of the room on the layout are in line with design requirements for the particular floor plan you are drawing. The size of the stairwell opening will alter accordingly.

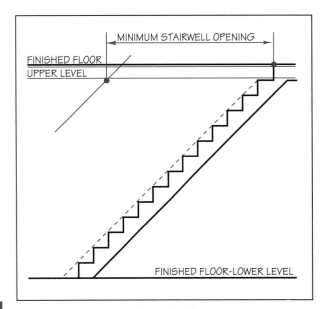

FIGURE 9-22H *Determine stairwell opening*

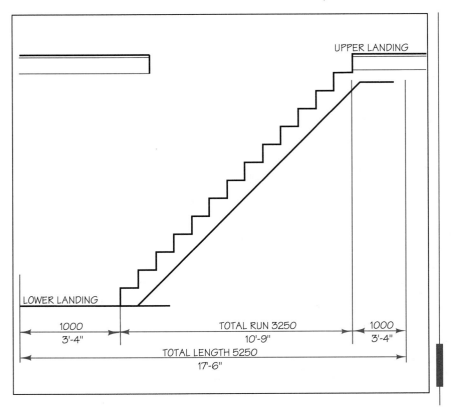

FIGURE 9-22I
Lay out total length

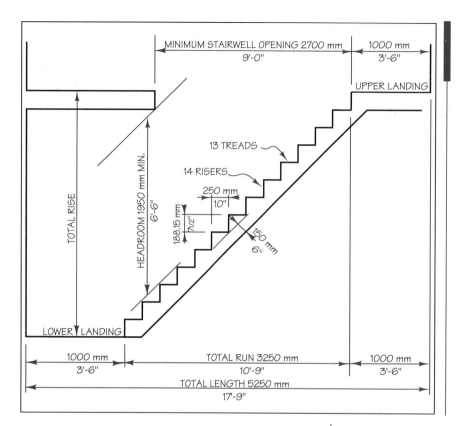

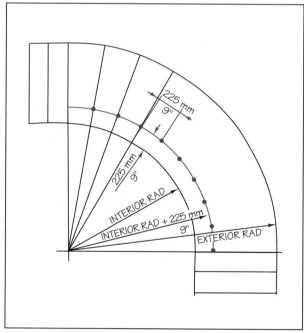

FIGURE 9-22J
Label and dimension stairway layout

CURVED STAIRS

Large contemporary houses tend to feature curved stairs. These stairs also have safety regulations applied to their construction. Curved stairs must be designed so that the narrow end of the tread is a minimum of 225 mm (9") deep at a point 225 mm (9") in from that edge of the stairs *(see Fig. 9-23)*.

To design curved stairs, set out the width of the stairs along two adjoining walls. By trial, decide on a suitable radius that will allow the correct number of treads around the arc with two to three straight treads at either end of the curved portion of the stairway.

From a single centre point, draw in the interior and exterior radius for each side of the stairs. Draw an additional radius equal to the interior radius plus 225 mm (9"). Along this radius, plot divisions of 225 mm (9") to determine the number of risers that may be constructed around the curve. Draw

FIGURE 9-23 *Designing curved stairs*

radial lines from the centre point through these divisions to form treads. Remember, all treads around the curve must be identical.

Check the total number of risers, including the straight stairs at the top and bottom. See that it equals the same number of risers that is correct for the design.

SPIRAL STAIRS

Spiral stairs are an attractive additional stairway. However, not only is it impossible to move furniture up a spiral staircase, but it is also difficult for children and disabled people to use. Therefore it cannot be the only stairway in a house.

The winders must be wedge-shaped treads at an angle of 30° around a central post. Headroom and a landing must be provided *(see Figs. 9-24A and 9-24B)*. All stairs must have handrails and guardrails for safety.

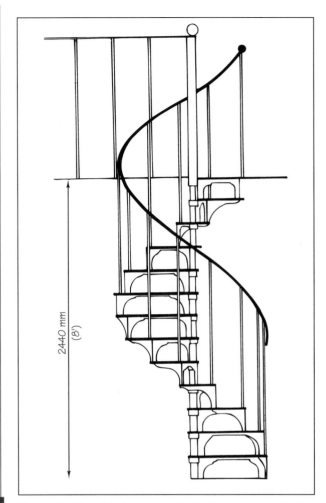

FIGURE 9-24B *Spiral stairs – side view*

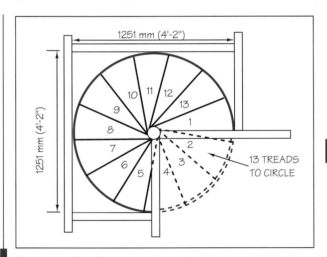

FIGURE 9-24A *Spiral stairs – aerial view*

1. Why should you not place stairways in two different areas of the house?
2. What are the major safety concerns in stairway design?
3. What calculations must be made when designing stairs?

1. Would you prefer to have a split-level house with short flights of stairs or a two-storey house with full flights of stairs? Explain your answer.
2. If you are designing your own two-storey house with a large entrance foyer, what stairway design would you choose to connect with the second floor? Explain your decision.

1. Make the calculations necessary for designing a residential stairway.

Data	Metric	Imperial
Room Height	2440 mm	8'-0"
Joist Size	235 mm	11 3/8"
Floor Finish	15 mm	5/8"

2. On an A3/B size sheet of paper and at a scale of 1:20 (3/4"=1'-0"), make a stair layout and determine the size of the stairwell opening using the data obtained from Assignment 1.

   Measure the height of a riser and the width of a tread. Then count the number of risers. From this data, calculate the six items necessary for stair design, including the total rise.

UNIT 4

Individual Room Design

OBJECTIVES

- To design a suitable area for the bedroom, living room, and dining room with adequate space for furnishings
- To understand the necessity for adequate closet space
- To learn the appropriate size and shape for small, medium, and large rooms

When designing a house, consider the probable size and placement of furniture in each room. Remember that changes in the homeowner's activities and lifestyle will occur, making it unwise to make a house design that is specifically related to the current activities of the homeowner. For example, a new hobby may need a studio to be built in the attic. Also, the original homeowner may move and the house will then have to accommodate other homeowners with different lifestyles.

BEDROOM DESIGN

NUMBER OF BEDROOMS

The number of bedrooms could determine the maximum population of a house. A three-bedroom house is the most common because it will accommodate a couple plus children of both sexes. Two-bedroom houses are not as popular because they are not as adaptable.

Additional bedrooms can be created in the basement; however a house cannot advertise the basement rooms as bedrooms unless the ceiling is a minimum of 1200 mm (4'-0") above grade. Four- or five-bedroom houses can be designed and any room not required as a bedroom may be used as a den, an office, or a children's play area.

FURNISHINGS

The furnishings for most bedrooms consist of large-sized pieces such as beds and dressers and smaller items such as night tables, an armoire, and a desk and chair. This must be taken into account when planning the layout of the room.

Some bedrooms may accommodate double, queen-, or king-sized beds while other bedrooms may have space only for a twin-sized bed. Two twin-sized beds need a great amount of space even if they are placed side by side because additional area must be allowed for making up the beds *(see Figs. 9-25A, 9-25B, 9-25C, and 9-25D)*. All bedrooms should also have space for a dressing area, a play area, or a work area.

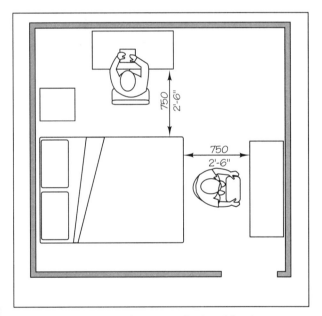

FIGURE 9-25A *Access between a bed and furniture*
Courtesy CMHC: The Use and Design of Space in the Home

MASTER BEDROOMS

Master bedrooms, which are usually larger than other bedrooms, are incorporated into many contemporary homes. In large houses, master suites may include a bathroom, with a Jacuzzi or whirlpool bath, desk space, and a sitting room.

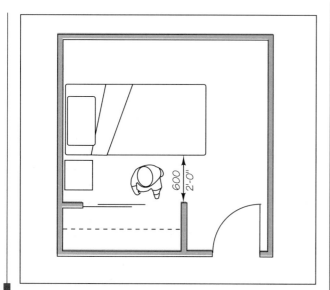

FIGURE 9-25B *Access between a bed and a closet*

Courtesy CMHC: The Use and Design of Space in the Home

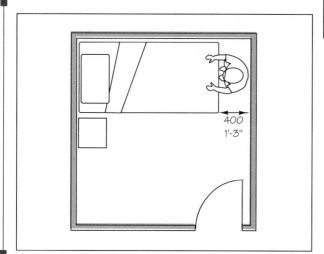

FIGURE 9-25C *Bed-making space*

Courtesy CMHC: The Use and Design of Space in the Home

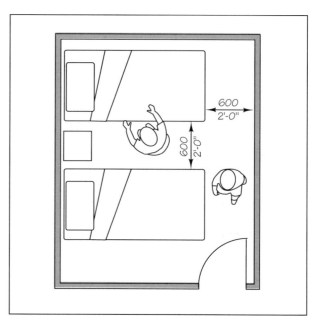

FIGURE 9-25D *Access between a bed and a wall*

Courtesy CMHC: The Use and Design of Space in the Home

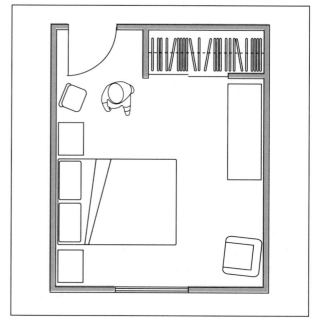

FIGURE 9-26A *Good circulation and dressing space*

Courtesy CMHC: The Use and Design of Space in the Home

Walk-in closets or dressing rooms are also frequently found in master suites. When designing a master bedroom, open space and additional furniture should be taken into account *(see Figs. 9-26A, 9-26B, and 9-26C)*.

CLOSETS AND WINDOWS

The size and number of closets is important in house design. Any clothes closet should not be longer than 1500 mm (5'-0") unless an intermediate support is provided for the clothes rod. The

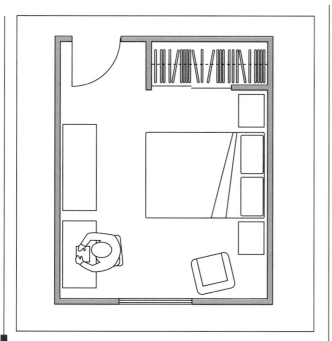

FIGURE 9-26B *Desks in a master bedroom*

Courtesy CMHC: The Use and Design of Space in the Home

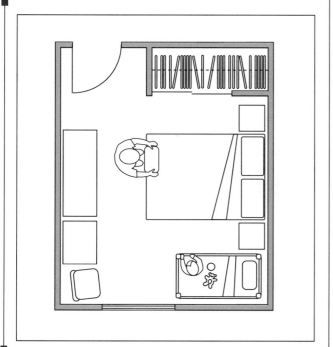

FIGURE 9-26C *Cribs, or other furniture, can be included in a master bedroom if there is adequate space.*

Courtesy CMHC: The Use and Design of Space in the Home

weight of hanging clothes is considerable and will cause the rod to bend if it is too long. Many clothes closets are now designed with fitted shelves for accessories such as shoes, ties, and handbags. Double-tiered rods will accommodate more items of clothing in the closet. Some space must be retained for full-length clothing such as coats and dresses.

A closet should be a minimum of 660 mm (2'-3") deep to allow hanging clothes on a rod. It is not advisable to make a clothes closet too deep as it is difficult to retrieve items stored behind a rack of hanging clothes.

Closets can have sliding doors, but only half of the clothes space will be revealed at a time; swing doors take up space in front of the closet when opened; folding and bi-fold doors are the most practical. Bi-fold and folding doors open up the entire front of the closet and take up the minimum amount of space when opened.

Windows in a bedroom should be 1000 mm (3'- 4") from the floor. This ensures privacy and allows furniture to be placed under them. It is often important to be able to use this space when arranging the furniture in a bedroom. A bedroom with windows placed on opposite or adjoining walls will have good cross ventilation of air.

The position of both closets and windows in a bedroom should be made with care so that rearrangement of furniture is easy. Because of the amount of wall space used up by closets and windows, and because of the large size of most pieces of bedroom furniture, it is advisable to plan the furniture layout in order to ensure a practical arrangement. Alternative furniture placement should also be planned to avoid an arrangement that is static.

In addition to bedroom closets, there should be a closet within 3000 mm (10'-0") of the front door of the house and another small closet at the rear door of the house for hanging outdoor clothing. Another useful addition is a full-size broom closet in the kitchen to store mops, brooms, and a vacuum cleaner.

A linen closet should be designed in the bedroom hall area preferably close to the bathroom for easy access to towels.

FIGURE 9-27A
A closet with sliding doors

FIGURE 9-27B
A closet with swinging doors

FIGURE 9-27C
A closet with bi-fold doors

APPROXIMATE SIZES OF STANDARD BEDROOM FURNITURE

	Metric	Imperial
Beds		
Single (Twin)	970 mm x 1900 mm	38 3/4" x 76"
Bunk	1040 mm x 1980 mm	41" x 79"
Crib	690 mm x 1320 mm	27" x 52"
Double	1350 mm x 1900 mm	54" x 76"
Queen	1520 mm x 2130 mm	60" x 85"
King	1830 mm x 2130 mm	73" x 85"
Dresser		
Small	1180 mm x 390 mm	47" x 15 1/2"
Large	1625 mm x 457 mm	65" x 18"
Drawers		
Small	610 mm x 406 mm	24" x 16"
Large	890 mm x 480 mm	35" x 19"
Night Table	610 mm x 380 mm	24" x 15"
Desk	1230 mm x 450 mm	49" x 18"

LIVING ROOM DESIGN

THE MULTI-PURPOSE LIVING ROOM

The design constraints on a living room are less specific than those on a bedroom because in a living room there is variation in furniture and use. The size and use of a living room will depend on whether there is a family room on the same level. Since family rooms are used for watching television, casual entertainment, and as a child's play area, they relieve a living room of the pressure of accommodating a wide range of activities. When there is a family room, the living room may become more formal and be used largely as a conversation area. Therefore it need not be very large. If there is only one major living area in the house, this room will have to serve a great variety of activities. It will have to be adaptable in its furniture placement and should therefore be quite large.

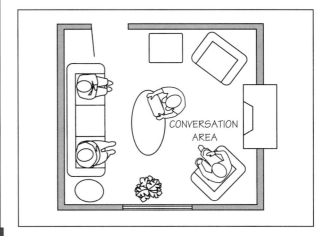

FIGURE 9-28A *Small living room – conversation arrangement, one focal point*

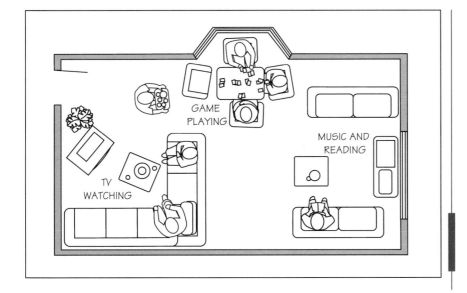

FIGURE 9-28B *Large living room – several focal points*

LIVING ROOM SIZES AND ARRANGEMENTS

Generally, a smaller living room should be square-shaped and should have one focal point. Conversely, a large room should be rectangular and its furniture should be arranged in two or more specific groupings, such as a conversation area and a television area.

ENTRANCES

The main entrance should have convenient access to the living room of a house. However, for the sake of privacy, the front door should not open directly into the living room. If this is unavoidable, particularly in a small house, your design should include a privacy screen that can be made by a wall or closet placed at right angles to the door and positioned between it and the living room. This feature will also reduce the impact of draughts and cold air entering the living room when the main door is opened in winter.

The door or entrance to the living room should not be placed diagonally across from any other entrance to the room or this would result in a traffic flow problem.

A living room is not always totally enclosed. Often there are not any doors attached to the entrances. This open style makes the living room a core area and it will appear more spacious and less formal in comparison with an enclosed living room. However, this type of room lacks a certain amount of privacy.

FIREPLACE AND WINDOWS

If a house is to have a fireplace, it will usually be placed in either the living room or the family room. A fireplace is most often used to give a cosy and inviting look to a room rather than as a form of supplementary heating. The average fireplace will take up 1500 mm (5'-0") of inside wall space and there should be enough space on each side of the hearth to accommodate chairs. A fireplace should not be placed on the northwest wall of a house as the pre-

vailing cold winds in winter will chill the chimney and inhibit the smoke from rising inside the flue.

Most living rooms or family rooms have large windows. This is another reason for not placing such rooms on the northwest side of a structure where they will be affected by the wind. The windows should overlook the best view from the house. If the large window overlooks the garden, then the outside area becomes an extension of the living room or family room.

DINING-ROOM DESIGN

STYLES OF EATING AREAS

Styles of eating areas range from formal and separate dining rooms to informal eating areas that are part of, or adjacent to, the kitchen. However, as in the case of bedroom design, the furniture for most dining areas is similar and consists of a table with chairs and a china cabinet. The major factors that must be considered in your design of an eating area are that enough space is provided for people to be seated and to eat or work comfortably at the table, and that there should be sufficient room around the table and chairs for food to be served conveniently. There is a definite minimum size for a dining room, based on the space allowances given.

SPACE ALLOWANCE

An absolute minimum of 850 mm (2'-10") should be allowed between the dining table and a wall or another item of furniture to permit enough room for a person to be seated at a table and eat a meal. For more comfortable access and to allow for food service, 1000 mm (3'-6") is preferable. To allow an aisle behind a seated person, a 1200 mm (4'-0") space is necessary (*see Figs. 9-29A, 9-29B, 9-29C, and 9-29D*). The majority of tables vary in width from 750 mm to 1200 mm (2'-6" to 4'-0"), therefore the narrowest width a dining area should be is 2700 mm (9'-0"). Most average-sized dining rooms are 3600 mm (12'-0") wide, which provides room for comfortable dining and for extra furniture.

A space of 600 mm (2'-0") should be allowed at each individual place along the table length.

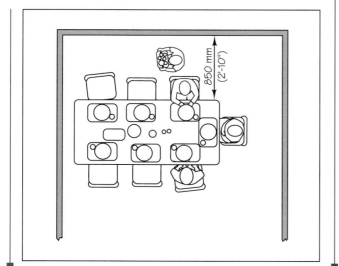

FIGURE 9-29A *Limited access behind a chair*

Courtesy CMHC: The Use and Design of Space in the Home

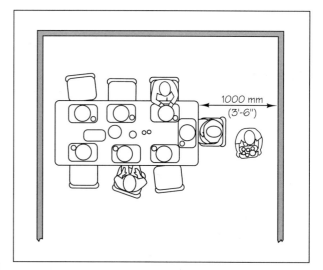

FIGURE 9-29B *Access behind a chair*

Courtesy CMHC: The Use and Design of Space in the Home

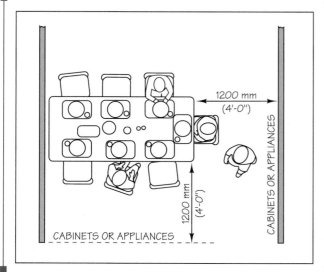

FIGURE 9-29C *Access between a table and cabinets or appliances*

Courtesy CMHC: The Use and Design of Space in the Home

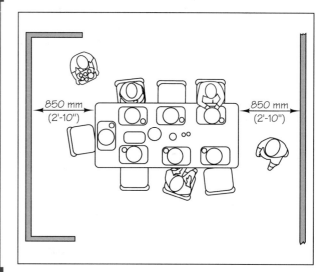

FIGURE 9-29D *Access between a table and a wall*

Courtesy CMHC: The Use and Design of Space in the Home

The minimum length of a dining area should be 3300 mm (11'-0"), which will allow a person to be seated at each end of the table and two persons along each side. Most average-sized dining room lengths are 4200 mm (14'-0"). Dining areas open to the living room appear to be more spacious and accommodate overflow numbers on special occasions.

For safety reasons, the dining area should be close to the kitchen with no changes in levels between them.

Some kitchens have a snack counter where casual meals are served. In this case, the counter is widened and projects over the supporting cupboards so that people may sit on stools and have adequate knee room under the overhang *(see Fig. 9-30)*.

Major Room Size Chart

Room Sizes

	Metric	Imperial
Bedrooms		
Small	2400 mm x 3000 mm	8'-0" x 10'-0"
Medium	3600 mm x 3600 mm	12'-0" x 12'-0"
Large	3600 mm x 4800 mm	12'-0" x 16'-0"
Living Rooms		
Small	3000 mm x 3600 mm	10'-0" x 12'-0"
Medium	4200 mm x 6000 mm	14'-0" x 20'-0"
Large	5400 mm x 8400 mm	18'-0" x 28'-0"
Dining Rooms		
Small	2700 mm x 3300 mm	9'-0" x 11'-0"
Medium	3600 mm x 4200 mm	12'-0" x 14'-0"
Large	4200 mm x 6000 mm	14'-0" x 20'-0"

When determining the size of any of the main rooms of the house, it is important to consider standard widths of floor covering in order to avoid purchasing extra lengths of costly material. Most floor covering materials are 3600 mm (12'-0") in width.

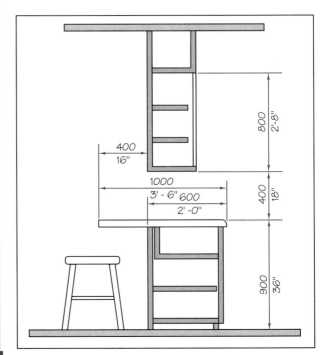

Figure 9-30 *Space requirements for a snack counter*

REVIEW QUESTIONS

1. Based on the number of people who can live comfortably in a house, what are some design considerations?
2. Describe some possible contents of a master bedroom.
3. Why should a family room be on the main floor? Which activities will take place in the family room? in the living room?

WHAT DO YOU THINK?

1. Often rooms have to be multi-purpose. Which rooms do you think could be used for two or more distinct activities?
2. Would you prefer to have a separate dining area or an eat-in kitchen? Give reasons for your answer.
3. If your living room is large, what shape would you prefer? What furniture groupings would you arrange?

ASSIGNMENTS

1. On the living room plans provided by the instructor, make two alternative furniture arrangements. Research sizes of standard furniture items from a current retail sales catalogue. Label all the furniture and indicate distances between the major pieces.
2. Using the information sheet provided by the instructor, calculate the sizes of the three dining areas requested. Sketch the layout for each problem before making the calculations.
3. Design an upper storey for the floor plan provided by the instructor on a sheet of vellum A4/A using the same scale as the floor plan.

UNIT 5

Drawing a Presentation Floor Plan

OBJECTIVES

• To relate site plan data to a floor plan design
• To develop a presentation floor plan
• To assess the quality of the design by using a checklist
• To use the correct symbols for a floor plan
• To dimension a presentation drawing floor plan

INCORPORATING DATA INTO THE FLOOR PLAN DESIGN

The type, size, and orientation of the house together with the relationship and size of the individual rooms will have been established by the work done on the site plan and preliminary drawings.

You now have sufficient data to prepare a presentation drawing of the floor plan. Any special features desired by the homeowner such as a fireplace, curved stairs, or whirlpool bath should be discussed before proceeding. The design should incorporate as many of the features favoured by the purchasers as possible and yet stay within the constraints of the proposed cost. Before proceeding, compare the design with the checklist that follows on page 225.

The floor plan is the most important element in the set of presentation drawings that will be submitted to the client. Usually the client will not be knowledgeable about house designs or skilled in the interpretation of technical drawings. The floor plans should show only the information that is of concern to a client:

1. the rated area or square footage of the house not including the basement area (this will determine the cost of the building and so will be a most significant figure for the client),
2. the overall size of the house,
3. the approximate size and the location of each room, which will be shown at the centre of each area,

4. the layout of the kitchen and the arrangement of cupboard space,
5. the location of bathroom facilities and their fixtures,
6. the interconnecting system of entries, passageways, and stairs.

DRAWING THE PRESENTATION FLOOR PLAN

All presentation drawings should be as attractive as possible. The clients will tend to equate your ability as a designer with the degree of care that is reflected in the drawings. Attention to neatness, colour, and artwork is important at this stage. The clients must have confidence in your work before they will commit themselves to taking the next step of building based on your design.

First you must select the medium in which you wish to work. In order to do this, you must be aware of the type of presentation you will make. For example, an ink drawing on display board that is coloured will make a strong visual impact in a formal presentation to a large number of people. A pencil or ink drawing on vellum, enhanced with colour pastels applied to the reverse side of the sheet, is both easy and inexpensive to produce. This type of drawing will have a pleasing but low-key effect in a presentation to a small group of people.

An ink drawing is more dramatic and much clearer than a pencil drawing, but it is more difficult to make the changes to inkwork that clients will usually require when they review the plans.

Floor plans for a residence are most often drawn at a scale of 1:50 (1/4" = 1'- 0"). Most designers and contractors are comfortable working with drawings at this scale as these proportions are familiar.

The floor plan is a view looking down on a section taken horizontally through the house at half the room height. This means that all doors and windows are shown on the section as well as all bathroom equipment, kitchen cupboards, and appliances.

The front or street side of the structure should always be placed at the bottom of the sheet to avoid errors in construction.

To begin drawing the floor plan, centre the basic structure on the sheet and outline the exterior shape of the house using construction lines. The shape of this section may be a simple rectangle or the house may have projections and **ells**, bay windows and recessed doorways, which will make a more complicated shape. It is wise to make your initial plan in light construction lines so that it will be easier to make the inevitable changes to the drawing as the design develops *(see Fig. 9-31A)*.

Next, place a second line inside this line to represent the thickness of the exterior frame wall of the building. The exterior walls would be drawn approximately 145 mm (5 1/2") thick. Remember, you are drawing at a scale of 1:50 (1/4" = 1'- 0"). Show the exterior wall as a frame wall at this time. Some houses will eventually be bricked but the brick is merely an added veneer of decorative material covering the frame wall and need not concern us at this stage of the drawing *(see Fig. 9-31B)*.

Now draw in the interior partitions using your preliminary drawings as a guide. The inside walls or partitions that define the rooms should be slightly thinner than the exterior walls. Still using construction lines, draw the inner walls at 130 mm (5") thick. Look at your drawing periodically to make sure that all the exterior walls are of equal thickness and all the interior walls are of equal thickness. As your design proceeds, you should make an effort to plan continuous walls through the structure and eliminate jogs as far as possible *(see Fig. 9-31C)*.

It is advisable that one of the sides in any room does not exceed 5000 mm (16'- 4"). This will make the selection of convenient joist sizes simpler when preparing the working drawing later on.

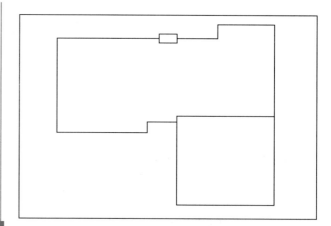

FIGURE 9-31A *Making a presentation drawing – the exterior line*

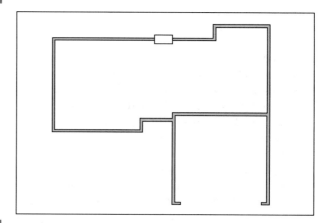

FIGURE 9-31B *Making a presentation drawing – the exterior wall*

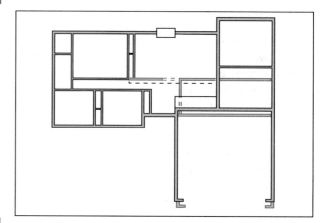

FIGURE 9-31C *Making a presentation drawing – partitions and eliminating jogs*

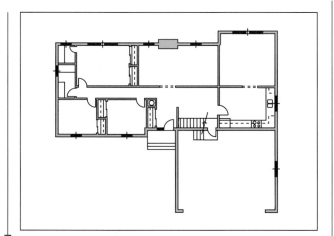

Figure 9-31D *Making a presentation drawing – doors, windows, and other details*

DOORS AND WINDOWS

Locate the doors and windows by drawing in the centre lines along the exterior walls. Approximate the width of the windows at this stage. The exact size of the windows and a supplier can be researched when making the working drawing. A window is indicated by two lines close together running lengthwise and central to the frame wall. These lines represent the glass. All windows are shown in this schematic manner *(see Fig. 9-32A)*. **Mullions**, which are the major vertical divisions between sashes (framed panels of glass that make up a window), are drawn as shown in *Fig. 9-32B*. Bay windows are drawn so that the lines indicating the extent of each sash are perpendicular to the wall containing it. The front corners of the bay window form support mullions between the adjacent sashes *(see Fig. 9-32C)*.

Apart from screen and storm doors, a door will always open into a house or into a room. The main entrance door can be made more imposing by using double doors or by putting a glass panel on one or both sides of the doorway. This is called **glazing**. Swing doors should always be indicated fully opened with an arc indicating the leading edge of the door as it swings open *(see Figs. 9-33A [Exterior] and 9-33B [Interior])*. Exterior doors are 810 mm - 975 mm (32"- 39") wide while interior doors are usually 760 mm - 860 mm (30"- 35") wide. Doors should be shown to have door frames

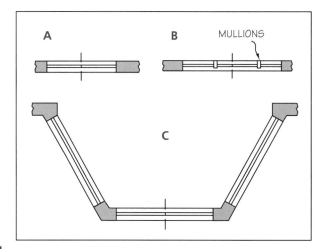

Figure 9-32A *Windows for presentation drawing floor plan;* **B** *Windows with mullions;* **C** *Bay window*

when they are at right angles to a nearby wall *(see Fig. 9-33C)*.

Bathroom doors need only be 600 mm (2'-0") wide as large pieces of furniture are not usually moved into a bathroom. Openings in walls or archways are shown as hidden lines *(see Fig. 9-33D)*.

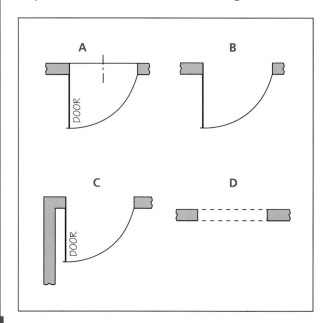

Figure 9-33A *Exterior swing door for floor plan;* **B** *Interior swing door for floor plan;* **C** *Door frame of swing door for floor plan;* **D** *Archway for floor plan*

STAIRWAYS AND CLOSETS

Now you can draw in the stairways and closets. The stairway should always be a minimum of 860 mm (2'-10") wide, wall to wall, and each tread should be drawn 250 mm (10") deep. As the floor plan is a section taken at half the room height, the stairs can be shown broken off after the eighth or tenth riser. After the tenth riser, detail the space underneath the remainder of the stairs *(see Figs. 9-34A and 9-34B)*.

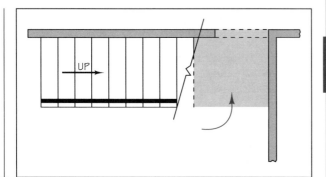

FIGURE 9-34A *Passageway under stairs*

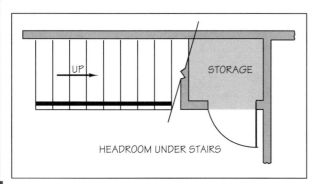

FIGURE 9-34B *Storage under stairs*

When stairways in a two-storey house are drawn, the plan view of the stairs will be similar to that shown in *Fig. 9-35A*, and in a split-level house the stairs will be similar to those shown in *Fig. 9-35B*. Remember, safety regulations demand that doors must open on to a landing when the stairs on the other side of the door are descending *(see Fig. 9-36)*.

Clothes closets should be 660 mm (2'-3") deep measured from inside of wall to inside of wall. The walls of the closets in most cases are the same

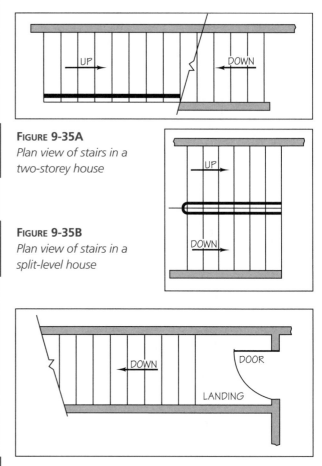

FIGURE 9-35A
Plan view of stairs in a two-storey house

FIGURE 9-35B
Plan view of stairs in a split-level house

FIGURE 9-36 *Door and landing for descending stairs*

thickness as the interior partitions because they will be constructed from the same size studs. Closets may be constructed in front of a room partition or recessed into it *(see Figs. 9-37A, 9-37B, 9-38A, and 9-38B)*. Occasionally, to save space, the

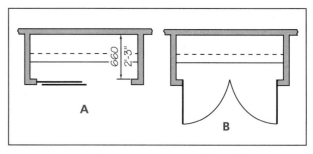

FIGURE 9-37A *Closets constructed in front of partition – sliding doors;* **B** *Swing doors*

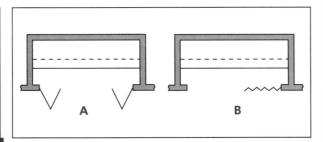

FIGURE 9-38A *Closets recessed into partition – bi-fold doors;* **B** *Folding doors*

studs will be turned sideways in a closet wall to make a narrower partition 75 mm (3") thick. This will have to be noted on the working drawing eventually *(see Fig. 9-39A).*

The types of doors used on closets should be indicated by standard symbols and the doors should always appear to be the correct size to fit the opening of the closets as shown on the drawing. The clothes rod is indicated by a hidden line running lengthwise down the middle of the closet. A full line is shown parallel to the hidden line on the open side of the closet to represent an overhead shelf. Closets are sometimes shown by a series of perpendicular lines *(see Fig. 9-39B).*

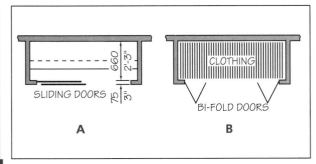

FIGURE 9-39A *Dimensioning closets with narrow partitions;* **B** *Schematic drawing*

BATHROOMS AND KITCHENS

Bathroom fixtures, kitchen appliances, and cupboards must be drawn to scale. Templates are available to assist you in doing this. Upper kitchen cupboards are shown in hidden line to indicate that they are above the section shown in the drawing *(see Fig. 9-40).*

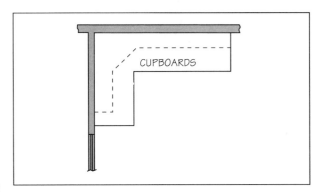

FIGURE 9-40 *Using a dotted line to indicate upper cupboards*

DARKENING IN THE PLAN

When you are satisfied that the plan cannot be improved upon, take a sharpened pencil and darken the object lines. When partition walls join exterior walls, leave a gap in the line work where the two walls intersect *(see Fig. 9-41).*

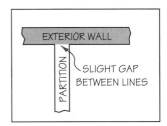

FIGURE 9-41
Method of showing partition meeting an exterior wall

Sharpen your pencil frequently to maintain a sharp dark line. Erase any extraneous lines. Construction lines that are very light will not show when a print is taken and therefore need not be erased.

Brick veneer that is 100 mm (4") thick may now be added to the exterior of the house if desired. The exterior walls with brick veneer will have a total thickness of 245 mm (10"). The overall dimensions of the house will not be changed to include the brick. The additional thickness added to show masonry or brick work is sectioned with lines drawn at 45° *(see Fig. 9-42).*

FIGURE 9-42
Brick veneer exterior

DIMENSIONING THE PRESENTATION FLOOR PLAN

Dimensioning the presentation floor plan is very simple. First draw in the overall dimensions. Remember, these dimensions extend from the outside of the stud to the outside of the stud *(see Fig. 9-43)*. Do not dimension any small projections or recesses at this stage but do dimension any large extensions such as a garage.

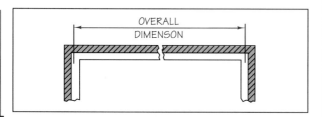

OVERALL
DIMENSON

FIGURE 9-43 *Overall dimensions – outside of stud to outside of stud*

In the centre of each room or area, label the use intended for that space. Directly under the name, give the size of the usable space. Only the general size of the room is required. Do not extend measurements into closets or small recesses. The horizontal distance of the room as shown on the plan should be shown first, followed by an *x* and then the vertical width of the room as shown on the plan should be given *(see Fig. 9-44)*.

ADDITIONAL NOTATION

A large dark arrow pointing into the house should be drawn indicating the main entrance to the house and a large outlined arrow also pointing inwards should be placed to show the side or rear exit.

An arrow should be superimposed on all stairs or steps indicating up or down from the level of the plan.

Above the title block, the total area or square footage of the house should be given. This area can be calculated by multiplying the length and width of each floor level, not including a basement area, and adding them together. A separate area for the garage should also be provided.

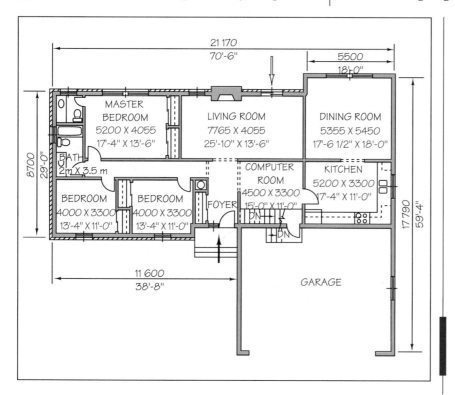

FIGURE 9-44
Dimensioning the presentation floor plan

House Design -
Checklist for Preliminary Floor Plan

1. Does the front door have side glass panels or some other features to make it stand out as the main entrance to the house?
2. Is the living room shielded from the front door by a divider or closet that provides privacy and protects the occupants from drafts?
3. Is there a coat closet less than 3000 mm (10'-0") from the front door?
4. Is less than 15% of the floor area used as corridors or stairways?
5. Have you arranged the traffic flow so that a person does not have to cross diagonally the living room to get to another part of the house?
6. Have you taken care to see that a major passageway does not cross the work triangle in the kitchen?
7. Do the upper kitchen cupboards stop well clear of the windows and do the upper cupboards pass over the top of the fridge and stove?
8. Is there a work triangle of less than 6000 mm (20'-0") in the kitchen?
9. Have the number of doors or entrances into the kitchen been cut to a minimum? Is the stove clear of these entrances?
10. Is there counter space in the kitchen beside the refrigerator, beside the oven, and on both sides of the sink?
11. Is there a short and easy route from the kitchen to the front door and from the kitchen to the garage or driveway?
12. Is all the plumbing located in one area of the house?
13. Would a person hit an elbow against the wall when shaving or using a hairdryer in the bathroom?
14. Is access to plumbing at one end of the bathroom indicated?
15. Is there both a broom closet and a linen closet on the main floors?
16. Is there somewhere to hang outdoor clothes near the entrances?
17. Is there easy access for children from an exterior door to a nearby bathroom?
18. If the stairs contain winders, are they wide enough to allow the passage of furniture?
19. Is there a stairwell opening approximately 900 mm × 2500 mm (3'-0" × 8'-4") at the top of the stairs?
20. Is there a square landing at the top and the bottom of all stairs?
21. Are the closets placed between the bedrooms for use as sound barriers wherever possible?
22. Will there be 900 mm (3'-0") minimum space at the sides and at the bottom of beds (bed 1900 mm [6'-3"] long) when in position?
23. Is the access to the attic in a convenient location such as the upper hallway?
24. Have provisions been made for a flue from the fireplace at each floor level?
25. Have you considered the fact that the garage floor is on grade while the finished floor level of the house is usually 600 mm (2'-0") higher than the grade?

An affirmative answer should be given to 80% (20) of these questions. If you cannot answer yes to at least 20 of the questions, start redesigning.

THE SECOND-STOREY FLOOR PLAN

If a second-storey floor plan is required, the design should be made at this time. Exterior walls and the stairway should be in line with the first-storey plan. Plumbing should be placed above the plumbing in the lower floor.

COMPLETING THE PRESENTATION PLAN

Now draw a border around the sheet on which the drawing has been made and add a title block to the bottom right-hand corner. Use the standard title block of your school. All title blocks should include spaces for the following:

1. title of drawing
2. scale of drawing
3. name of draftsperson
4. date of drawing
5. drawing number

INITIAL PRESENTATION

Have the floor plan approved before the rest of the presentation drawings are made. A presentation of the floor plan should be made directly to the clients so that any queries may be answered immediately. It is a good idea to leave a print of the plan with the clients for their review.

Discuss suggested amendments with the clients even though they may be impractical, may be costly to undertake, or may ruin the traffic flow of the house. It is important that the clients understand that as many of their ideas as possible have been incorporated into the design. Make notes of the suggestions that are to be included on the final working drawing of the floor plan. If the changes are extensive, a completely new presentation drawing may be needed and will have to be resubmitted to the client. However, do not change the initial presentation drawing as this will provide a record of your design. Sometimes, after frequent changes, a client will revert to the original design suggestions. Minimal changes can be made directly on the working drawing at a later date with no change to the presentation drawing.

SAVING CLASSROOM TIME

When making a full set of presentation and working drawings, the following procedure is suggested in order to save class time.

A. The Basic Floor Plan *(see Fig. 9-45)*
1. Make a good drawing of your design on vellum.
2. Show the overall dimensions placed far enough from the drawings to allow at least two dimensions to be placed between the overall dimensions and the exterior of the house at a later time.
3. Name the purpose for which each room is to be used by lettering the name neatly in the centre of each area.
4. Draw in kitchen and bathroom equipment.
5. Put an arrow on all stairs and steps showing direction up or down from the major floor level of the plan.

The notations you have made on this drawing will be required on both presentation and working drawings.

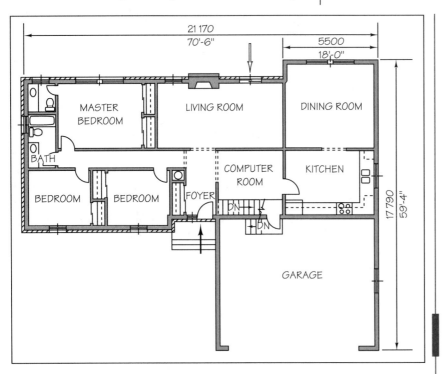

FIGURE 9-45
Basic floor plan

B. The Presentation Floor Plan

1. Make a print of the basic drawing.
2. Using pen or an HB pencil, add the overall sizes of each room directly below each room name.
   Example – Living room
   　　　　6000 mm × 3900 mm
   　　　　(20'-0" × 13'-0")
3. Place a large dark arrow at the front entrance and an outlined large arrow at the rear or side entrance.
4. Give the rated area of house above the title block.
5. Title the print *Presentation Drawing*.

The additions are shown in blue on the illustration of a presentation floor plan. The print now has all the information required for a presentation drawing *(see Fig. 9-44)*.

C. The Original Drawing of the Floor Plan

1. Make the changes suggested by the instructor to improve the design on the original vellum drawing. Do not change the presentation drawing as this will provide a record of your original design. Since most clients will make some changes to the primary design, the final working drawing of the floor plan will usually differ from the original presentation drawing.
2. Retain this drawing on vellum. This drawing will be fully dimensioned at a later time and become part of the working drawings from which the house will be constructed. If CAD has been used to draw a basic floor plan, put the dimensions for the presentation drawing on another layer. Save these two layers and print as a Presentation floor plan.

　　To obtain a working drawing, make any changes necessary to the basic floor plan and save as working floor plan. Put dimensions on another layer at a later date. Print these two layers as part of the working drawings.

REVIEW QUESTIONS

1. What type of linework will you use to begin making your design? What type of linework will you use to complete the presentation drawing?
2. What is the purpose of a presentation drawing?
3. How is a presentation floor plan dimensioned?

WHAT DO YOU THINK?

1. Why might it be worthwhile to make a coloured presentation drawing?
2. Why should you discuss with the client any changes to the presentation plan?
3. Why should you not make alterations on your original presentation drawing?

ASSIGNMENTS

1. On graph paper using 4 squares = 1 m (1 square = 1'-0"), draw the floor plan of your home or a friend's home. Sizes may be paced out using a scale of 1 stride = 1 m (3'-0") approximately. Incorporate all the correct symbols and dimension the plan as for a presentation drawing.
2. Using the basic floor plan provided by your instructor, add the upper storey you designed for Chapter 9, Unit 4, Assignment 3 (scale 1:50 [1/4" = 1'-0"]) and dimension as for a presentation drawing.

DESIGNING THE HOUSE

THE PROJECT

At this point you are ready to begin designing the floor plan for the presentation drawings you will show to your clients. Now you will have developed an idea of the household needs of the client and the size of house they are able to afford.

You will have made a site plan and will know the maximum size of house that will fit on the chosen lot. Also, you will have chosen the preferable orientation for the various areas of the house.

Follow instructions A or B below according to whether you are making an original design or a revision of an existing plan.

A. To Design an Original Floor Plan

Step 6: Making a Preliminary Floor Plan Design

a. Plan the orientation of rooms using bubbles.

b. On graph paper or with CAD, sketch in the arrangement of the rooms in a single-line format using the approximate sizes you have selected. Use a scale of 4 squares = 1 m (1 square = 1'-0").

c. Make a copy of the plan and indicate the traffic pattern for two members of the family for a typical day by using two different coloured pencils.

d. Review your plan and make amendments to your preliminary design to produce the best possible traffic flow.

e. Draw a preliminary floor plan design in a single-line format showing the probable size and location of all rooms, stairs, and entrances at a scale of 1:50 (1/4" = 1'-0").

Step 7: Designing the Kitchen and Bathroom Facilities to Suit Your Preliminary Floor Plan Design

a. Design the kitchen, considering the orientation of the kitchen and driveway.

Decide on the type of layout you will use and where the work triangle will be positioned.

The initial planning should be done at a scale of 1:20 (3/4" = 1'-0"). The scale used for the final drawing, which will be incorporated into the floor plan design, is 1:50 (1/4" = 1'-0").

b. Rate your kitchen design using the assessment sheet supplied by your instructor and make your own appraisal of the kitchen in a written statement.

c. Design the main bathroom facility and decide on the location and number of additional washrooms.

Decide on the layout for each of the bathroom facilities. The initial planning should be done at a scale of 1:20 (3/4" = 1'-0"). The scale used for the final drawing, which will be incorporated into the floor plan design, is 1:50 (1/4" = 1'-0").

Step 8: Designing the Stairs

a. Do a layout for each of the stairways in order to determine the size of the stairwell openings. The layout should be at a scale of 1:20 (3/4" = 1'-0").

b. Draw a plan view of the stairs at a scale of 1:50 (1/4" = 1'-0") as it will appear at each floor level. Show the landing area at the beginning of the stairs. These plan views will be incorporated into the main floor plan designs.

Step 9: Checking the Design

a. Draw the plan of the living room at a scale of 1:20 (3/4" = 1'-0"). Arrange suitable furniture groupings in this room using retail sales catalogues for sizes. This exercise will indicate whether your living room is a practical size and shape.

b. Review the preliminary floor plan design thoroughly and make changes on the basis of additional knowledge you have acquired. Check the drawing, using the checklist supplied on page 225.

Step 10: Making the Presentation Drawing

a. On vellum, make a finished presentation drawing of the floor plan for your major project to a scale of 1:50 (1/4" = 1'-0").

b. Dimension this drawing as for a presentation drawing or make a basic drawing on vellum and print it. Now turn the print of the basic drawing into a presentation drawing of a floor plan by adding appropriate dimensions and retain the original vellum drawing for a working drawing.

B. To Adapt a Design and Redraw the Presentation Floor Plan

Select a suitable house plan from a magazine, making sure that the size and orientation of the floor plan is suitable for your lot.

Step 6: Making the Preliminary Floor Plan Design

a. Revise the plan so that it is more suitable for the lot by sketching the floor plan in single-line format on graph paper. Use a scale of 4 squares = 1 m (1 square = 1'-0").

b. Make a copy of the sketch and indicate the traffic pattern for two members of the family for a typical day, using two different coloured pencils.

c. Assess the design and amend your plan to create a good traffic flow.

d. Draw a preliminary floor plan design in a single-line format showing your revisions at a scale of 1:50 (1/4" = 1'-0").

Step 7:   Kitchen and Bathroom Facilities

a. Draw the kitchen layout as in the original design showing the work triangle at a scale of 1:20 (3/4" =1'-0"). Amend the design if necessary.

b. Draw the main bathroom plan at a scale of 1:20 (3/4" =1'-0"). Amend if necessary.

Step 8:   Stair Design

Draw a plan view of the stairs at a scale of 1:50 (1/4" =1'-0") as they will be seen at each floor level. Show the landing area at the beginning of the stairs. These plan views will be incorporated into the floor plan designs.

Step 9:   Checking the Design

a. Draw the plan of the living room at a scale of 1:20 (3/4" =1'-0"). Arrange suitable furniture groupings in this room, using retail sales catalogues for sizes. This exercise will indicate whether your living room is a practical size and shape.

b. Review the preliminary floor plan design thoroughly and make changes on the basis of additional knowledge you have acquired. Check the drawing, using the checklist supplied on page 225.

Step 10:   Making the Presentation Drawing

a. On vellum, make a finished presentation drawing of the floor plan for your major project to a scale of 1:50 (1/4" =1'-0").

b. Dimension this drawing as for a presentation drawing or make a basic drawing on vellum and print it. Now turn the print of the basic drawing into a presentation drawing of a floor plan by adding appropriate dimensions and retain the original vellum drawing for a working drawing.

CHAPTER **10** | *Elevations*

ALL CLIENTS WOULD LIKE to have a picture of how their house will appear when it is complete. The most realistic way of achieving this is by a **perspective drawing** rendered to show the exterior materials and the landscaping relating the building to its environment. In order to make a perspective drawing, elevations, which are two-dimensional orthographic drawings of at least two sides of the house, are essential.

A perspective, or an **elevation drawing**, will indicate the style of the house. In Chapters 6 and 7 you have been made aware of aesthetic considerations in design. This knowledge enables you to plan the external features of the house so that the house will be attractive. Experienced designers often plan the functional and aesthetic elements of a house simultaneously.

If it is necessary to save time and money on the presentation drawings, a front elevation can be used instead of the perspective. Materials and landscaping can be added to this drawing to create a realistic illustration *(see Figs. 10-1A and 10-1B)*.

FIGURE 10-1A

Presentation drawing before landscaping

Jensen: *Architectural Drawing and Design for Residential Construction* published by McGraw-Hill Ryerson Ltd.

FIGURE 10-1B

Presentation drawing after landscaping – added realism and effect

Jensen: *Architectural Drawing and Design for Residential Construction* published by McGraw-Hill Ryerson Ltd.

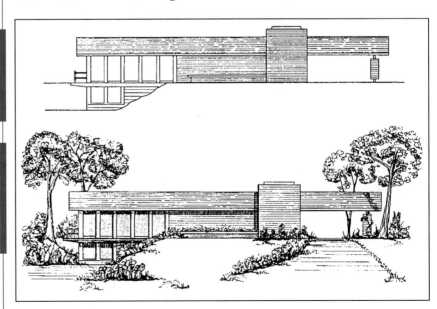

UNIT 1 | Elements of Elevations

OBJECTIVES

- To be able to name various roof and window types
- To appreciate how to apply various styles to the exterior of a house
- To understand the purpose of a presentation elevation drawing
- To be able to name various window types
- To understand the basic criteria of a good design

TYPES OF ROOFS

The purpose of a roof is to protect the interior of the house from the elements and also to make the structure more rigid. The key style feature is the shape of the roof, as it forms such a large element of the design. The most common roof styles are outlined below *(see Fig. 10-2)*:

THE GABLE

Features of the gable roof are:

1. It is one of the most frequently used styles for roofs.
2. It is a simple roof to construct and therefore is comparatively inexpensive.
3. The gable can vary from extreme slopes, as in an A-frame, to a shallow slope featured in ranch-style houses.
4. Two gable roofs can intersect one another when a house has a projection, such as a garage.
5. A gable roof can have added dormers and shed roofs to provide light for the upper level.
6. A gable roof has wide overhangs on two sides only.
7. The gable gives a strong horizontal line to the design of the structure.

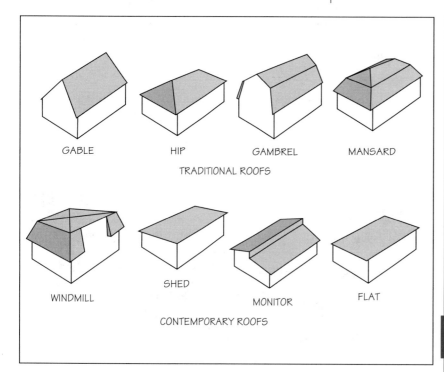

FIGURE 10-2
Types of roofs

GABLE HIP GAMBREL MANSARD

TRADITIONAL ROOFS

WINDMILL SHED MONITOR FLAT

CONTEMPORARY ROOFS

THE HIP

The hip roof is often misnamed a cottage roof. Its features are:

1. The hip is a variation on the gable with slopes on all four sides.
2. It is more complicated and expensive to construct than a gable.
3. The hip roof usually has a medium slope of approximately 10:5 (12:6).
4. It has wide overhangs on all sides to protect the windows from the sun, making it ideal for a sunny climate.
5. It is used on both traditional and post-modern-style houses.

THE GAMBREL

Points of interest about the gambrel roof are:

1. It is a Dutch colonial roof that was originally used on barns to provide greater headroom at an upper level.
2. It requires complicated construction so it is not often used today.

THE MANSARD

1. The mansard was originally designed by one of the great architects of France, after whom it is named.
2. It is related to the gambrel in the same way as the hip is to the gable, that is, it slopes on all four sides.
3. It is a very complicated roof to construct.
4. It has narrow windows inset into the roof for light.
5. It allows use of the area directly under the roof.

THE WINDMILL

The windmill roof is a contemporary adaptation of the mansard.

1. It has sloping sides but a flat top.
2. It is used on two-storey houses to create a division of materials between the upper and lower storeys.
3. Wooden shingles are often used in its construction.
4. It has windows in the upper storey that are cut into the sides of the roof to provide light.

THE SHED

1. The shed is really half of a gable roof, but as there is no supporting thrust from opposing members, the rafters must be larger in section to support live loads such as snow.
2. It is easy to construct and relatively inexpensive.

THE MONITOR

1. The monitor is two shed roofs at different levels with a short vertical wall separating the opposing sides of the roof.
2. It can have windows inserted in the short wall above eye level to provide lighting and privacy.
3. It is ideal for a house built on a sloped lot.

THE FLAT ROOF

1. The flat roof requires stronger members to support live loads.
2. It is not completely flat but usually has a slope of 20:1 (24:1.2) for drainage.
3. The covering is constructed of layers of tar, felt, and gravel, which is called a built-up roof.

Most other roofs found on residential buildings are variations of these basic types. To minimize the effect of live loads, houses built in windy areas should have shallow or flat roofs, while those in heavy snow areas should have steep roofs to allow the snow to fall off easily.

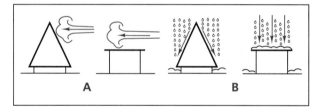

FIGURE 10-3A *Wind load on roofs;* **B** *Snow load on roofs*

STYLE FOR THE EXTERIOR

To decide on the style for the exterior of the house, make a series of **thumbnail sketches**. These sketches are small freehand drawings that will allow you to create an impression of how the elements of the structure will go together aesthetically. You can plan the **fenestration**, which is the placement and grouping of the windows, and other unique features of the style you wish to emulate.

These thumbnail sketches of the elevations must relate to the floor plan. You can draw a variety of different styles for the exterior elevations of the same floor plan *(see Fig. 10-4)*. Care must be

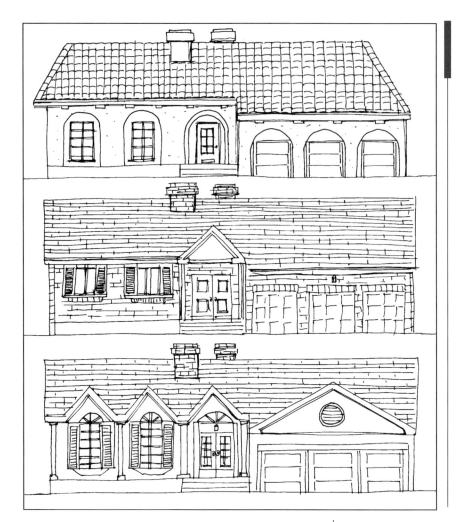

taken to see that all of the design elements such as the roof, doors, and windows are in keeping with the style required for each sketch. For instance, post-modern homes have sharply peaked gable roofs. The doors and windows often feature semi-circular skylights or round tops. The façade will be informally balanced and this will be reflected in the floor plan.

FIGURE 10-5

Post-modern-style house

DRAWING THE ELEVATIONS

The purpose of presentation elevation drawings is primarily pictorial. When you have decided upon the style, make a drawing to a scale of 1:50 (1/4" = 1'-0"). This size of drawing will allow you to elaborate some of the details from your thumbnail sketch and help you to keep the details in proportion. Keep all of your work in construction lines until you are satisfied with the design.

To begin this drawing, make a series of horizontal construction guidelines across the paper as shown in *Fig. 10-6A* for a one-storey house, and *Fig. 10-6B* for a two-storey house. If you are drawing a split-level house, the series of construction lines must be placed relative to each other on either side of the division wall *(see Fig. 10-6C)*.

The following are horizontal guidelines you would use in drawing an elevation:

1. The grade level is the level of earth around the house. Even for a level lot, the grade will vary from the front to the rear of the house. Ideally, the grade will be approximately 750 mm (2'-6") lower at the rear of the house to allow basement windows to be used without resorting to window wells. If the lot slopes naturally, the house should be designed to take advantage of this and the elevations drawn accordingly.

2. The top of the sub-floor is the floor level before any finish such as wood, tile or carpet has been laid down. The top of the sub-floor is usually 600 mm (2'-0") above the grade.

3. The top of the windows or the eave line is usually 2050 mm (6'-10") above the finished floor.

4. The room height or finished ceiling line does not show on the exterior of the building but is an essential element in the construction so it must be indicated. Room height is usually 2440 mm (8'-0").

5. The upper finished floor of a two-storey house will be approximately the depth of the joist above the finished ceiling of the lower level. As we have not determined the size of the joists at this stage, a distance of 250 mm (10") will be adequate for this drawing. Then continue with the horizontal lines spaced for the upper storey as shown in *Fig. 10-7*.

6. The height of the ridge above the ceiling must be calculated. See instructions for calculating the height of the ridge on page 237.

7. The top of the chimney is 600 mm (2'-0") above the ridge line. Dimensions need not be added to elevation drawings, which are part of the set of presentation drawings.

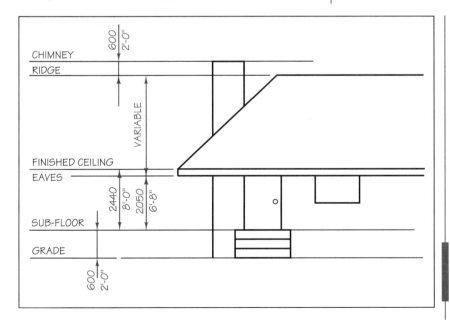

FIGURE 10-6A
Construction lines for a one-storey house

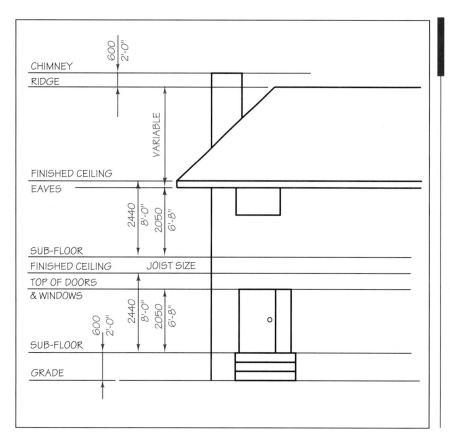

Figure 10-6B
Construction lines for a two-storey house

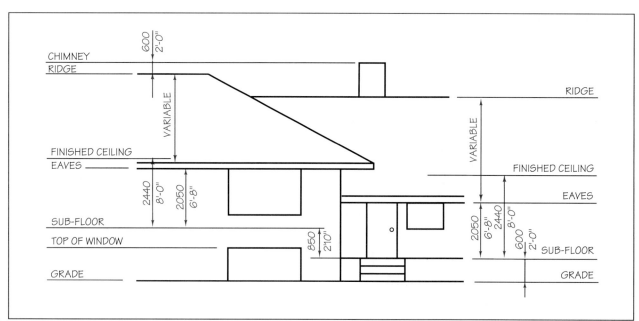

Figure 10-6C   *Construction lines for a split-level house*

FIGURE 10-7
Tudor-style house
Vertical and Horizontal Lines
Spaced for Upper Storey

CALCULATING THE HEIGHT OF THE RIDGE

In order to draw the roof on the elevation, you must establish the height of the ridge line. After you have decided on the type of slope that the roof is to have, that slope must be related to a **pitch ratio**. The pitch ratio is the proportion of the run or span of the roof to the rise of the slope. The pitch of the roof is shown by a symbol *(see Figs. 10-8A, 10-8B, and 10-8C)*. For a metric drawing, the run is related to 10. For an imperial drawing, the run is related to 12. Examples of probable slopes:

1. An A-frame house might have a pitch ratio of 10:20 (12:24).
2. A traditional house might have a pitch ratio of 10:5 (12:6).
3. The shallowest slope that a shingled roof can have is 10:2.5 (12:3).

When a ridge line is central to the structure, the height of any roof can be estimated by applying the ratio to the width of the house divided by two. Example — A house is 21 000 mm (70'-0") wide and has a pitch ratio of 10:5 (12:6). To estimate the rise of the roof from the ceiling follow the example that follows.

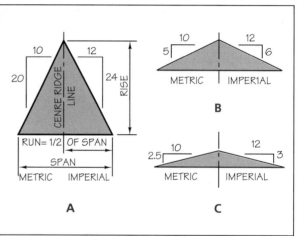

FIGURE 10-8A   *Pitch symbols – A-frame;*   **B** *Pitch symbols – traditional;*   **C** *Pitch symbols – shallow slope*

Divide the width of the house by 2:

$$\frac{21\ 000\ mm}{2} = 10\ 500\ mm \qquad \frac{70'\text{-}0"}{2} = 35'\text{-}0"$$

Apply the pitch ratio:

$$\frac{10\ 500\ mm \times 5}{10} = 5250\ mm \qquad \frac{35'\text{-}0" \times 6}{12} = 17'\text{-}6"$$

On the elevation, draw in the horizontal line to represent the height of the ridge at the calculated distance from the ceiling line and add the chimney line 600 mm (2'-0") above it.

Now you are ready to fill in the external features using vertical lines which can be projected from the floor plan to the elevation.

EXTERIOR DOORS

Next, plan the location of the exterior doors. The doors will fit in between the floor line and the eave line. Doors fall into two main categories: panel doors, which are solid, and slab doors, which are hollow. Modern exterior doors can be made of wood, plastic, or steel. Leaded lights, which are decorative glass panels, are available as door inserts or as additional panels for one or both sides of the doorway. Exterior doors are usually 810 mm (2'-10") wide and double exterior doors are somewhat wider. Glass sliding doors, which come in a variety of widths, usually give access to a patio. Consult manufacturers' brochures for details.

FENESTRATION

Now consider the placement and grouping of the windows. Usually windows are placed either directly under the soffit, which is the underside of the roof overhang, or are placed at a height of 2050 mm (6'-10") from the floor level. This means that from the interior, the windows will be at the correct height for someone standing inside a room to look out. In either case, this will leave approximately 400 mm (16") wall space above the window on the inside of the room.

Windows should be grouped in an attractive sequence on the exterior of the house. Windows on the first storey should also be placed so that they are at the same height as the doors. Too many different sizes or shapes of windows in one elevation are not attractive.

TYPES OF WINDOWS

Windows are made up of sashes, which are framed pieces of glass. Some may open for ventilation, while others will be fixed and provide illumination only. The hinged side of windows is shown on a drawing by a hidden line forming a triangle. The apex of the triangle points to the hinged side of the sash *(see Fig. 10-9A)*. The direction of sliding windows, which also includes double- and single-hung windows, is shown by an arrow *(see Fig. 10-9B)*. The major vertical divisions between sashes are called mullions and these divisions are shown on the floor plan *(see Fig. 10-10)*. The minor vertical and horizontal divisions are called **muntins**.

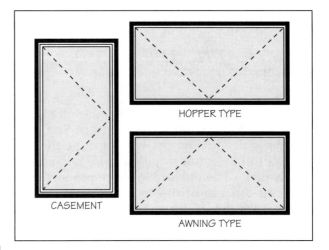

FIGURE 10-9A *Hinged windows*

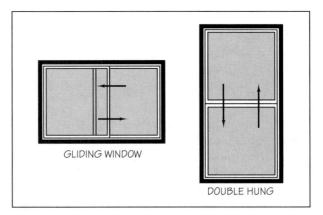

FIGURE 10-9B *Sliding windows*

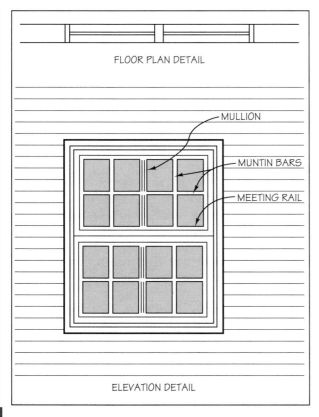

FLOOR PLAN DETAIL

MULLION

MUNTIN BARS

MEETING RAIL

ELEVATION DETAIL

FIGURE 10-10 *Window terminology*

On a double-hung window, the horizontal frame members that meet are called **meeting rails**. If the window is to be divided into small squares or diamond panes, removable muntins are provided as inserts, allowing for easy cleaning.

There are several different types of windows.

1. A fixed sash is a framed part of the window that does not open and can be used in combination with other sashes that do open.
2. A casement sash is a window that is hinged to open vertically like a door. It can open either inwards or outwards, but if the casement swings outwards then the screens are placed on the inside. Modern casement windows pivot to facilitate cleaning from the inside.
3. Hopper or awning windows are hinged at the top (awning) or bottom (hopper) and can project into or out of a room. These windows can be made to pivot for ease of cleaning also.

4. Sliding windows are windows in which the sashes are designed to slide past one another horizontally when opened. These windows can be removed from the inside for easy cleaning; the screens are on the outer side.
5. Double- and single-hung windows have sashes that are designed to slide past one another vertically when opening. Either both sashes or only the lower one can be movable. These windows can be removed for easy cleaning; the screens are on the outside.
6. A jalousie window is one that is made up of a series of horizontal strips of glass that can be cranked open.
7. Bay windows are made up of a series of sashes with the side sashes placed at angles of 30°, 45°, 60°, or 90°. These windows can be cantilevered out from a wall or can be supported by similarly shaped foundation walls.
8. Bow windows project out from the wall, and the individual sashes are placed around a shallow curve.
9. Arch windows have half round lights at the top of a window. This is usually a fixed sash above a casement window.
10. Solarium windows are glass extensions to rooms; they are a recent development and come in many styles. Consult manufacturers' catalogues for details.

Windows are used in a house to provide light and air. They are also an integral part of the architectural style. The living areas of the house should have a window area equal to 10% or more of the floor area. The bedrooms and bathrooms should have at least 5%. Because the heat loss through a window is much greater than that lost through an external wall, avoid using a lot of glass on the north and east sides. If all large windows are placed on the southern exposure, the heat loss will be less apparent and the windows may even aid in the heating for part of the year.

Factory-sealed double- and triple-glass windows are available as well as special heat-resistant and cold-resistant glass. Nevertheless, heat is lost more readily through windows than any other part of the house. Modern windows are usually

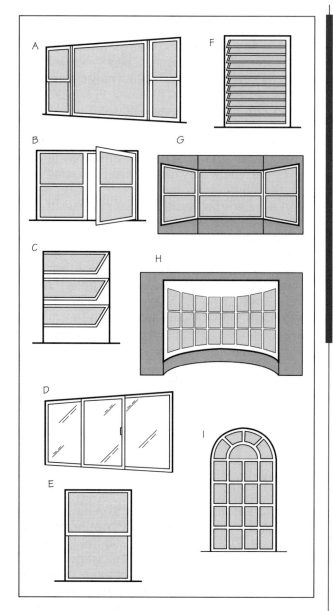

FIGURE 10-11A *Fixed-pane window with movable sections*

B *In-swinging casement window – opens inward by use of a crank, or operated by hand*

C *Awning type of window – has wide, horizontal sashes that open outward to any angle.*

D *Sliding glass doors – often set into a wall construction, but sometimes part of a "modern glass wall"*

E *Double-hung window – two sashes*

F *Jalousie window – narrow horizontal strips of glass that crank open to any desirable angle*

G *Bay window – three or more windows set at an angle to each other*

H *Bow window – sometimes called a circular bay window*

I *Arched window – any window arched at the top*

weather stripped, and all windows should be caulked around the frame to minimize the infiltration of exterior air into the house.

GOOD DESIGN CRITERIA

Go over your work with the following design criteria in mind. The front of the building should have a dominant feature. The front door is an obvious choice. It can be enhanced by being projected forward or inset into the structure. The front door can also be emphasized by side glazing, by which panels of glass are inserted on one or both sides of the door. A skylight or round top can also make the entrance look important. Steps to the front door can be enhanced by railings that direct the eye towards the entrance.

A building should have balance; either formal balance (the doors and windows are identical on each side of the front door) or informal balance. Informal balance is more difficult to achieve. The various elements on either side of the dominant feature of the façade, which is probably the front door, should appear equal in colour, texture, weight, and interest value. By holding your drawing up to a mirror, you can spot design errors concerning balance more easily than from the drawing itself.

It may be necessary to change the location of some of the components of the floor plan in order to incorporate elements of the style or to achieve the type of balance you desire.

Complete your design by adding a chimney and indicating the exterior materials as shown in *Fig. 10-12.*

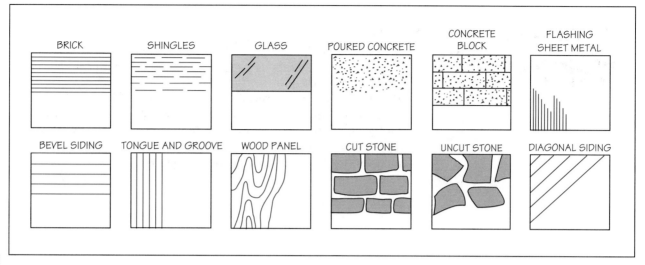

FIGURE 10-12   *Material symbols for use on elevations*

REVIEW QUESTIONS

1. What is the purpose of a presentation elevation drawing?
2. Describe the six different roof styles and suggest where they might be used.
3. List the horizontal construction guidelines you would use in order to draw an elevation.

WHAT DO YOU THINK?

1. What is the advantage of making thumbnail sketches of elevations?
2. Which type and style of house do you prefer? What elements would you include when designing a house in that style?
3. What design criteria would you use to make the front of a house interesting?

ASSIGNMENTS

1. Sketch an elevation on graph paper, or do this as a CAD project, of your own home or a friend's home. Using the scale 4 squares = 1 m (1 square = 1'-0"), draw in the appropriate construction lines before beginning.
2. Using the drawings you made in Chapter 9 for a two-storey house, make several thumbnail sketches in order to select a suitable style for the house. Then draw elevations of the front and one side for this house at a scale of 1:50 (1/4" = 1'-0") on A3/B sized sheets of vellum.

ELEVATIONS FOR THE PRESENTATION DRAWINGS

THE PROJECT

Step 11:
Create the style for the floor plan that you developed in Chapter 9.
a. Make a series of thumbnail sketches in order to discover the style that is best for your design.
b. Draw two presentation elevations to a scale of 1:50 (1/4" = 1'-0") using the horizontal construction guidelines suggested in this chapter. One elevation should be of the front of the building and the other of the side that will be shown in the perspective. Incorporate the design you have selected from the thumbnail sketches.

CHAPTER 11

Pictorial Drawing

IT **IS DIFFICULT** for most people to visualize, by looking at floor plans and elevations, what a house will look like when it is built. A pictorial drawing showing several sides of the building as well as the landscaping is usually provided as a visual aid for the client.

Interiors of the house are also illustrated to show either the functional layout or to create an aesthetic appeal for the design. Special detailed areas such as a fireplace, kitchen, bathroom, or foyer may be shown in a pictorial style for the same reasons.

The pictorial may be drawn in oblique, isometric, or perspective methods. The most popular is the perspective drawing. This method shows the building without distortion, as you would see it in real life.

You should be familiar with the basic styles of oblique, isometric, and perspective drawings. Also you should develop a unique style of rendering your pictorial drawings, thereby becoming a more versatile architectural draftsperson.

UNIT 1

Perspective Drawing – Multi-View Projection

OBJECTIVES

- To understand comparisons between oblique, isometric, and perspective drawings
- To appreciate the significance of a perspective drawing relative to a set of presentation drawings
- To draw an exterior and interior one-point perspective
- To draw an exterior two-point perspective
- To make an enlarged exterior perspective
- To draw lines that do not touch the picture plane in perspective

When a floor plan is to be projected into the illusion of three-dimensional space, three basic approaches are used. One is known as an **oblique drawing**, another is called an **isometric drawing**, and the third is referred to as a **perspective drawing**.

OBLIQUE AND ISOMETRIC DRAWINGS

The oblique and isometric forms of three-dimensional drawing are commonly used by draftspeople when the drawing must be done quickly. It is faster to draw either of these styles because they are drawn with standard angles of 30°, 45°, and 60° and isometric uses a 30° angle at all times. All width, height, and length lines are drawn to actual scale and in sets of parallel lines. These techniques create a distorted illusion of the object but are acceptable for many applications.

The oblique drawing has the front view drawn parallel to the picture plane and the side view drawn at an angle of 30°, 45°, or 60°. This is an unrealistic method of viewing an object but is easy to plan *(see Fig. 11-1)*.

The isometric drawing shows the object viewed from the front corner with all the horizontal lines

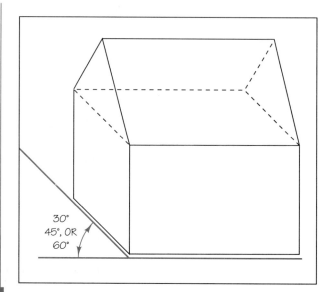

FIGURE 11-1 *An oblique drawing*

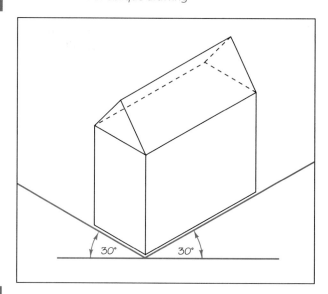

FIGURE 11-2 *An isometric drawing*

drawn parallel and at 30° *(see Fig. 11-2)*. The isometric view is usually preferred because there appears to be less distortion to the object.

PERSPECTIVE FOR TECHNICAL DRAWINGS

There are two methods of layout used in drafting a perspective of a building. The first method is explained in this unit and depends on a **multi-view projection**. It requires a large surface on which to construct the drawing. The second method is explained in Unit 2 and uses the **measuring point system**. This requires a smaller work area and can readily be adapted to the size of drawing required. The choice of method is one of personal preference. Both methods of perspective drawing can be made using one, two, or three **vanishing points**

ONE-POINT OR PARALLEL PERSPECTIVE

A **one-point perspective** can be clearly seen when looking at railroad tracks. You will notice that the tracks appear closer together as they move into the distance. If this process is taken to infinity, the lines will converge at one point called the **vanishing point** *(see Fig. 11-3)*.

One-point perspective is used to show a structure that has one side parallel to the horizon. You need to assume that the viewer is standing at a certain distance in front of that side of the building. The viewer's location is known as the **station point**. The final drawing will look similar to an oblique drawing except that the receding lines will not be parallel but will converge towards the vanishing point.

MULTI-VIEW PROJECTION FOR ONE-POINT PERSPECTIVE

When preparing to draw a one-point perspective by multi-view projection, it is necessary to lay out two separate views: a plan view and an elevation view. The elevation drawing will eventually become the perspective drawing. The **plan view** is drawn looking down on the layout to show the relative positions of
1. the **picture plane line**, which is the foremost surface of the drawing,

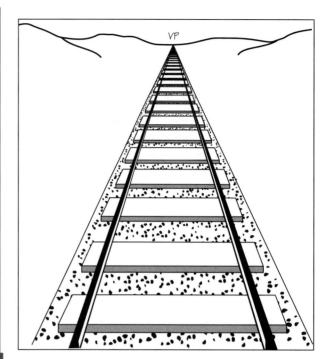

FIGURE 11-3 *One-point perspective*

2. the plan view of the building drawn to scale, and
3. the station point or location of the viewer.

The front of the building should be located on the picture plane line as it is only at this position that the structure can be measured at a known scale in the elevation view.

The **elevation view** is developed by projecting the building lines perpendicularly down from the plan view. The front elevation will be seated on the **ground line**, which should be drawn across the sheet at a convenient place underneath the plan view. Complete the drawing by using the true heights of the various features that are shown to be on the picture plane line in the plan view.

A **horizon line**, which is a line set at the eye level of the viewer, should be drawn parallel to the ground line. Eye level is usually 1600 mm (5'-4") from the ground line. The same scale as that used for drawing the plan view should be used. However, the level of the horizon line can be lowered if you wish the viewer to appear seated or raised as if the viewer were standing on a platform. The vanishing point will always be located

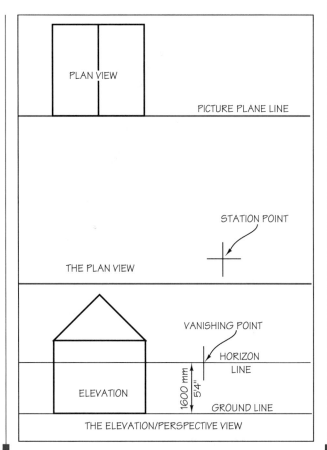

FIGURE 11-4A *A multi-view layout for one-point perspective*

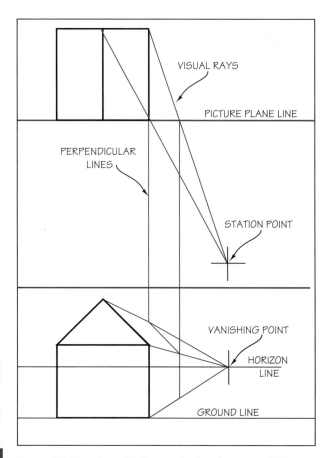

FIGURE 11-4B *A multi-view projection for one-point perspective. Determining the depth of the building.*

on the horizon line (in the elevation view) and it will also be perpendicular to the station point (in the plan view).

The plan view and the elevation view provide the layout necessary to complete a one-point perspective. If there is not enough vertical space on the paper, these two views can be overlapped.

COMPLETING THE PERSPECTIVE

Starting with the plan view, in light construction lines draw the visual rays from the viewer's eye by joining the major elements, such as the corners of the building and the roof overhangs, to the station point.

In the elevation view, with converging construction lines join the matching elements of the structure to the vanishing point.

To determine the depth of the building or to locate any feature along the side of the structure, drop perpendicular lines from the points where the appropriate visual rays cross the picture plane line in the plan view. Relate these lines to the converging lines projecting from the building to the vanishing point in the elevation view. Gradually, the perspective drawing will be formed *(see Fig. 11-4B)*.

INTERIOR PERSPECTIVES

One-point perspective is the most effective way of showing interior views of a house. The picture plane line can be shown at the front of the room and all furnishings drawn in to scale on this line and projected back into the picture *(see Fig.11-5A)*. If a larger drawing is required, the rear wall of the room can be used as the measuring plane and objects can be

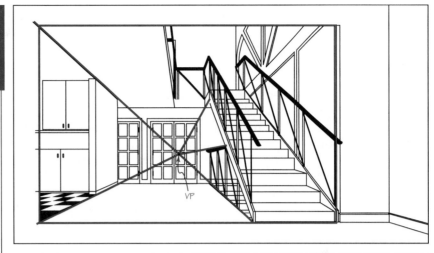

FIGURE 11-5A
*One-point interior —
comparison of size using
front picture plane for
measurement*

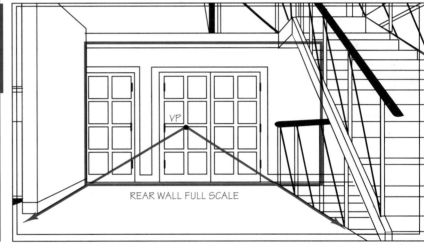

FIGURE 11-5B
*One-point interior —
comparison of size using
rear picture plane for
measurement*

drawn to scale on this surface and enlarged by projecting the visual rays forward *(see Fig. 11-5B)*.

TWO-POINT PERSPECTIVE

One-point perspective has similarities to an oblique drawing in the same way that two-point perspective has to an isometric drawing. In two-point perspective, a corner of the structure faces the viewer. However, the receding lines on each side of the corner are not parallel (as in an isometric drawing) but converge to vanishing points at either side.

Although the initial layout for making a two-point perspective drawing is more complicated than for a one-point, the actual construction of perspective depths in the elevations is identical for each case.

MULTI-VIEW PROJECTION FOR TWO-POINT PERSPECTIVE

A plan view and an elevation view are also necessary for preparing a two-point perspective by multi-view projection. The plan view is a view looking down on the layout and shows the relative position of

1. the picture plane line,
2. the floor plan of the building,
3. the station point.

Only one corner of the building will touch the picture plane line and it is only at this point that the structure can be measured at a known scale in the elevation view.

The floor plan will be set at an angle to the picture plane line. The most commonly used angles for rectangular buildings are 30° and 60° with the long side being positioned at 30° to the horizontal. A 45° angle is most commonly used for a square building.

The station point should be in line and perpendicular to the front corner of the building. The proportions of the building will appear normal if the station point is positioned in such a way that the visual rays going to each corner of the structure do not exceed an angle of 30°. This usually means that the station point will be 1.5 to 2 times the width of the house (measured parallel to the picture plane line) in front of one of the side corners of the building *(see Fig. 11-6)*. The elevation/perspective view comprises the ground line, the horizon line, and the vanishing points. A scale drawing of the orthographic elevation must be on hand to determine true heights.

POSITIONING THE DRAWING ON THE PAPER

Use a floor plan at a scale of 1:50 (1/4" = 1'-0") and an A1/D or larger sheet of paper. For an adequate sized perspective drawing, start the layout by drawing the picture plane line approximately 150 mm (6") from the top of the sheet. Then place location points at the extreme ends of this line. Determine which corner of the building you will view and at what angle you will position the floor plan to obtain the best perspective view. Project angular lines at these angles downward from the location points. The station point will be where these lines cross. Draw a vertical line through the station point to touch the picture plane line. This point indicates where the corner of the plan view should be located. This line will also become the measuring line and all measurements will be taken from the point where the measuring line and the ground line intersect *(see Fig. 11-7A)*.

A speedy way to incorporate the floor plan into the layout is to make a print of your original drawing. Draw in the overhangs and ridge lines of the

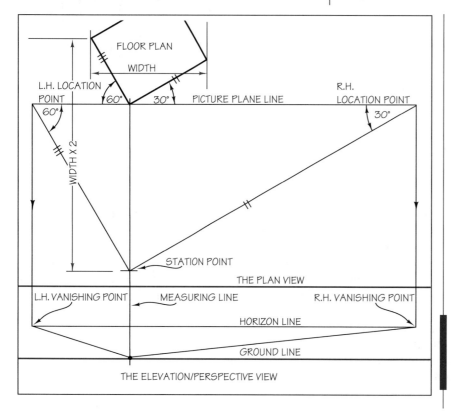

FIGURE 11-6

Multi-view layout for two-point perspective showing location of vanishing points

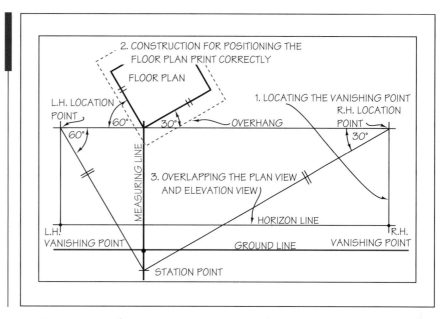

roof on the print and cut it out along the edges of the roof overhangs. To position the floor plan correctly on the layout, draw in the selected angles on either side of the point on the picture plane line where the corner of the floor plan is to be located. Draw in additional lines to represent the extent of the roof overhang in front and parallel to these lines. Then line up the cut-out edges of the print with the lines you have drawn and tape the print down to the layout.

To begin the perspective, draw in the ground line and horizon lines in an appropriate place on the paper. The two views may overlap if the vertical size of the drawing sheet is limited. Locate the vanishing points by dropping perpendicular lines to the horizon from the two location points. Draw angular lines from each vanishing point to where the measuring line and the ground line meet. These lines will form the base line of the structure (*see Fig. 11-7B*).

COMPLETING THE PERSPECTIVE

As in all pictorial drawings, you should draw a box to contain the structure before adding details. Any projections such as a garage or any recessed portions such as an entry should be added or taken from the main perspective box once the basic shape and size have been established.

Determine the depth of the house as you did for one-point construction. It is useful to draw a separate box on top of the eaves when drawing in the roof because of the sloping lines and overhangs involved (*see Fig. 11-8*).

ENLARGING A PERSPECTIVE

If the size of the drawing appears to be smaller than is desirable, it is possible to make an enlarged perspective using the layout that has already been set up.

We know that the further the object is positioned behind the picture plane line, the smaller the object will appear in perspective. It is therefore logical that the further the object is in front of the picture plane, the larger it will be in the perspective view.

To enlarge the perspective drawing, move the picture plane line back from its initial position on the layout. Theoretically this new line can be positioned anywhere, but it is most practical to have it run through one of the corners of the floor plan. The front corner of the structure will now be in front of the newly positioned picture plane line.

From where the new picture plane crosses the floor plan, drop a perpendicular line to the

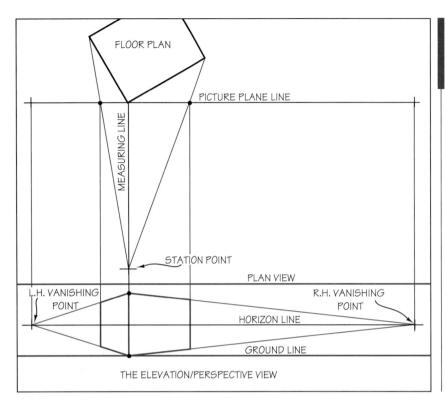

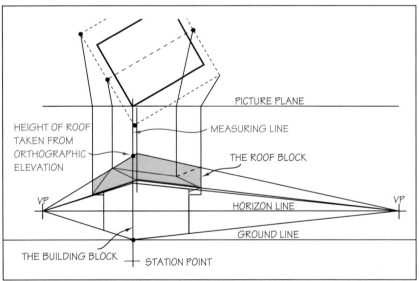

Figure 11-8
Blocking in the structure and drawing the roof

ground line in the elevation view. Since measurements can be made only at the point where the object touches the picture plane, this perpendicular line will become the new measuring line. The revised picture plane will cut across the floor plan at two points. Select the point closest to the corner of the floor plan touching the picture plane as the measuring line *(see Fig. 11-9).*

To draw the base line of the building for the enlarged perspective view, draw a converging line

Figure 11-9
Enlarging a two-point perspective

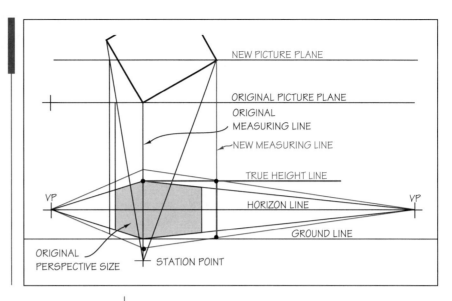

NEW PICTURE PLANE

ORIGINAL PICTURE PLANE

ORIGINAL MEASURING LINE

NEW MEASURING LINE

TRUE HEIGHT LINE

HORIZON LINE

GROUND LINE

VP

VP

ORIGINAL PERSPECTIVE SIZE

STATION POINT

from the vanishing point on the same side as the measuring line so that it will pass through the point where the measuring line and the ground line cross. Project this line forward until it reaches an extension of the line drawn perpendicularly from the front corner of the floor plan. Where the converging line and the corner line intersect, construct another line going back to the vanishing point on the other side of the drawing. These two converging lines will form the base lines of the building. Proceed with the projection of depth lines as for any perspective drawing but remember to use the new picture plane line and the new measuring line at all times. As a part of the floor plan of the building is in front of the picture plane line, some depth lines will have to be determined by extending visual rays back to the picture plane line.

The perspective will become enlarged because

1. the building is partially in front of the picture plane, and
2. the measuring line is on a corner at the side of the building rather than being at the front corner.

Note: This method of enlarging is not totally accurate. Therefore, it will produce only a realistic perspective if the picture plane line is not moved too far back from its original position.

LINES THAT DO NOT TOUCH THE PICTURE PLANE

As measurements can be made only for lines that touch the picture plane, it is evident that additional construction will be necessary to establish the height of any object that does not touch the picture plane directly. To find the correct height relative to the object's location in the plan view, connect a corner of the object to the picture plane line by a line drawn parallel to the angle used for the main block of the drawing. From the point where this angular line crosses the picture plane line, drop a perpendicular line to the ground line in the elevation view. Height measurements can then be made from where these lines intersect. The correct relative height will be established for the object by drawing converging lines to the vanishing point.

REVIEW QUESTIONS

1. Which two views must be used in multi-view perspective drawings? What lines or points must be included in each?
2. Why is the enlarged method that is explained in the chapter not totally accurate?
3. How do you set up the drawing to ensure you are using the paper to the fullest extent?

WHAT DO YOU THINK?

1. Why does a perspective form such an important part of a set of presentation drawings?
2. Why do you think one-point perspective would not make a suitable exterior drawing of a house?
3. When making a two-point perspective, why is a 45° angle used for a square house and 30° or 60° for a rectangular house?

ASSIGNMENTS

1. Draw a one-point perspective of buildings A and B shown on the assignment sheet provided by your instructor.
2. Draw a one-point perspective of the garage assignment provided by the instructor.
3. Draw a one-point perspective drawing of the kitchen interior provided by the instructor. Assume heights and details not given.
4. For the floor plan of the house provided:
   a. Draw an enlarged two-point perspective using picture plane 1.
   b. Draw a two-point perspective using picture plane 2, by placing a piece of vellum on top of the original drawing.
5. On the layout of blocks provided by your instructor:
   a. Draw a two-point perspective using picture plane 1.
   b. Draw an enlarged two-point perspective using picture plane 2, by placing a piece of vellum on top of the original drawing.

UNIT 2

Perspective Measuring Point System and Grids

OBJECTIVES

- To learn the applications of the measuring point system
- To be able to draw a one-point exterior and interior perspective using measuring points
- To be able to draw a two-point exterior and interior perspective using measuring points
- To learn the applications of perspective grids
- To draw in perspective using a grid

APPLICATIONS OF THE MEASURING POINT SYSTEM

The measuring point system of perspective can be applied to one-point or two-point perspective drawings for either exterior or interior views. The measuring point system differs from the projection system in three ways.

First, with the measuring point system, it is not necessary to place a plan view or elevation in a position relative to the desired view. Therefore, it allows large structures to be drawn on an average-sized drafting table and drafting paper. Second, the size of the finished drawing is seen after only a few lines are drawn, saving valuable time. The third difference is that the size of the drawing can be increased or decreased by simply changing the scale of measurement, without redoing the whole drawing.

It is recommended that you learn the measuring point system, as well as the multi-view projection system, in order to draw large homes or buildings to scale, quickly and efficiently.

USING THE MEASURING POINT SYSTEM FOR ONE-POINT (PARALLEL) PERSPECTIVE

To lay out a scaled drawing in one-point perspective using the measuring point system, use the following steps:

1. Draw the horizon line across the approximate centre of your drawing paper. Using a desired scale of your choice for the drawing, draw the ground line 1600 mm (5'-4") below the horizon line and parallel to it *(see Fig. 11-10)*.

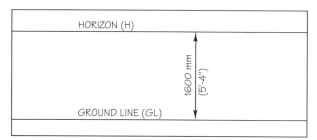

FIGURE 11-10 *Measuring Point System – One-Point Perspective   Step 1*

2. Draw the line of sight (LS) perpendicular to and through the horizon line and the ground line. Where the line of sight intersects the horizon line, it forms the vanishing point (VP), and where the line of sight intersects the ground line, it forms the **station point** (SP) *(see Fig. 11-11)*.

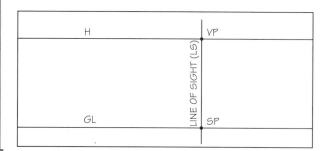

FIGURE 11-11 *Step 2*

3. Place a 45° set square along the ground line so that you can draw 45° lines from the station point through the horizon line. The points where the 45° lines intersect the horizon line become the **left measuring point** (LMP) and **right measuring point** (RMP) *(see Fig. 11-12)*.

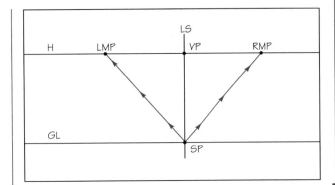

FIGURE 11-12 *Step 3*

4. Using the desired scale and starting at the station point, measure, at an equal distance to the left and right along the ground line, one-half of the total measurement of the side of the object you choose to look at. From each of these two points of measurement, draw a line to the vanishing point *(see Fig. 11-13)*.

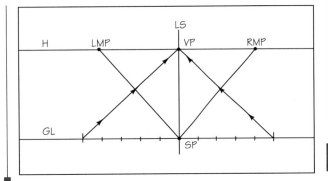

FIGURE 11-13 *Step 4*

5. To locate the depth of the object in perspective, you can measure the other dimension of the object from either the left or right points of measurement drawn in Step 4 along the ground line towards the station point. From this dimension point, draw a line to the measuring point *on the same side of the line of sight* from which you began to measure this dimension *(see Fig. 11-14)*.

6. Where the line drawn to the measuring point intersects the line from the vanishing point on the same side of the line of sight as the measuring point, draw a line parallel to the horizon to

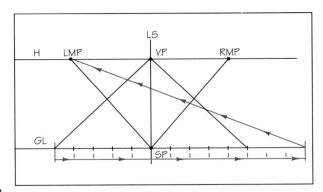

FIGURE 11-14 *Step 5*

the opposite line from the vanishing point. This line will now complete the base rectangle of the object in perspective on the ground plan *(see Fig. 11-15)*.

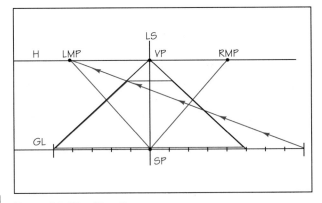

FIGURE 11-15 *Step 6*

7. Draw perpendicular lines from the four corners of the rectangle through the horizon line. Height measurements can be placed in scale on vertical lines that touch the ground line. All heights are projected in perspective by drawing visual ray lines from the height point to the vanishing point *(see Fig. 11-16)*.

To draw all details of the object, you simply read the dimensions from the plans of the object and repeat Steps 5 through 7 to draw them in perspective to scale. If you wish to enlarge or reduce the size of the drawing, change the scale accordingly. The distance between the horizon line and the ground line determines the eye level of the viewer.

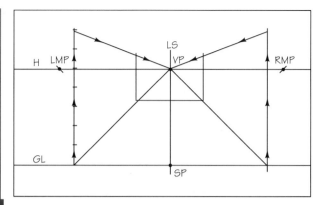

FIGURE 11-16 *Step 7*

The closer together these lines are drawn, the more you are looking up at the object, while the farther apart they are drawn, the more you are looking down on the object.

USING THE MEASURING POINT SYSTEM FOR TWO-POINT PROJECTION PERSPECTIVE

To draw a building to scale in two-point perspective using the measuring point system, use the following steps in your drawing:

1. Draw the horizon line across the approximate centre of your drawing paper. Then draw the line of sight perpendicular to the horizon line. Using a scale of your choice, measure down from the point of intersection the length of the building and place a dot on the line of sight to represent the station point *(see Fig. 11-17)*.

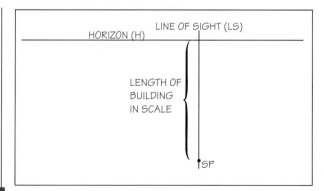

FIGURE 11-17 *Measuring Point System – Two-Point Perspective   Step 1*

2. Place a set square so that the 90° corner is on the station point and the two sides of the square are angled upward towards the horizon line. Each of these sides represents an end or a side of the building. By rotating the set square left or right, you can visualize how much of the building you would see. When you have decided on the best angle of view, draw a line from the station point along each of the sides of the set square until they touch the horizon line. These two points will be the **left vanishing point** (LVP) and the **right vanishing point** (RVP) *(see Fig. 11-18)*.

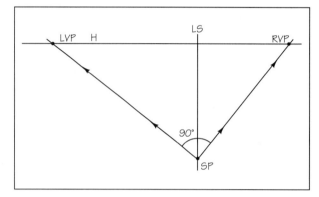

FIGURE 11-18 *Step 2*

3. Using the distance from the left vanishing point to the station point as the radius of a circle and the left vanishing point as the centre, draw an arc from the station point through the horizon line. The point of intersection is called the left measuring point. Repeat this procedure, using the distance from the right vanishing point to the station point as the radius and the right vanishing point as centre to locate the right measuring point on the horizon *(see Fig. 11-19)*.

4. Using the desired scale, measure down the line of sight 1600 mm (5'-4") and through this point, draw the ground line parallel to the horizon. Also from this point, draw a line to the left vanishing point and one to the right vanishing point. These **base lines** (BL) represent the closest planes of the building and closest corner on the ground, in perspective *(see Fig. 11-20)*.

5. Starting where the ground line meets the line of sight, mark off the ground line in the desired

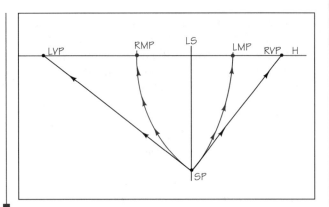

FIGURE 11-19   *Step 3*

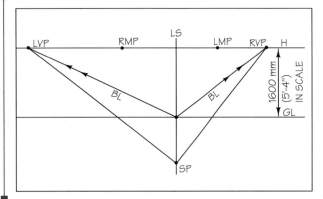

FIGURE 11-20   *Step 4*

scale in both directions. Also mark this scale up the line of sight starting at the same point (*see Fig. 11-21*).

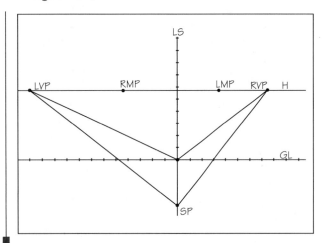

FIGURE 11-21   *Step 5*

6. Reading the dimensions from the floor plans and elevations, measure in scale the left and right sides of the building along the ground line starting where the ground line meets the line of sight. Project measurements to the left of the line of sight to the left measuring point, and measurements to the right of the line of sight to the right measuring point. Where these lines meet the base lines, project them to the left and right vanishing points (*see Fig. 11-22*).

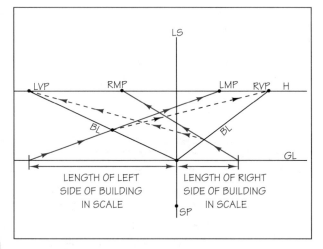

FIGURE 11-22   *Step 6*

7. Draw vertical lines from the points along the left and right base lines to meet the height lines (*see Fig. 11-23*).

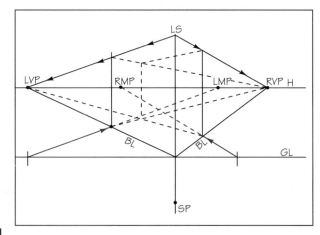

FIGURE 11-23   *Step 7*

8. All height lines are measured along the line of sight and then projected to the left or right vanishing point *(see Fig. 11-24)*.

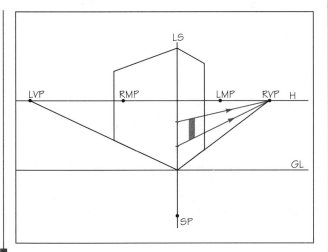

If you wish to enlarge or reduce the size of your drawing, simply change the scale of measurement. The distance between the ground line and the horizon line will determine the eye level and create the illusion of either looking up or down at the building.

PERSPECTIVE GRIDS

Perspective grids are preprinted perspective drawings of a cube divided horizontally and vertically in equal sections to scale. These grids are available in one-point, two-point, and three-point perspectives. They are also available in a variety of scales. Preprinted perspective grids make it easier and faster to draw in perspective.

The two-point grids are drawn to show the cube so that the base lines are at 30° and 60° angles and also in sets to show the base lines at 45° angles. Perspective grids are very useful if you

have numerous perspective drawings to produce because it saves constructing the projected lines from the floor plan or elevations.

Before deciding to use a perspective grid, you should consider which view of the house would look the best, which special features you would like to see, and what landscaping you would see from various views. These considerations may reveal that the perspective grid angles are not suitable and it would be better to use another perspective method.

Since these perspective cubes are divided on all sides into equal modules, all the dimensions of the building can be plotted within the perspective cube grid. The size of the drawing can be determined by the choice of the scale of the grid.

Use the perspective grid by placing it under the drafting paper and drawing the building within the cube using the predetermined vanishing points of the cube itself. The perspective grid may be used for both interior and exterior perspective drawings *(see Fig. 11-25)*.

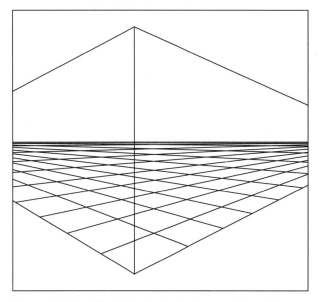

FIGURE 11-25 *Line shot of a typical perspective grid*

REVIEW QUESTIONS

1. What are three advantages of using the measuring point system?
2. In one-point perspective, what kind of set square is used to locate the measuring points on the horizon?
3. How do you enlarge or reduce your drawing when using the measuring point system?
4. How does your viewpoint affect the distance between the ground line and the horizon line?

WHAT DO YOU THINK?

1. What features of a house would you consider when choosing your point of view for a perspective drawing?
2. When would you not choose to use a perspective grid to make a perspective drawing of a house or building?

ASSIGNMENTS

1. Use the measuring point system to draw a one-point perspective of the kitchen layout from the assignment sheet provided by your instructor.
2. Draw a two-point perspective of the house from the assignment sheet provided by your instructor, using the measuring point system.

UNIT 3 | Special Applications of Perspective

OBJECTIVES

- To learn how to draw equal divisions in perspective
- To learn how to draw cast shadows in perspective
- To learn how to create the illusion of perspective
- To learn how to draw figures in perspective

The study of perspective is an interesting and involved area of pictorial drawing. To effectively illustrate exciting new designs, a thorough understanding of perspective for the pictorial artist is required.

There are a few special applications of perspective that you should learn because they are often used in pictorial drawing. Four such applications are drawing equal divisons in perspective, drawing shadows in perspective, drawing the illusion of perspective, and drawing figures in perspective.

DRAWING EQUAL DIVISIONS IN PERSPECTIVE

In architectural design some of the building components, such as windows, doorways, or columns, are often arranged equally along an area or wall. To draw equally spaced objects in perspective, one of the following two methods can be used.

Method One – This method is excellent for drawing objects and spaces that are both equal and are without a given confined distance.

1. Draw the converging top and bottom lines, representing the height of the object, to a vanishing point *(see Fig. 11-26)*.
2. Draw parallel vertical lines to form the first space *(see Fig. 11-27)*.
3. Divide the first vertical line in half and from this point draw a converging line to the vanishing point *(see Fig. 11-28)*.

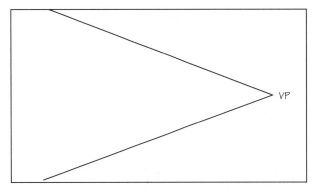

FIGURE 11-26 *Drawing converging lines of height for equal divisions*

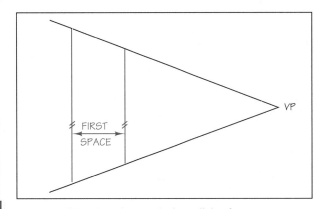

FIGURE 11-27 *Drawing vertical parallels of space*

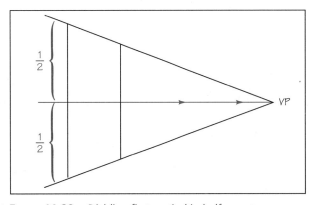

FIGURE 11-28 *Dividing first vertical in half*

4. Draw a line from the bottom of the first vertical line through the next vertical line at the point where the centre converging line intersects that vertical line. Continue the line until it meets the top converging line. This point locates the distance of the next space in perspective; the space is indicated by drawing a vertical line to the bottom converging line *(see Fig. 11-29)*.

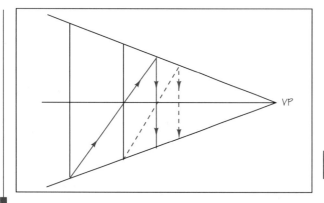

FIGURE 11-29 *Drawing equal divisions in perspective*

This procedure is repeated by beginning at the bottom of the second space to locate the third space. All equal spaces can be located in perspective using this system.

Method Two – The second method is the most accurate for dividing equal or unequal spaces within a defined distance, such as a number of windows and doors along a wall.

1. Draw the wall in perspective using a vanishing point and a horizon line *(see Fig. 11-30)*.

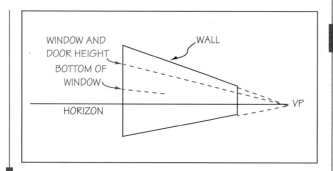

FIGURE 11-30 *Locating height lines in perspective*

2. Draw a line parallel to the horizon from the bottom of the nearest corner of the wall towards the vanishing point. Then, starting at the nearest corner, mark off along this horizontal line all the dimensions of the windows, spaces, and doors in the proper scale *(see Fig. 11-31)*.

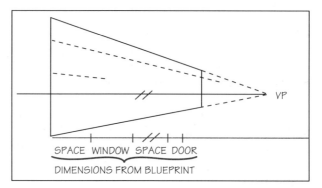

FIGURE 11-31 *Locating width dimensions*

3. Locate on the horizon line a point that is the same distance from the vanishing point as the distance from the vanishing point to the bottom nearest corner *(see Fig. 11-32)*. This point is the **measuring point** (MP).

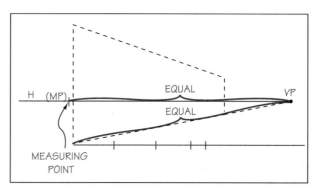

FIGURE 11-32 *Locating the measuring point*

4. Draw lines from each of the measured points along the horizontal line to the measuring point until they intersect the base line of the wall *(see Fig. 11-33)*.
5. By drawing vertical lines up the wall from the points of intersection, the wall is divided into the correct spaces for windows and doors *(see Fig. 11-34)*.

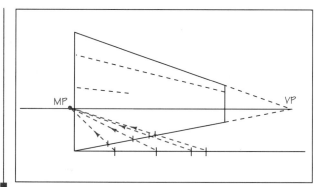

FIGURE 11-33 *Locating width measurements onto the base of the wall*

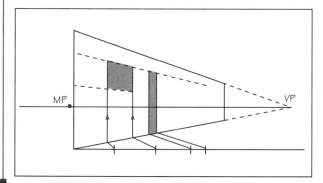

FIGURE 11-34 *Projecting width measurements up the wall to complete windows and doors*

Both of these methods for dividing space in perspective can be used for dividing horizontal planes as well as vertical planes *(see Fig. 11-35)*.

DRAWING SHADOWS IN PERSPECTIVE

Shadows are cast from the sun or from another source such as a light bulb. The main difference between the sun (natural light) and a light bulb (artificial light) is the direction of the light rays. Sun rays are considered to travel in parallel lines because the sun is so much larger than the earth. Light rays from a bulb, however, radiate in all directions from the centre of the bulb. You should learn the following two simple methods of casting shadows to add more realism to your pictorial drawings.

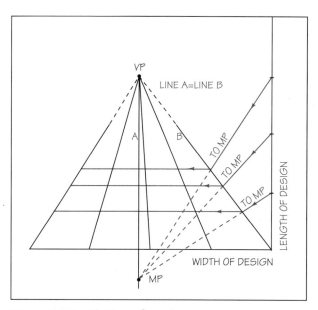

FIGURE 11-35 *Plotting a floor design*

CASTING SHADOWS WITH THE SUN PARALLEL TO THE HORIZON

This method offers a quick but accurate system of indicating cast shadows. Only two construction lines are required to locate each corner of the shadow: a ground line and a sun ray.

1. Select the angle at which the sun is shining on the house. Usually an angle of 45° is used to allow the use of a standard set square.
2. Draw sun rays through the corners of the house that will cast the shadow *(see Fig. 11-36)*. Remember that corners at the back of the house may also cast shadows, so note the hidden lines used in the diagram to locate the back corner of the house.
3. Project vertical lines from these corners to the base of the house *(see Fig. 11-37)*.
4. Draw lines parallel with the horizon from each corner located on the ground at the base of the house. Extend these horizontal lines, called **ground lines**, until they intersect with the sun ray that was drawn through that point of the house *(see Fig. 11-38)*.
5. By drawing lines to join each of these intersections, the shadow is outlined on the ground *(see Fig. 11-39)*.

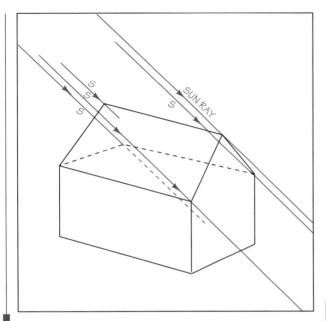

FIGURE 11-36 *Locating sun rays on an object*

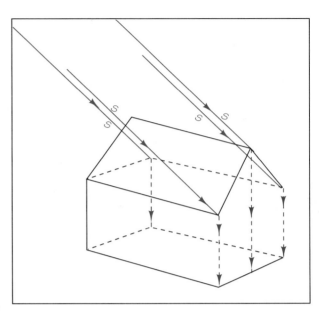

FIGURE 11-37 *Locating shadows casting points down to the ground*

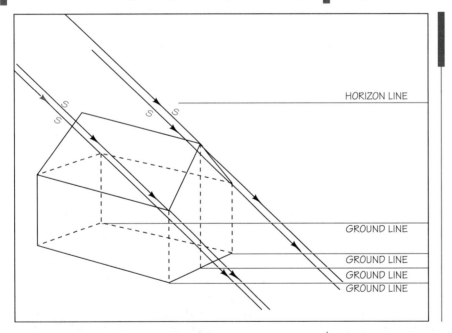

FIGURE 11-38
Locating ground lines parallel to the horizon

CASTING SHADOWS FROM A LIGHT BULB

An understanding of casting shadows from a light bulb will add depth and interest to interior pictorial drawings. Since all the light rays radiate from the centre of the light bulb, all the ground lines will radiate from the centre of the bulb and be projected down to the floor.

1. Draw a line from the light across the ceiling, down the wall, and horizontally across the floor to intersect with a vertical line that has been

Figure 11-39

Shadow formed where sun rays meet groundlines

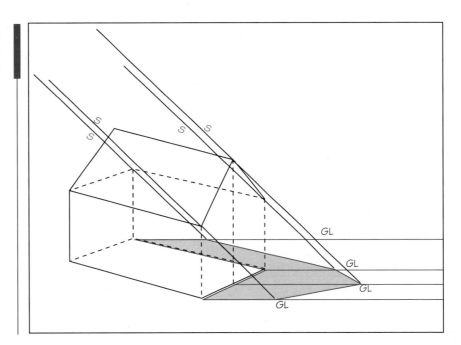

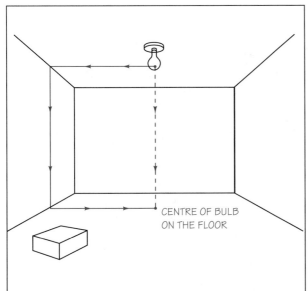

Figure 11-40 *Locating the centre of the light bulb on the floor*

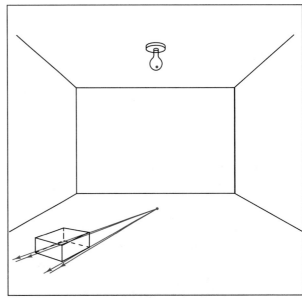

Figure 11-41 *Locating the ground lines of the shadow*

drawn from the light towards the floor of the room *(see Fig. 11-40)*.

2. Draw radiating lines from the intersected point through the parts of the object that are touching the floor *(see Fig. 11-41)*.

3. Draw radiating lines from the centre of the light bulb through the points of the object that will cast the shadow. Extend each line to meet the radiating line on the floor that corresponds to that part of the object *(see Fig. 11-42)*. Join the points of intersection to form the shadow *(see Fig. 11-43)*.

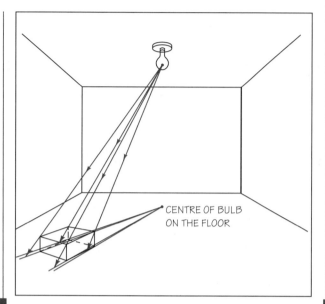

FIGURE 11-42 *Locating the light rays striking the object points that will cast the shadow*

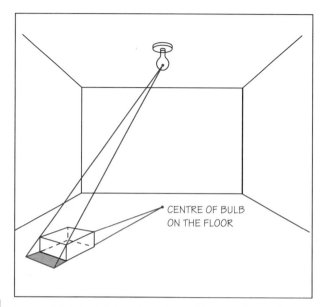

FIGURE 11-43 *Joining the points of intersection to form the shadow*

DRAWING THE ILLUSION OF PERSPECTIVE

One form of pictorial drawing often used for the promotion of new houses being built in quantity is a front elevation rendered to appear three dimensional. This technique allows the developer to show alternative front elevations of one standard floor plan. The method is quite easy and quick to render and is therefore economical.

The illusion of three dimensions is achieved by creating the appearance of a one-point perspective drawing. Recesses and overhangs on the house are given the appearance of depth by casting shadows from them onto the perspective; the vertical lines indicating the ends of the roof are drawn at a slight inward angle. This makes the roof appear to slant away from the front.

If the height of the roof is also drawn about 25% lower on the elevation, the illusion of a slanting roof is increased. Drawing cast shadows under the fascia board, window sills, and front entrance also creates depth. The illusion of perspective and three dimensions is made complete by drawing a sidewalk and driveway, each with its own single vanishing point, to project slightly forward. Extra touches such as shrubs or trees complete the illusion (*see Fig. 11-44*).

FIGURES IN PERSPECTIVE

Although figures are seldom drawn in a pictorial drawing of a single house, they are almost always shown in the drawing of a proposed residential development or a proposed commercial project. The body proportions of humans are relatively the same, making them easier to draw in perspective. Adult males are eight heads high and adult females are seven and one-half heads high.

1. When the horizon line is above eye level in relationship to the building:
    a. Using an area of the building that is about the height of a human, such as a doorway, draw lines from the vanishing point through this height and extend them to the desired location of a figure. Draw the first figure within this height (*see Fig. 11-45*).

Figure 11-44   *Shrubs and trees complete the illusion of perspective*

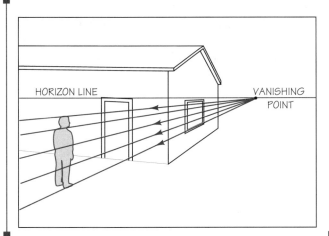

Figure 11-45   *Locating the first figure in proportion and perspective*

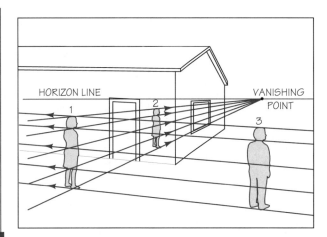

Figure 11-46   *Locating other figures in proportion and perspective*

b. Draw lines from the shoulders, waist, and knees of the first figure to each of the vanishing points. All other figures can be drawn proportionately along these converging line *(see Fig. 11-46)*.

2. When the house is in the correct relationship to the horizon line and if the horizon line is drawn at normal eye level, the eyes of a person standing on the ground anywhere in the picture will be on the horizon line unless the person is much smaller.

REVIEW QUESTIONS

1. What is the main difference between natural light and artificial light?
2. How many construction lines are required to locate each corner of a shadow?
3. What is the most common angle used to draw sun rays? Why?
4. When might a pictorial drawing that uses the illusion of perspective be used?
5. For an elevation drawing, suggest two methods that create the illusion of depth.

WHAT DO YOU THINK?

1. Why are figures not used in pictorial drawings of a single house?
2. Why are figures used in residential development or commercial project pictorials?
3. When do you think it would be appropriate to use figures of children in a drawing?

ASSIGNMENTS

1. Using one of the two methods described, draw a row of eight columns that are equally spaced in perspective. Leave all construction lines on your drawing.
2. Using method two of dividing spaces in perspective, draw a wall and arrange three equally proportioned windows and one door that is twice as wide as a window on the wall in perspective.
3. Draw a box in pencil using two-point perspective. Cast a shadow of the box using 45° sun rays that are parallel to the horizon and shine from the left. Leave all construction lines on your drawing.
4. Draw the front elevation of a simple small bungalow and render your drawing in pencil to create the illusion of perspective.
5. Draw six figures in perspective that are all standing in various locations on the drawing. Leave all construction lines on your drawing.

PROVIDING A PICTURE

THE PROJECT

Part of your major project is to show the completed house three dimensionally. This may be done through a pictorial drawing, a model, or both. The following procedure is suggested to produce a pictorial drawing:

Step 12: Select the view of the front and end of the house that will show the best features.

Step 13: Draw the house in two-point perspective using either the multi-view projection system at a scale of 1:50 (1/4" = 1'-0") using an A1/D size sheet of paper or the measuring-point system at a scale of 1:25 (1/2" = 1'-0") using an A2/C size sheet of paper.

Step 14: Choose the items for embellishment, such as walkways, driveways, trees, and shrubs. Draw these in outline form on the perspective drawing.

Step 15: Remove all construction lines so that the house and surroundings remain outlined. It is sometimes better to retrace the outline of the house and surroundings on to a clean A2/C size sheet of drafting paper or illustration board.

Step 16: Before rendering the house, read Chapter 13.

CHAPTER 12 | Model Making

PRIOR TO THE TWENTIETH CENTURY, models played an important role in construction because it was not possible to reproduce architectural drawings in quantity. Measurements would often be taken directly from the model to build the structure.

Twentieth-century technology produced several methods of making multiple copies of drawings. Blueprint machines, photographic machines, and eventually photocopiers made it easy for those who needed a set of building plans to have them. Therefore, the need for architectural models declined slightly. But the rapid growth in new materials and new building techniques has now caused an increase in the use of models. Model making is a very lucrative career and, in many large cities, professional model-making services are available to architectural firms.

There are many advantages to using a model:

1. Complicated areas of construction, such as roofs, are easy to understand and visualize from a model.
2. Most people are able to visualize the finished structure from a model more clearly than from two-dimensional drawings.
3. Spatial areas around and within the building can be compared to surroundings for practical and aesthetic design.

Architectural models are commonly made in five categories: massing models, solid models, rough hollow models, detail hollow models, and test models. Each type has its own function.

MASSING MODELS

Massing models are used for large projects involving several new buildings to be located among existing buildings; for example, a downtown redevelopment project or a multiple low-rental housing complex. These models are usually intended for planning by the architectural firm and do not require much detailing. Since the scale of the buildings is quite small, blocks of wood are cut to represent the

FIGURE 12-1

A massing model for an apartment project

Hohauser, S. *Architectural and Interior Models: Design and Construction*, Van Nostrand Reinhold Co.

buildings. Cardboard roads and pieces of sponge to represent trees are glued onto a particle board base *(see Fig. 12-1)*. Often these models are painted in one neutral colour for speed and economy.

SOLID MODELS

The solid model is similar to the massing model but has more detail and colour. To allow for this, a larger scale may be used. Blocks of wood are glued together to form the basic shapes of the proposed buildings and are then glued onto a landscaped base representing the lot.

This type of model is most often used to show the clients how the project will look when completed. Very large buildings, such as skyscrapers or condominiums, are the types of structures requiring the use of a solid model *(see Fig. 12-2)*.

ROUGH HOLLOW MODELS

Architects will often build a rough hollow model to help visualize or solve intricate structural problems. A roof design that has several pitches or angular directions can be easily constructed and fitted to the model to solve design problems. Hollow models are made from illustration board, cut and glued to form hollow boxes with very little detail. As well, the model is generally made from one coloured board, usually white, to save time.

FIGURE 12-2

A solid block model for a low income housing project

Hohauser, S. *Architectural and Interior Models: Design and Construction*, Van Nostrand Reinhold Co.

FIGURE 12-3

A rough hollow model for roof design

The scale of these models is the same as the drawings to more clearly see the conversion from two dimensions into three dimensions. House design problems are ideally visualized from a rough hollow model *(see Fig. 12-3).*

DETAIL HOLLOW MODELS

This is the most commonly used model. The full detailing, landscaping, and colouring show the clients what the building will look like. It is the ideal model to use for public projects or corporations where fund raising is necessary from many sources *(see Fig. 12-4)*. Hollow models can also be made so that the roofs are removable, allowing the interior plan to be seen. Residential projects of large homes will use models of the various house styles available to help potential customers make their selection. Professional model-making supplies are generally used by architectural firms, but very attractive models can be made from *found* materials such as sawdust, yarn, wallpaper, and sponges. Models of interiors are also made using the hollow methods.

TEST MODELS

Test models are sometimes referred to as structural models. They are made to a scale that will conveniently show the structural members, with or without the exterior covering *(see Fig. 12-5)*. Wood, plastic, or metals are used to create a realistic simulation of stresses on material. These models may be used in wind tunnels, put under pressures, distorted, or burned under controlled conditions. Results of testing are analysed and computed to validate designs or alter design forms.

You can learn a great deal about architectural design by constructing a model. The best model to make when considering residential design is the detailed hollow model. A removable roof is optional since it is used primarily to show a very unusual interior layout. Most residential models have a fixed roof.

FIGURE 12-4 *Detailed hollow model of Head House Square redevelopment*

Hohauser, S. *Architectural and Interior Models: Design and Construction*, Van Nostrand Reinhold Co.

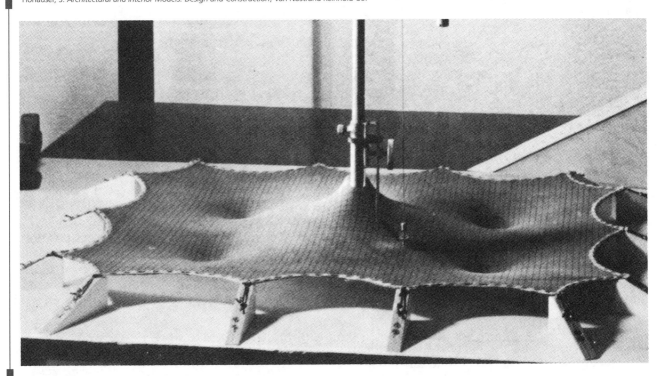

FIGURE 12-5 *A test model for designing a tent structure*

Hohauser, S. *Architectural and Interior Models: Design and Construction*, Van Nostrand Reinhold Co.

UNIT 1

Beginning the Model

OBJECTIVES

- To learn about model-making materials
- To learn how to add details to the model
- To learn how to construct a base
- To learn how to construct the building

MODEL-MAKING MATERIALS

PAPER AND CARDBOARD

There are many papers and boards available for model making. The finish and weight, or thickness, is what determines the cost. Papers are categorized as coated (smooth), text (rough), or specialty (patterned or textured). Frequently used papers are bond, construction, watercolour, pastel, and brown wrapping paper. A heavy paper is available in several colours and is referred to as cover stock. To indicate windows on a model, a thin, flat, black paper is available, called bible paper. Textured wallpapers are excellent to use for model making.

Cardboards are also made with smooth, rough, or textured finishes. The thickness of a board is referred to in points; the larger the point number, the thicker the board. For example, an average illustration board is about 3 mm (1/8") thick and is called an 80 point board. The most common boards are illustration, mounting, bristol, matting, and mill boards.

The newest board materials are those that have a styrofoam core. These boards are available in various thicknesses and are very good for large models because of their strength and light weight. They are referred to as **foam-core** or **alligator boards**. An X-acto knife will easily cut foam-core boards and the boards can be glued or painted. *Caution: When using an X-acto knife, be careful not to cut yourself with the extremely sharp blades.*

PAINTS AND MARKERS

Water-base paints are the easiest and most effective to use for models. The opaque watercolours, called **gouache**, are the most versatile. Acrylic or oil-base colours should not be used except where a glossy finish is desired to create a texture.

Markers of various sizes create excellent textural effects such as bricks, shingles, or stone. The permanent, waterproof colours are better to use, since the model may require a lot of handling. Most markers come in fine point, bold point, and broad chisel point shapes. They are instant drying and fast to work with.

Matt or dull finish spray varnishes are sometimes used to waterproof and protect painted areas of the model. Although these are transparent, they will usually cause the colours to darken slightly.

GLUES AND TAPES

The fastening together of model parts must be done with great care for two important reasons. First, all pieces must fit perfectly together to give a strong joint, so care in applying the glue and fitting is essential. Second, glue joints should not have excess glue dripping on finished surfaces, or the end result will look untidy. Also, excess glue is difficult to paint over.

These problems will be reduced if a quick-setting glue or a contact type glue is used. White carpenters' glue works well if not applied too heavily. It allows pieces to be moved into exact position, then held while the glue sets, which is usually one or two minutes. This glue is useful for glueing paper, cardboard, wood, or cloth materials. White glue has other advantages:

1. It is water based and therefore easy to wipe off excess.
2. It is white, and therefore easy to see for applying.
3. It dries transparent, making it nearly impossible to see on the finished model.

A plastic container with a small, conical applicator is excellent for applying the glue. An easy way to apply an even coat of glue along the cardboard edge of a wall or roof is to spread a bead of glue, a little longer than the section to be glued, on a piece of waxed paper. Simply set the edge of the section to be glued into the bead and then place it on the model.

Small tubes of contact cement are an excellent method of assembling parts that require a strong bond. By carefully running a bead of contact cement along the location lines and also along the corresponding edges of the model, the pieces may be moved into place. Allow the pieces to sit until the glue is dry and then gently press them together. This assures an instant, strong bond.

Tapes are useful to hold parts temporarily in place while glue dries or to allow parts to be removed and reassembled. Masking tape works well for this purpose. To bond larger pieces together on their flat surfaces, two-sided carpet tape is quick and clean to use.

Art-supply stores also carry a number of different coloured striping tapes. These are excellent for detailing such elements as windows, roadways, and linear textures on models. They are available in sizes from very narrow to broad widths.

WOODS AND PLASTICS

Balsa wood has been used for all types of model making. It is available in stick form, sheet form, and block form. Balsa wood is easily cut with an X-acto knife or razor blade and is easy to glue together. Although it is relatively strong, balsa wood has the disadvantage of being easily damaged. Painting balsa wood is not very easy since the wood is quite porous and paint tends to soak in deeply, leaving the wood grain exposed. Therefore, it should be painted first with a prime coat containing a filler.

Plywood or particle board is much stronger. These woods are also available in a variety of thicknesses and forms. For models that will be moved around a lot for display, plywood bases are preferred for strength.

Plastic materials can be used where smooth, glossy areas are desired. For example, a thin layer of clear plastic when placed over a sheet of blue paper that is cut out to resemble a swimming pool will create the shine of water. Plastics are available in various thicknesses and colours. A special glue that bonds plastics must be used. Thin sheets of plastic can be curved or moulded by carefully heating the plastic.

ACCESSORIES

Materials that can be used to add textures and details to models are almost endless. The imagination of the model maker and the type of model effect that is to be achieved are the guiding factors. The following list is a brief outline of some common materials used on architectural models: sandpaper for roofs, walls, and ground; wallpaper for textures and patterns; cake decoration candies for earth, flowers, and vegetation; scouring pads for trees, shrubs, and hedges; dried flowers, weeds, and leaves for trees, shrubs, and hedges; sponges and pipe cleaners for trees and vegetation; sawdust or cat litter sprayed green for grass or left natural for earth; sand and white aquarium sand for gravel and roof textures; scissors, X-acto knives, and straight-back razors for cutting; stick-on symbols and dry transfer symbols for details.

CONSTRUCTING A BASE

The base of the model is very important to the overall plan. Many hours of detailed model making can be wasted if the base is not strong enough to avoid warping. There are two types of bases: the solid one-piece and the framed, layered base.

If the house model is to be sitting on a flat lot, the solid base may be suitable. Materials used for flat, solid bases are tintest, or railroad board, and plywood, or particle board. All of these materials are available in 1 cm (1/2") thickness. This dimension allows the drilling of small holes for gluing model trees securely. A heavy, sometimes cumbersome, model may result from using thick bases. Plywood and particle board is made in 0.5 cm

(1/4") thickness. A lighter-weight model would result from using this thickness.

The framed, layered base is the most functional to use. It is strong and lightweight and allows a variety of contours to be erected. The frame is made from wood strips about 1 cm × 2.5 cm (1/2" × 1"). These pieces are cut to length and nailed together on the edge, like a picture frame, using mitred corners or butt joints. Extra support strips may be added to prevent the top surface sagging *(see Fig. 12-6)*.

The top surface can be covered with plywood or particle board 3 mm (1/8") thick. Millboard also makes a strong, workable base if 100-point board is used. You can glue or nail the surface to the frame and supports. To create the various contours and elevations of a lot that is not flat, cut layers of cardboard to match the patterns on the traverse drawings *(see Fig. 12-7)*. Each of these contours is glued in position to create the high and low areas.

To allow the base of the house itself to remain flat, a tracing of the house plan should be drawn on each layer and carefully cut out, so that the house will sit down into the layers *(see Fig. 12-8)*. After gluing the house in position, the individual edges of the contours can be left exposed, or a gradual rising and falling effect can be made by

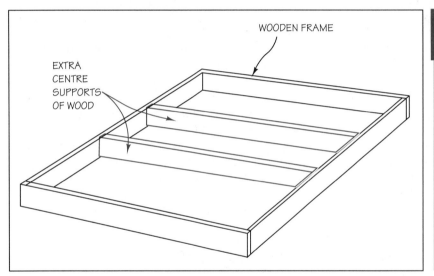

WOODEN FRAME

EXTRA CENTRE SUPPORTS OF WOOD

FIGURE 12-6
Extra support members for a wood frame base

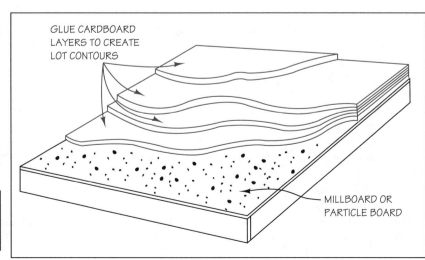

GLUE CARDBOARD LAYERS TO CREATE LOT CONTOURS

MILLBOARD OR PARTICLE BOARD

FIGURE 12-7
Creating lot contours with cardboard layers

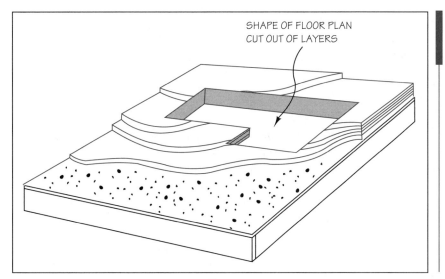

Figure 12-8

Cutting out the floor plan to allow the house model to sit flat

SHAPE OF FLOOR PLAN CUT OUT OF LAYERS

Figure 12-9

Covering the edges of the contours for a smoother finish

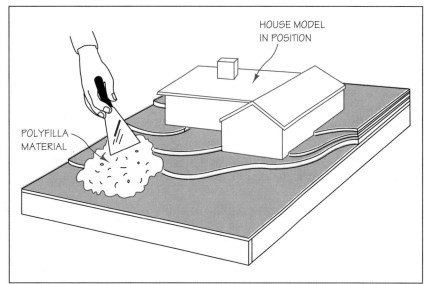

HOUSE MODEL IN POSITION

POLYFILLA MATERIAL

blending plaster or Polyfilla material over the edges *(see Fig. 12-9)*.

Most of the texturing, painting, and detailing of the lot should be done before the house is fastened in place. Only the trees and shrubs should be left off and added later. This will allow the painting of the base to be done without interference from the house model.

The edges of the frame can be painted to match the ground colour or can be painted to resemble a frame in black, white, grey, or brown.

CONSTRUCTING THE BUILDING

CUTTING

To properly cut and fit in the model construction, work on a flat work table rather than a tipped drafting table. A sheet of thick millboard or mounting board should be used to cut on to avoid damaging the table-top.

When cutting thick cardboard, use several cutting strokes rather than one heavy cut. This will assure smoother, straighter cuts. An ideal cutting guide is a steel straight edge, available at most art supply stores. An X-acto knife with a number 24 blade or a number 11 blade is the best instrument to cut card. All cut edges should be perpendicular to make smooth, solid glue joints. If thick board is to be bent, a partial cut should be made. Always fold away from the cut *(see Fig. 12-10)*.

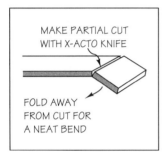

FIGURE 12-10
How to bend thick cardboard

ASSEMBLY

It is much easier to construct the house on its own base and then attach the house to the landscaped lot than to assemble it directly on the lot. This approach allows you to make changes or corrections without damaging the lot base. It is also easier to manipulate the house for fitting details. Similarly, you may find that it is more convenient to construct parts of the house, such as the garage or an extension, separately and then attach them to the main house.

You will need one or two copies of the floor plan and elevations of the house that can be cut up and used as patterns. The following is a step-by-step method of constructing the house model.

1. Carefully cut out the print of the floor plan and trace the outline onto a piece of thick cardboard. If the model is to have a removable roof to show inside walls, then glue the floor plan print onto the cardboard. This allows you to glue interior partitions in the exact locations. Cut the floor plan out of the cardboard base.
2. Cut out and trace the prints of the wall elevations onto thick cardboard. This board may be white or a coloured matting board that is similar to the exterior brick or siding. Walls may be made individually or may be arranged in sequence to be cut and folded as one piece *(see Fig. 12-11)*.

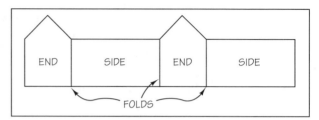

FIGURE 12-11 *Walls of a model made from one piece of cardboard*

Remember to allow for the thickness of the cardboard when measuring the length of each wall. Butt joints are usually used, therefore only one thickness of board needs to be deducted in the measurement. *Do not glue the walls in place.*

3. Render all the textures and details on the walls before cutting them. Coloured pencils, sharpened to a chisel point, may be used to indicate bricks. Two or three colours that are similar in colour but different in tones give a more realistic effect. Do not use colours that are too bright; earth tones are more natural. Mortar lines can be suggested by drawing horizontal lines in scale, with an HB pencil, over the colour. Markers or paint can also create brick textures.

   If wallpaper or other sheet covering is used for the walls, sufficient additional paper must be left on the long sides to wrap around the corners for a neat look.

   Since windows appear dark, use black bible paper to detail them. Cut out the black paper to suit the window size and glue it in position. The window frame or mullions can be indicated with paint, pencil, or strips of tape.

   Wood siding is best suggested by drawing HB pencil lines on the board, either horizontally or vertically. Doorways can be pasted on the wall after they have been drawn on thinner bond or coloured paper.

4. After all the details are added to the walls, carefully cut them out. Test fit the walls onto the floor plan base and adjust dimensions as needed. Glue the walls to the base as squarely and perpendicularly as possible *(see Fig. 12-12)*.
5. Draw the overall size of each roof area required. The dimensions for the roof must be taken from the elevations, not the floor plan *(see Fig. 12-13)*.

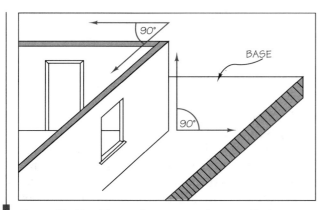

FIGURE 12-12   *Glue walls square and perpendicular*

Roofs can be made from coloured matt board for rough planning models. If the shingle texture is preferred for the detail model, strips of construction paper or sandpaper can be laid in overlapping rows. The roof should be partially cut through at the ridge line, to allow a clean fold.

Dormers should be constructed separately and then glued to the main roof. Test fit the roof before glueing to the walls. For houses that have the chimney on an outside wall, chimney cut-outs

must be made while the roof is flat. Inside chimneys can be made separately and glued on top of the roof. To give the roof thickness, glue strips of thin cardboard on the edges to represent the fascia boards and trim.

6. Fit the house carefully onto the lot, making any adjustments. Glue the house firmly in position. Fit and attach any separate extensions such as the garage, steps, dormers, or bay windows. After allowing all glue joints to dry thoroughly, the model is ready for the final details.

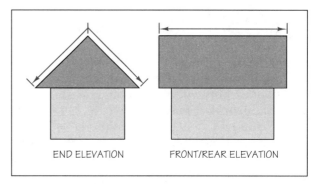

FIGURE 12-13   *Establishing roof dimensions*

REVIEW QUESTIONS

1. What are the five common types of models?
2. Which of the five types is most often used?
3. List five kinds of cardboard used for model making.
4. What are two reasons that model parts must be fastened carefully?
5. Why is the house model built separately from the lot model?

WHAT DO YOU THINK?

1. Why do you think models are used more for commercial projects than residential projects?
2. You are having an architect design a large house for you. Explain why you would or would not ask for a model to be made.

ASSIGNMENTS

1. Construct a rough hollow model of a bungalow using white cardboard. No colouring or details are necessary. The house size is 15 cm x 10 cm (6" x 4"). The front and rear walls are 8 cm (3") high. The ends are gabled and are 13 cm (5") high to the peak. Attach the roof to the house with an optional overhang.
2. Construct one dormer and attach it to the house model in Assignment 1.

UNIT 2 | Completing the Model

OBJECTIVES

- To learn the embellishments of a model
- To learn model identification
- To learn how to photograph a model

EMBELLISHING THE MODEL

Embellishment helps to establish proportions, creates atmosphere within the model, and gives the model a finished professional look. The type of embellishment may vary depending on the type of model making, who the model is for, or how the model is to be used. Standard items used to embellish a model are shrubs, trees, flowers, cars, people, roadways, and identification. Special items that may be used for specific buildings include fountains, pools, fencing, sculptures, and lighting. House models are generally embellished with standard items. Remember to keep all items in the same scale as the model and avoid adding too much embellishment or your model may look cluttered. The house should remain the focal point of interest.

SHRUBS

Green scouring pad material can be bought in large sheet sizes, and various shrub shapes can be cut from it. Once the basic shape is cut, pull the pad apart slightly to create a natural look to the shrub. Glue shrubs on the model in clusters of various sizes using white glue. Scouring pad material is also available in a reddish-brown colour. Hedges made from this material are very effective and easily glued straight or curved. Green sponges of various tones are good to use as shrubs when torn into rough pieces or shaped as conical evergreens. Also, lichen is available at model supply stores in a variety of colours.

TREES

Deciduous trees can be made from actual twigs of trees or shrubs. They can be left bare or foliage can be simulated by gluing pieces of sponge to them. Torn pieces of construction paper can also be glued to twigs to represent trees. Shredded paper towelling can be soaked, mixed with wallpaper paste, and formed into rough ball shapes. After drying, the trees can be painted in greens or other colours and glued to a twig representing the

FIGURE 12-14
A student model, detailed and embellished

tree trunk. Model trees are available at model supply shops *(see Fig. 12-15)*.

FIGURE 12-15 *Examples of ready-made model trees*

Hohauser, S. *Architectural and Interior Models: Design and Construction*, Van Nostrand Reinhold Co.

FLOWERS

When applying flowers to the model, think of them in flower beds and use one colour of flower in each cluster. Place a layer of white glue over the flower-bed shape; while the glue is wet, sprinkle in coloured cake decorations. An effective flower bed can also be made by placing a thick layer of patching plaster over the bed and gently pushing confetti into the top surface.

CARS

Although small model cars are readily available, be sure they are in correct scale to the house. Simplified car shapes can be cut from wood and painted. These cars can be left with a flat bottom with wheels painted on.

ROADWAYS

Driveways can be painted or strips of construction paper can be cut and glued in the desired shape. Grey or black is the most suitable colour. If the driveway is going to be painted on, use masking tape along the edges to keep a neat finished paint edge.

PEOPLE

Most models of a single house do not use figures of people because it is assumed that the person for whom the model was made is the potential owner. Therefore another figure becomes distracting. However, models of larger housing projects may use a few figures to show the scale and to add a feeling of life to the project. Either simplified figures cut out of cardboard or plastic figures from model supply shops can be used but the scale must match the model. Balsa wood is excellent for carving simplified human forms.

IDENTIFICATION

There are two blocks of identification to be used on a model. The most important one is the title block. This identifies the building and therefore is usually the larger of the lettered signs. The style of lettering should be carefully chosen. It should be in harmony with the style of building, easy to read, and not too large. On a separate piece of cardboard, letter the title neatly in ink or with dry transfer letters. A border should be drawn around the title block as well. Cut the title block out of the cardboard and glue it on the model so that it can be read when you are looking at the front of the house. It is best to place the block slightly in from the edge of the base. The title block will state the name of the house, if there is one, and the name of the proposed owner.

There may also be a lettered block that lists the scale of the model and the architect's or builder's firm name. This information block should match the style of the title block, but be smaller in size. It may be glued beside the title block or in one corner but should not detract from the model.

PHOTOGRAPHING THE MODEL

Models are photographed as a project record for filing; to have photo prints for advertising and promotion; and to show the model as the completed building in natural surroundings *(see Fig. 12-16)*. There are five rules for good model photography.

1. The background must be suitable to the model in subject and scale.
2. The camera viewpoint must make the model look like a real structure.
3. The foreground, midground, and background should be in natural focus.
4. The optical vanishing points should appear as they would in real life, without distortion.
5. The model and landscaping must fill the picture so that no part of the edge or frame of the model is seen.

FIGURE 12-16

A model photographed to show it in the natural setting

Hohauser, S. *Architectural and Interior Models: Design and Construction*, Van Nostrand Reinhold Co.

REVIEW QUESTIONS

1. List five standard items used for embellishing a model.
2. Describe two ways of making model trees.
3. What two identification blocks are used on a model?
4. List three rules for good model photography.

WHAT DO YOU THINK?

1. Detailed models of large architectural projects can cost thousands of dollars. Do you believe such models are necessary? Explain your answer.

ASSIGNMENTS

1. Construct several trees and shrubs, both coniferous and deciduous, suitable for use on your model which will be at a scale of 1:50 (1/4" = 1'-0").
2. Construct approximately half a dozen figures involved in various actions using cardboard and a scale of 1:50 (1/4" = 1'-0").
3. Construct several simplified car shapes in keeping with the scale of the model and paint them.

A MODEL OF THE HOUSE

THE PROJECT

After completing the study of Chapter 12, you are ready to begin constructing a model of your house design. Follow the assembly steps as outlined in Chapter 12, Unit 1.

Step 17:

Plan the modelling of the lot to harmonize with the style of the house model. Remember that your model is part of the overall presentation of your house design and therefore must co-ordinate with all the other drawings.

CHAPTER 13 | *Promotional Presentation*

THE PROMOTIONAL PRESENTATION is often the deciding factor as to whether an architectural project is accepted or rejected. A great deal of planning, therefore, should be put into the presentation. There are several important areas to consider when preparing a plan of presentation. These areas can be more clearly defined through asking the following five questions:

1. What is the reason for the presentation?
2. Who will be at the presentation?
3. What will be involved in the presentation?
4. How will it be presented?
5. What will be the follow-up?

There are many things to consider when answering each of the questions.

1. When deciding what the presentation is for, you must consider such factors as: is it intended to sell the design to the client; is all or part of the presentation to be used for advertising in newspapers, or as a press release to the public; or is the presentation expected to help raise funds to build the project.

2. Larger architectural projects are often presented to groups of people, such as a board of directors or city council, rather than to one person. This factor could also affect where the presentation will be made. If it is to be held in a large room, the drawings, models, etc. would have to be rendered in an appropriate scale to be clearly seen. The model or drawings may be shown as a static display, or they may have to be moved about. Identification and written explanations might vary also, depending on whether there will be a verbal presentation as well as a pictorial presentation. Consideration should also be given to the amount of time it will require to make the presentation.

3. Determining what will be presented is extremely important. The presentation could include a written report, a set of the plans, a pictorial rendering, sectional drawings, interior drawings, charts, and a model. If the project is a renovation or addition to an existing building, you may wish to include before-and-after drawings. The choice of medium for the pictorial drawing is usually made after consideration of the points previously outlined in the second part above.

4. To determine the type of presentation, you should carefully consider such factors as the order in which each part will be shown and the methods that will be used to explain the design. Even the arrangement of people to whom the presentation is being made is important, to ensure that everyone can see the design drawings clearly. You could hand out extra sets of the plan to allow each person to follow the presentation.

5. There are many ways to include follow-up information in a presentation. Condensed printed copies of the proposal may be offered as take-home reading. Simplified drawings of the floor plans and a reduced pictorial drawing may be used as handouts. These are most often used as promotion at open house displays in new subdivisions. Individual house models may be displayed as a group at the builder's office. Pictures or slides of the scale model can also be reproduced for handouts. Advertisements in local newspapers are common and usually include a pictorial rendering of the house.

You should remember that the promotional presentation drawing is not intended to show every detail of the house. The main purpose of the drawing is to show the most interesting and pleasing view of the house, rendered in a technique that depicts the house as an exciting new structure to build. A pictorial drawing should show how the house will look upon completion, while creating an aesthetically pleasing picture.

UNIT 1 | Media

OBJECTIVES

- To learn pencil techniques
- To learn ink techniques
- To learn watercolour techniques
- To learn marker techniques

The material used to render a picture of a house is called a medium. For example, a drawing done in pencil lines and tones is said to be done in pencil medium. Sometimes more than one material is used, and this type of drawing is called a **mixed-media** drawing. Regardless of the choice of medium, three important factors should be considered. The first factor is **contrast of tones**, using light, medium and dark tones within the picture. The second factor is **composition**, arranging the house, trees, sky, and ground on the paper to look balanced. The third factor is **cleanliness**. It is important to keep your drawing clean and fresh by avoiding too much erasing and using a piece of paper under your pencil hand to avoid smearing the tones.

PENCIL TECHNIQUES

Pencil is the most common medium used for drawing houses because of the speed and flexibility it provides. The pencil is a transparent medium but can be used in an opaque method. If the tones are shaded lightly, a transparent effect can be achieved; however, in areas that are to be opaque, an increase of pencil pressure will create dark, solid tones.

When creating a pencil drawing, shade in the background tones first, such as the sky. Shade in light tones and then gradually work over the entire picture to increase the darker areas. This approach, of shading light to dark, makes it easier to correct mistakes and avoids smearing the tones.

After blocking in the sky *(see Fig. 13-1)*, shade in the light and medium grey parts of the house *(see Fig. 13-2)*. Try to work from the top of the picture towards the bottom, to help keep it clean. Avoid completing the textures at this stage so that the picture can be equally balanced in texture later.

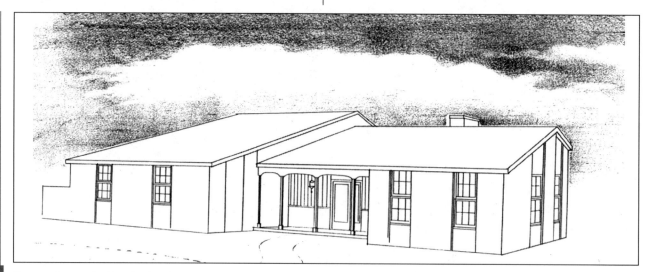

FIGURE 13-1 *Blocking in the sky*

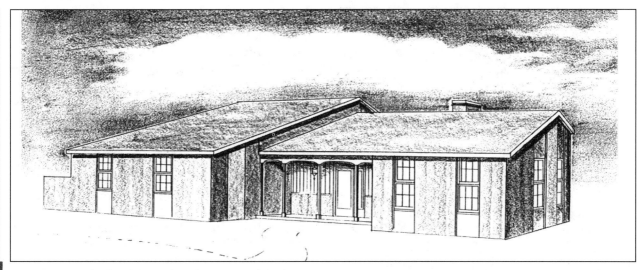

FIGURE 13-2 *Shading light and medium parts of the house*

When the house is shaded, the ground tones should be carefully drawn. Remember to keep the pencil strokes in perspective to each other. One way to make grass strokes is to imagine that you are cutting the grass back and forth in parallel lines. This will create an effective *cut-grass* look to the lawn. The ground tones should be lighter at the horizon and become darker as they approach the foreground.

The trees and shrubs can now be blocked in *(see Fig. 13-3)*. By placing darker trees against lighter areas and lighter trees against darker areas, a feeling of depth will be achieved. *Fig. 13-4* shows some basic shapes of trees and shrubs.

After sketching the landscaping, you are ready to add the dark tones and textures. Shadows and very dark tones give the drawing a look of realistic depth. Keep the greatest amount of texture and

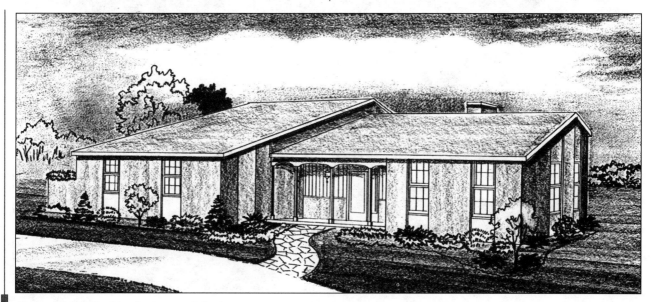

FIGURE 13-3 *Blocking in trees and shrubs*

FIGURE 13-4 *Basic shapes of trees and shrubs*

contrast of tones in the most important part of the picture. This area is known as the **focal point** of the picture. Sometimes the picture can be *framed* by suggesting part of the foliage of a large tree that is beside the viewer *(see Fig. 13-5)*. This helps to display darker tones at the top of the picture and balance the sky with the ground.

Another pencil technique is to use coloured pencils. The same procedure should be followed for colour, with some important considerations. The colours must be carefully planned since pencil crayons are more difficult to erase. Avoid harsh, bright colours on the house to maintain a natural look to the picture. Skies appear natural if they are not too bright and are coloured in various tones of blues, blue-greens, and touches of yellow. White areas should be made by allowing the white paper to show. Colour from light to dark. Avoid using black alone. Dark areas should be coloured first with a dark blue or brown, and then the black pencil applied over top. This creates a near-black colour as seen in nature.

A mixed-media drawing technique can also be effective by using coloured pencils and regular drawing pencils together. When working with this

FIGURE 13-5 *Foliage frames the picture.*

technique, it is easier to apply the regular pencil tones over the colour for shading, rather than putting the colour over the pencil lead.

To protect your pencil drawings from smearing while being handled, they can be sprayed with a fixative. There are two types of fixative, **workable**, which means you can do further shading on your drawing after it has been sprayed, and **permanent**, which should be used only when the drawing is totally finished.

Through practice, you will develop a pencil-rendering technique that is very appealing and uniquely your style.

INK TECHNIQUES

Pen-and-ink drawings are preferred if the drawing is going to be reproduced in a newspaper ad. The fine detail and the darker areas are more easily reproduced for printing because they are black, not grey.

The illusion of dark or light tones is made by placing ink lines closer together or farther apart. Because ink is difficult to erase, it is better to shade the light tones first. Unlike pencil shading, the sky effect should be shaded in last. It is easier to determine how much ink shading is needed in the sky after the drawing is completed, to avoid making the sky appear too dark. Sometimes it is best not to use any tones in the sky, but rather a simple line effect to indicate clouds *(see Fig. 13-6)*.

When using lines for shading, your drawing will look more controlled and professional if you keep the lines parallel or in perspective.

Linework can be done with straight thick or thin lines drawn with a ruler and pen *(see Fig. 13-7)*. Another effective style is to draw each line free-hand and twice. If you let the two lines vary slightly, the finished work will appear straight but have an architectural sketchy appearance *(see Fig. 13-8)*. Notice that the corners of the object are sharp and crisp because the lines overlap each other and extend slightly past the ends. This technique is more difficult to do than it appears, so you should practise on small objects first.

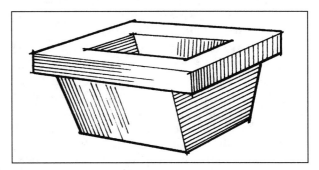

FIGURE 13-7 *Line shading with thick and thin lines*

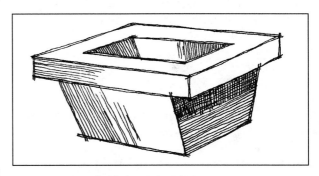

FIGURE 13-8 *Double-line ink technique*

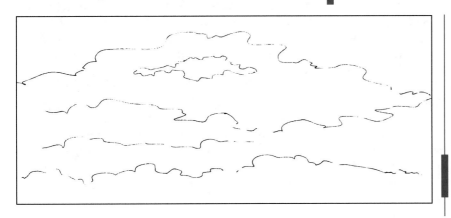

FIGURE 13-6
Indicating clouds with lines

A totally different ink technique is called **ink and wash**. With this technique, ink is applied in the larger areas with a brush. To make a variety of light to dark tones, dilute the ink by adding water to it. To create a light grey area, add a small drop of ink to a puddle of water. Mix them thoroughly and then brush the tone of ink onto your drawing.

Applying the ink and wash by brush can be done in several ways. The area to be painted can first be dampened with clear water, using the brush; while the area is damp, you can apply the ink wash. This technique is called **wet on wet** and produces soft tones with blurred edges *(see Fig. 13-9)*. Another method is to apply the ink wash onto the dry board, creating a sharp tone with hard edges *(see Fig. 13-10)*. To create textures, such as grass, trees, shrubs, wood, or brick, pick up the ink-wash tone with the brush. Then push down on the hairs of the brush so that they fan out in all directions. This will squeeze most of the tone out of the brush. While the brush hairs are fanned out, gently pull the brush across the board *(see Fig. 13-11)*. This technique is called **dry brush**. Practise these techniques separately and combined for various architectural effects.

WATERCOLOUR

The most dramatic technique for a pictorial presentation is full-colour illustration. A medium called **gouache watercolour** is best to use. Gouache colours are opaque but can be used as transparent washes. Coloured paintings of houses or architectural buildings are done as a combination of opaque and transparent techniques.

You can apply the paints in the same manner as outlined for ink and wash. Usually the sky and other large, light-toned areas are painted first. Darker colours are gradually applied over the light tones, with the darkest shadows and colours painted last. Highlights and white accents can be added using opaque white watercolour.

Remember that the house is the most important part of the painting; therefore do not use too many bright colours around it. Using natural yellows, oranges, blue-greens, sandy browns, and

FIGURE 13-9 *Wet-on-wet technique*

FIGURE 13-10 *Using a wash on a dry board*

FIGURE 13-11 *Dry-brush technique*

dull reds is most effective. When painting the grass and trees, use a variety of green tints and tones. For the trees or grass in the distance, add some white to the green, plus a small touch of red to dull the green.

Rendering full-colour paintings for architectural projects is usually done by trained professional artists. If this career is of interest to you, you should look into taking an art course as well. Practise rendering bricks, trees, grass, shingles, etc. in colour several times before attempting a complete illustration.

MARKERS

Architectural marker sets are available at art supply stores. They consist of colours that are compatible with building materials. The markers come in three styles: broad chisel shapes, blunt pointed shapes, and fine sharp pointed shapes.

Choose markers that are permanent. Plan the colours carefully before applying them to the drawing, because they are very difficult to erase. The colours may be applied over each other to create new colours or textures. Most markers will bleed a little, causing a slightly blurred edge.

Because markers show individual strokes quite noticeably, it is important that you keep the marker strokes parallel and in perspective.

Trees, shrubs, or objects that have random direction to their structure allow you to stroke the marker in various directions to create the textures. Always put the caps back on the markers immediately to avoid having them dry up. Although markers are fast and quite effective, using them well requires a great deal of practice. Some markers can be painted over with opaque watercolour to create special effects or to add fine details.

REVIEW QUESTIONS

1. What is a mixed-media drawing?
2. What part of a pencil drawing should be shaded first?
3. Describe a wet-on-wet technique.
4. Describe a dry-brush technique.
5. What are gouache colours?

WHAT DO YOU THINK?

1. How do you think computers might be used for pictorial renderings?

ASSIGNMENTS

1. Shade the front elevation of the house, supplied by your instructor, in pencil technique. Suggest foundation planting as well.
2. Render the same elevation drawing on a new sheet, using pen and ink or a fine-tip black marker technique.

UNIT 2 | Completing the Preparation for the Promotional Presentation

OBJECTIVES

- To understand the importance of embellishments to a presentation drawing
- To learn how to matt drawings
- To learn how to identify drawings
- To learn how to protect drawings

The complete presentation of a proposed house design includes several items. There may be a written design report, site drawings, survey plans, complete working blueprints, pictorial drawings, and a model.

EMBELLISHING THE PRESENTATION DRAWING

It is important to embellish or add extra details to pictorial drawings and presentation drawings. House drawings are most often embellished with landscaping. Figures and vehicles can also be used to add a feeling of life and activity to the presentation. Drawings of commercial buildings are more heavily embellished.

There are three important reasons to embellish a presentation drawing:

FIGURE 13-12 *An embellished presentation drawing*

1. to show comparison of scale,
2. to add interest, excitement, and animation,
3. to suggest a positive appearance to the project and thereby gain support for the building proposal.

MATTING

Pictorial drawings should be matted to give a professional, finished appearance to the pictures. All items must be clearly identified and protected against handling abuse. A **matt** is the cardboard frame that is placed around the pictorial drawing. Mattboard is available in numerous colours as well as black, white, or off-white tones. The proportion of the matt to the drawing is flexible, but the matt should never overpower or distract from the drawing. Usually the colour of the matt is subdued and neutral in tone. Ivory, tan, grey, off-white, or black are the most often used colours.

A double matt is used if a touch of stronger colour is desired to accent the colour of the building. To make a double matt, one matt is cut to form a slightly larger opening than that of the other matt. The larger matt is usually the pale neutral colour and the smaller matt is made from the stronger colour. By placing the larger matt on top of the smaller matt, only a narrow strip of colour is seen *(see Fig. 13-13)*.

FIGURE 13-13 *A double matt*

The following steps should be used to make a matt for a pictorial drawing:

1. Measure the width and height of the area of the pictorial drawing that you wish to display. Draw this rectangle on the matt board allowing space for Step 2.

2. Add a minimum of 50 mm (2") to each side to establish the width of the matt. Add the same dimension — 50 mm (2") — to the top of the picture and the same *plus approximately one-third* — 60 mm (2 1/2") — to the bottom of the picture to establish the height of the matt *(see Fig. 13-14)*.

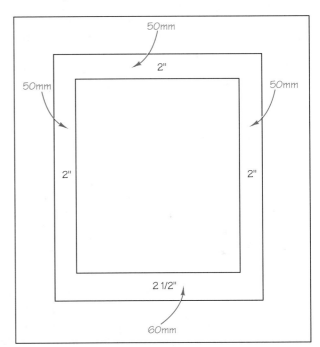

FIGURE 13-14 *Establishing the width and height of the matt*

A general guideline is that the larger the drawing, the wider the matt should be made.

3. Using an X-acto knife and a straight ruler, cut out the centre section of the matt to form a frame with the inside the same size as your drawing. Most matts are cut on a 45° angle for appearance, but a clean, straight cut is most important.

Avoid trying to cut through the mattboard with one cut. A smoother cut will be made if you use several strokes for each cut.

4. Check the matt on the drawing for size and position before gluing the matt to the drawing. The matt can then be glued in position with white glue or the drawing may be taped to the back of the matt with masking tape.

IDENTIFICATION OF DRAWINGS

Presentation and pictorial drawings should be clearly identified so that they can be examined by several people without any confusion or explanation. The identification block should include the name of the project, the client's name, and the architect's or designer's name. For example, a pictorial drawing of a house would be identified as:

> PINERIDGE MANOR
> Proposed home for
> Mr. and Mrs. D. Light
> R. Robinson, Architect

Since the identification is done primarily through words, it is important that the words are clearly legible and neatly lettered. Capital letters are usually used for the main title unless there are several words in the title; it is then better to use capitals and small letters for easier readability.

Avoid using letter styles that are too fancy. Simple Gothic or Roman letters give a pleasing, professional look to the title *(see Fig. 13-15)*. Use the same style of lettering on all the drawings to create a unified presentation. Lettering can be done by hand, using pen and ink, or preformed pressure-sensitive letters can be purchased in sheet form in a variety of letter styles.

BORDERS

Titles for pictorial drawings may or may not require a border. Sometimes a pictorial drawing will have a border drawn around the entire picture in place of a matt. When this technique is used, the title may be incorporated in the border.

Borders should be kept simple and can be drawn in ink or pencil, or made from pressure-sensitive borders, similar to pressure-sensitive letters. Decorative border tapes are also available. These tapes come in various widths of line and are applied along a straight ruler. An X-acto knife will cut the tape at the correct lengths to form the corners.

IDENTIFICATION PLACEMENT

When placing the titles on various presentation drawings, you should try to put them in the same place on each drawing. The lower right corner is the most readable and usually does not interfere with the drawing itself. Avoid having titles or descriptions randomly placed on a drawing. Group them together in a balanced and attractive arrangement. The most important title should be displayed in the largest letters, with the remaining information displayed in smaller letters.

PROTECTING THE DRAWINGS

Presentation and pictorial drawings require a lot of work and should be kept clean to make the greatest impression on the client. Each piece should be

GOTHIC GOTHIC
ROMAN ROMAN

FIGURE 13-15
Gothic and Roman letters

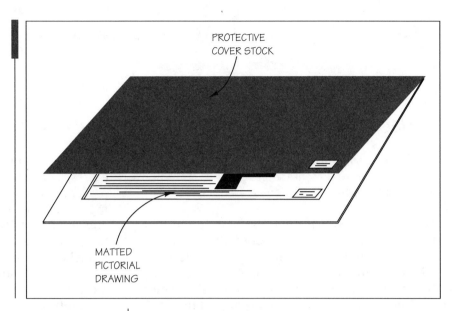

FIGURE 13-16
Protecting the drawing

PROTECTIVE
COVER STOCK

MATTED
PICTORIAL
DRAWING

covered with a thicker paper, called *cover stock*, to protect the drawing *(see Fig. 13-16)*. Even a complete set of blueprints can be stapled between two sheets of cover stock to keep them flat and clean.

If the drawings or plans are to be discussed for possible changes, a sheet of clear drafting paper should be fastened over the drawing. This will allow changes to be drawn or sketched on it without damaging the original drawing.

A title for each piece should be placed on the protective cover so that each drawing can be quickly identified.

REVIEW QUESTIONS

1. What are the most common details used for the embellishment of a house?
2. What is a matt? What is the purpose of a matt?
3. What information should be on an identification block?
4. Why should drawings be covered for presentation?

WHAT DO YOU THINK?

1. Do you think there should be legal limitations placed on embellishing a drawing to avoid misleading the buyer? Explain your reasons.

ASSIGNMENTS

1. Sketch in pencil six figures in various poses. Use simple geometric styles. Poses can be seen among students in the class.
2. Produce two hand-lettered identification blocks for your house design: one with a border around the block and one without a border.

UNIT 3 | The Presentation

OBJECTIVES

- To learn to assemble a report
- To learn how to present the design
- To learn how to follow up the presentation

One of the most satisfying parts of designing a house can be the meeting between you and the client. If the design is properly presented, the clients' excitement at seeing their proposed new home is very rewarding to the architect or designer.

Your personal appearance is important when making your presentation. Dress professionally and be well groomed. Arrange the presentation at a place, date, and time that is most convenient to the client. Be punctual and prepared with writing material, as well as your architect's scale, in case measurements have to be clarified. Have a tape measure available in order to measure room sizes, for example.

Remember to be pleasant, confident, and positive about your design proposal. Take your time and allow time for the clients to comprehend your design plans.

THE DESIGN REPORT

Technical information that would help justify the design, such as building codes, lot structure, or special design needs, is best documented in a written report. This allows the clients to study these details at their leisure. The written report may also include charts, sketches, or photographs, to visually support the written data. Your report should be contained in a binder and properly identified.

Information in the report should be arranged in chronological order. For example, site specifications may be presented first, followed by structural considerations, and then data concerning the interior or exterior materials.

PRESENTING THE DESIGN

Make sure that the clients can easily see you and each segment of your presentation. Much of your presentation will require psychologically preparing the clients to accept and desire your design concepts. To help achieve this goal, show them the finished house design first. This should be the model or the pictorial drawing of the house. The visual impact usually helps to put the clients in a receptive mood.

Carefully explain the overall design concept and elaborate on the unique features of the design, such as bay windows, patio areas, or structural features. Give the customers a chance to become enthusiastic about their *new* home.

The blueprints of the floor plans should then be displayed. Give the flat, covered set of plans to the clients, so that they can follow your explanations as you work from your set of the plans. Most prospective homeowners prefer to see the ground-floor plan first, the second-floor plan next, and the basement plan last. Explain the layout of the house, beginning at the front entrance. Emphasize special features of each area as you move through the plan.

After you have perused each floor plan and the elevations, return to the ground-floor plan for a more scrutinized discussion. Technical construction details, lot orientation, and detail drawings can also be explained at this time. The written report may be referred to at this time to help answer questions or to reinforce the design concept. Allow sufficient time for the clients to study your plans and express comments.

THE FOLLOW-UP

Since there is usually a feeling of excitement during the presentation, it is easy to forget suggested changes or information. You should listen carefully to the clients' comments or requests and write them down. Changes to the floor plans can be sketched directly on your set of plans for future redrawing.

Suggest to the potential homeowners that they examine the plans for a few days and record any changes they may wish to make on the blueprint. Contact the clients in one week to arrange another meeting, at which time the plans can be finalized.

*R*EVIEW QUESTIONS

1. What is the purpose of a written design report?
2. Why is it important to present the model or pictorial drawings first to the client?
3. How many sets of blueprints should you use in your presentation? Why?

*W*HAT DO YOU THINK?

1. Do you think that, in the future, computer-designed presentations may be used in conjunction with videotapes for home viewing? Explain your thoughts briefly.

*A*SSIGNMENTS

1. Write a brief report outlining the design concept of your house. Your report should consider the orientation of the house to the lot, the design style you chose, and the advantages of your design.

PRESENTATION TO THE CLIENTS

THE PROJECT

Step 18:

The presentation of your house design should include:

- two complete sets of working blueprints;
- a pictorial drawing of the house or a model of the house;
- necessary diagrams or charts to explain your design concepts;
- a written report explaining your design.

One set of blueprints should be properly covered and identified for the client's use. The pictorial drawing and the presentation charts, etc. should be identified and covered. The model should be clean and identified. Your written report should be placed in a binder and identified on the cover.

Remember to keep a similar style and appearance to all your presentation pieces to create a professional impression.

Step 19:

Present your house design in a pleasant, positive manner; however, be willing to listen to other ideas and perhaps compromise on parts of the design.

WORKING DRAWINGS

Part Four shows you how to design a set of working drawings to meet construction standards. Making these drawings will be of value to any student interested in architectural design, construction, and electrical and heating systems.

14

Working Drawings: Plans

THE MAJOR DIFFERENCE BETWEEN a set of presentation draw-ings and a set of working drawings is the purpose for which the drawings are intended. Presentation drawings are used by people who wish to select a plan in order to have a house built. Most people are not familiar with blueprints; therefore, the dimensioning must be very simple and easy to understand. The **working drawings**, however, are used by professionally skilled craftspersons, who are used to reading technical drawings. Therefore, a much more thorough and sophisticated dimensioning technique is necessary.

This chapter refers to the plans which, together with the elevations, make up a set of working drawings. In a complete set of drawings, these plans are usually placed in the sequence in which they will be used on the job:

1. a **plot plan**, which shows the location of a building on a specific lot;
2. the **foundation plan**, which shows how the building will be supported;
3. the **floor plans**, which are fully dimensioned to show the layout of each room.

UNIT 1 | Plot Plans

OBJECTIVES

- To utilize information from the survey plan and the site plan to draw a plot plan
- To draw a plot plan to a suitable scale
- To provide adequate information for locating the house on the lot according to local by-laws

INFORMATION FOR THE PLOT PLAN

A great deal of the preparatory work for the plot plan was already done when the site plan was made. However, the presentation of plans to the client frequently brings about dimensional changes. It is therefore advisable to check both the survey plan and the site plan to see that they compare and that the changes requested are suitable for that particular lot.

Compare the following items on the survey and site plan:

1. Do the lot number and the location refer to the actual lot the client wishes to build on?
2. Are the compass orientation and all bearings and distances in agreement with each other?
3. Have all iron bars been noted?
4. Has the datum line for elevations been recorded and have contours and elevations been included for a sloping lot?
5. Have existing buildings, rock outcrops, drainage direction, and any other details that will affect the location of the house been noted?
6. Has the name of the qualified surveyor and the date the survey was taken been given?

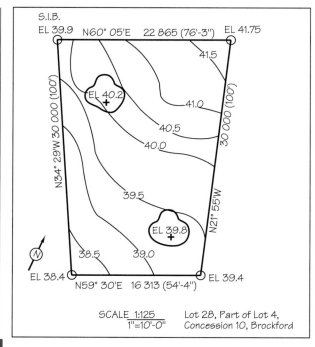

FIGURE 14-1A *Survey plan*

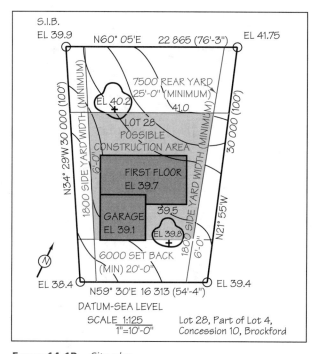

FIGURE 14-1B *Site plan*

THE PURPOSE OF A PLOT PLAN

With the previous information verified, the plot plan can now be drawn. The purpose of the plot plan is to show the location of the house on the lot, together with the size of the structure and the location and width of the driveway. As this drawing will be used to stake out the property prior to digging the area for the foundations, it is not necessary to include a great amount of detail on the plan. Although contour lines and salient elevations, such as the level of the floor, should be shown if the lot is sloped, an uncluttered drawing giving only relevant information is preferable.

Landscaping details are incorporated into a plot plan if there is any other excavation to be done, such as that for an inground swimming pool, a septic tank, or a major change to the existing contours. Most earth works will be done at the same time; therefore it is convenient to have them noted on a single drawing. In this case, it may be necessary to draw the plot plan at a larger scale *(see Fig. 14-2)*. Detailed landscape instructions that do not involve earth moving to any great

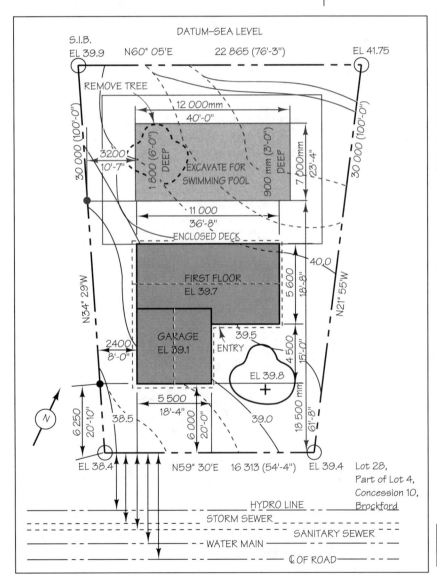

FIGURE 14-2
Plot plan with swimming pool

degree should be put on a separate landscape drawing (see Chapter 7). This work will likely be carried out after the construction is completed.

DRAWING THE PLOT PLAN

A relatively small drawing is required for the plot plan. A scale of between 1:125 and 1:250 (1" = 10'-0" or 1" = 20'-0") will be suitable for an average-sized lot. The plot plan and the foundation plan are usually placed on the first sheet of the working drawings as these drawings will be used at the beginning of construction. The plot plan should be arranged so that the front of the house is parallel to and faces the bottom of the sheet. All the other plan views of the house should be drawn facing the same way so that the drawings easily relate to each other and chances of error are minimized *(see Fig. 14-3)*.

The property lines should be drawn in phantom-type lines, which are a series of one long line followed by two small dashes. For a neat looking

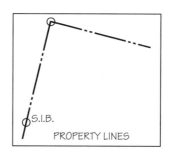

FIGURE 14-4
Property lines

drawing, arrange your linework so that the long lines go around the corners. Draw a small circle at each change of bearing angle around the perimeter *(see Fig. 14-4)*.

DIMENSIONING THE PLOT PLAN

The plot plan must be dimensioned in a similar way to the survey plan, giving a bearing and a distance along each property line. These dimensions should be placed outside the drawing and lettered so that the information can be read from the bottom right-hand corner of the page.

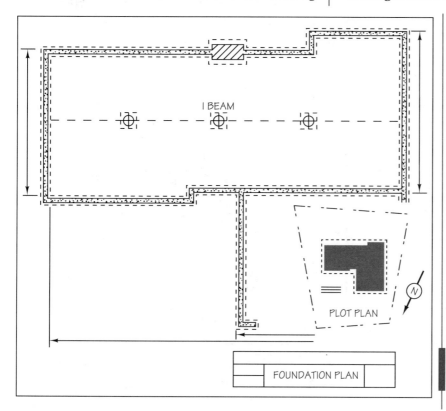

FIGURE 14-3
Plans face bottom of sheet

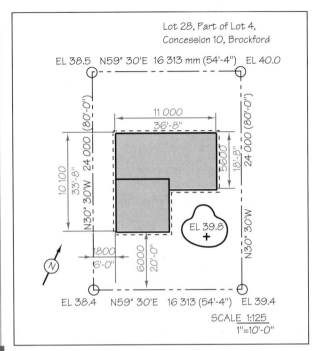

FIGURE 14-5A *Dimensioning a rectangular lot*

The north symbol, the lot identification, and the scale must be clearly located to one side of the drawing.

The overall dimensions of the house must be given and the house located on the lot with the correct setback and side yard. To do this, show the distances from the property lines to the front and to the left-hand side of the house. This will be a simple matter if the lot is rectangular *(see Fig. 14-5A)*. If the lot is pie-shaped or has irregular sides, care must be taken to locate the exact point from which the side yard is to be measured *(see Fig. 14-5B)*.

On some lots, the property line is an arc along the roadside of the lot. In these cases, the setback must be measured from the front of the building to a tangent line drawn from the crown of the curve *(see Fig. 14-5C)* and which is parallel to the front of the house.

Remember that side yards and back yards are always quoted as minimum distances in the

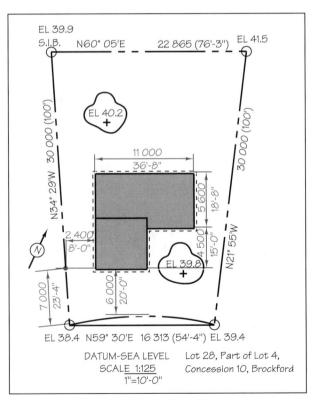

FIGURE 14-5C *Dimensioning a lot with a curved property line*

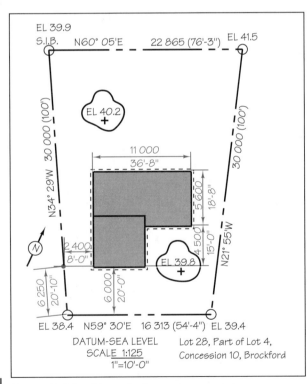

FIGURE 14-5B *Dimensioning an irregular lot*

municipal by-laws; therefore, larger dimensions at these locations are acceptable. The setback at the front, however, frequently refers to the building line and in most cases must be adhered to.

ADDITIONAL INFORMATION

In order to enhance the drawing, the building itself may be cross-hatched and the overhang of the roof and the ridge line added in dashed lines. The entrance to the house can be indicated by an arrow, and the driveway should be drawn in and the width dimensioned. The distance of the utility lines from the property line is additional information that will be useful on the plot plan. However, every effort should be made to keep this particular drawing simple because its function is to indicate where and how large the hole for the foundation is to be *(see Fig. 14-6)*.

CHECKLIST FOR A PLOT PLAN

1. Has the lot been identified?
2. Is the house clearly located on the lot from two sides?
3. Have the overall sizes of the house been shown?
4. Is the front of the house facing the bottom of the sheet?
5. Is the north symbol shown?
6. Does each of the property lines have a bearing and a distance?
7. Can the dimensions all be read from the bottom right-hand corner of the drawing?
8. Is the scale of the drawing given?
9. Have all iron bars been shown?
10. Has the driveway been shown and dimensioned?

(Optional)
11. Has the entry been indicated?
12. Has the area of the house been cross-hatched?
13. Has the roof overhang been shown in a dashed line?
14. Has the elevation of the garage and the first floor been given?
15. Have elevations of contour lines been included?

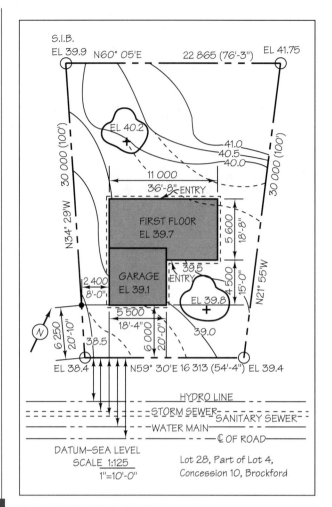

Figure 14-6 *Final plot plan*

REVIEW QUESTIONS

1. What is the purpose of a plot plan?
2. What information should be checked before drawing the plot plan and where should this information be found?
3. What dimensions are essential to the plot plan?

WHAT DO YOU THINK?

1. Why is it necessary to have the front of the house always facing the bottom of the sheet?
2. Why is it advisable to limit the information on a plot plan?

ASSIGNMENTS

1. Using the survey plan A and site plan B, provided by the instructor, draw a plot plan. This is an appropriate CAD assignment.
   a. Check the accuracy of all information.
   b. Draw a plot plan using a scale of 1:250 (1" = 20'-0"). A two-storey house plan with a single garage is to be placed on this lot.
   c. Go over the client's request indicated below in order to determine the final size of the house.

Client's Request
The house plan that has been selected by the client will be supplied by the instructor. This house has been changed by the client to a two-storey house with no garage. This is an appropriate CAD assignment.

UNIT 2 | Floor Plans

OBJECTIVES

- To recognize the function of a floor plan in a set of working drawings
- To understand the importance of accuracy for the floor plan
- To draw a fully dimensioned floor plan
- To select the correct joist size, spacing, and direction to give support to an interior

THE IMPORTANCE OF THE FLOOR PLAN

As it was for a set of presentation drawings, the floor plan is the most important element in a set of working drawings. A great amount of vital information is made available to a building contractor by the floor plans; the foundation plans are developed directly from them. Exceptional care must be taken to ensure that the information on the floor plan is absolutely accurate. The floor plan not only must interpret the needs of the client correctly but must be structurally viable as well.

USING THE FLOOR PLAN DRAWING

In Chapter 9, Unit 4, *Making a Presentation Drawing*, it was suggested that if no major design changes were involved, the students could make a print of the basic floor plan and that this print then be used for the presentation drawing. This procedure will save time as the original basic floor plan can now be dimensioned as a working drawing.

COMPUTERIZED ESTIMATING PROCEDURES

Professionally in the past, the actual drawing was not always altered in accordance with redimensioning. For simple changes, the time and expense involved in redrawing was not justified. The contractor was interested only in the dimensions as written and would never scale something directly from the drawing itself. However, now that many lumber yards and builders' suppliers are making their material estimates by computer, the short cut is no longer feasible professionally. To make a material quantity estimate, a computer operator now moves a *mouse* over the actual drawing. The calculations necessary for determining the amount of studs, plates, sheathing, etc. are made automatically, based on the distances travelled by the *mouse* rather than from the written dimensions.

This means that all drawings must be extremely accurate. Working drawings are completely redrawn professionally even if the changes required are minimal. If the drawings have been

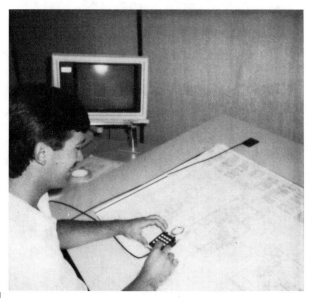

FIGURE 14-7 *Computer operator using a mouse to make a material quantity estimate*

made with a CAD system, the drawing itself will be adjusted automatically to fit with any computer changes in dimensioning.

DRAWING THE UPPER STOREY

When drawing an upper storey, a designer must ensure that all the exterior walls, chimneys, and stairwells are shown in the correct relationship to the corresponding features on the plan of the first floor. This is best accomplished by placing a piece of vellum over an accurately drawn first-floor plan, then tracing the major walls and stairways so that they will be in the correct position. Usually the exterior walls of the upper storey are placed on top of the lower exterior walls for support. If this is not possible, special supports such as posts and beams must be included to carry the weight of the upper wall.

If the lower portion of a structure is to be faced with brick veneer and the upper storey is to be sheathed with wood siding, then the dimensions of the upper structure must be extended by 125 mm (5") on each end of the wall where the adjoining

wall is brick faced. This provides the top edge of the brick veneer with protection from the weather by the wood siding, which will overlap it *(see Fig. 14-9).*

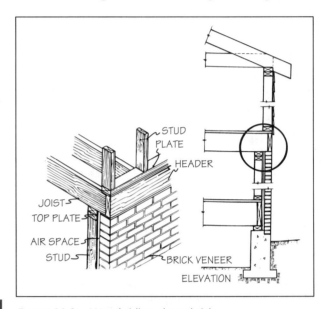

FIGURE 14-9 *Wood siding above brick*

Hepler/Wallach: *Architecture: Drafting and Design*, 5/e © 1987.
Reproduced by permission of Glencoe/McGraw-Hill Educational Division.

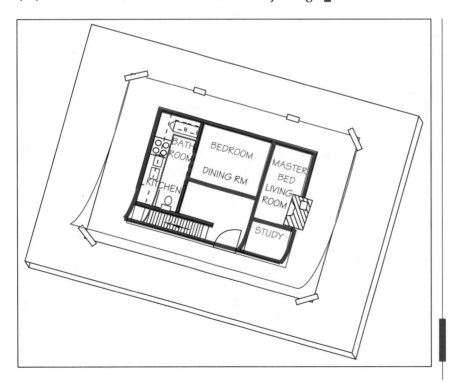

FIGURE 14-8
Tracing the upper-floor plan

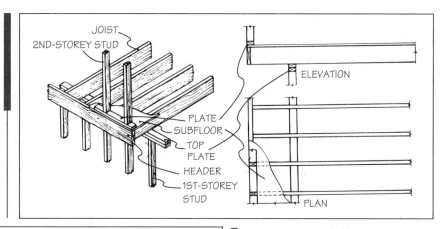

FIGURE 14-10A

Cantilever at second-storey level — joist perpendicular to exterior wall

Hepler/Wallach: *Architecture: Drafting and Design*, 5/e © 1987. Reproduced by permission of Glencoe/McGraw-Hill Educational Division.

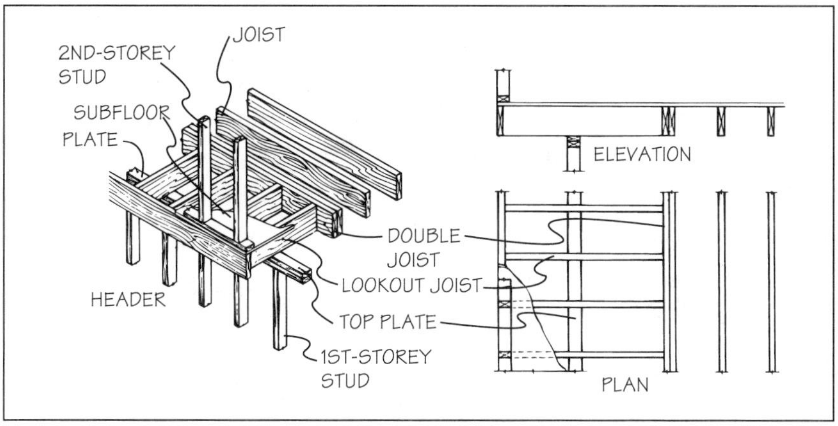

FIGURE 14-10B *(left)*

Cantilever at second-storey level — joist parallel to exterior wall

Hepler/Wallach: *Architecture: Drafting and Design*, 5/e © 1987. Reproduced by permission of Glencoe/McGraw-Hill Educational Division.

FIGURE 14-11 *(below)*

Waste lines must be larger than water-supply lines.

Hepler/Wallach: *Architecture: Drafting and Design*, 5/e © 1987. Reproduced by permission of Glencoe/McGraw-Hill Educational Division.

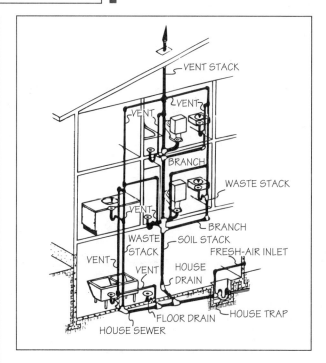

Sometimes a second floor is cantilevered, or extended, past the supporting wall. In this case, the extension should not exceed one and a half times the depth of the joist supporting it *(see Fig. 14-10A)*.

Where possible, interior second-storey partitions should be in line with those at a lower level or at least within 750 mm (2' -6") of a supporting wall. If this is not practical, double headers or trimmers should be placed in the first-floor ceiling to support the weight of the interior second storey walls *(see Fig. 14-10B)*.

Ideally, upper-storey plumbing should be placed directly above the plumbing in the lower storey to avoid costly runs of piping and to ensure the efficiency of the hot-water system. Soil stacks to which all toilets are connected must lead directly to the house foundations from each floor level. Particular care must be taken that soil stacks do not pass through any living room or dining room *(see Fig. 14-11)*.

DIMENSIONING A FLOOR PLAN

The uses of a working drawing of a floor plan determine the way that the drawing will be dimensioned. A working drawing must be dimensioned to show the exact location of all the major features of a house, such as the partitions, doors and windows, and the size of the closets.

To develop a neat and concise method of dimensioning, all the major structural dimensions should relate to one of the three specific types of dimension lines discussed below.

1. The overall dimension extends from the outside edge of the exterior stud on one side of the building to the outside edge of the exterior stud on the opposite side. Exterior sheathing and brick veneer will not be included in the overall dimensions. The builder has to know where to erect the frame walls and is not concerned with the actual overall size of the building when completed *(see Figs. 14-12A and 14-12B)*.

2. Dimensions to the centre lines of doors and windows should form a complete line of dimensioning and should add up to the original overall dimensions *(see Fig. 14-13)*.

3. Dimensions controlling the placement of partitions are usually superimposed on the floor plan itself and can be drawn using one of the methods shown in *Figs. 14-14A, 14-14B, and 14-14C*. The methods selected should be used throughout all the plan drawings. When added together, the lengths of any sequence or group of dimension lines should always equal the length of the corresponding overall dimension.

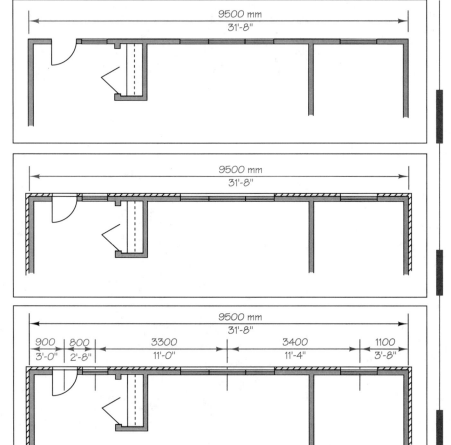

FIGURE 14-12A
Overall dimension in frame wall — outside of stud to outside of stud

FIGURE 14-12B
Overall dimension for brick veneer

FIGURE 14-13
Centre lines of doors and windows

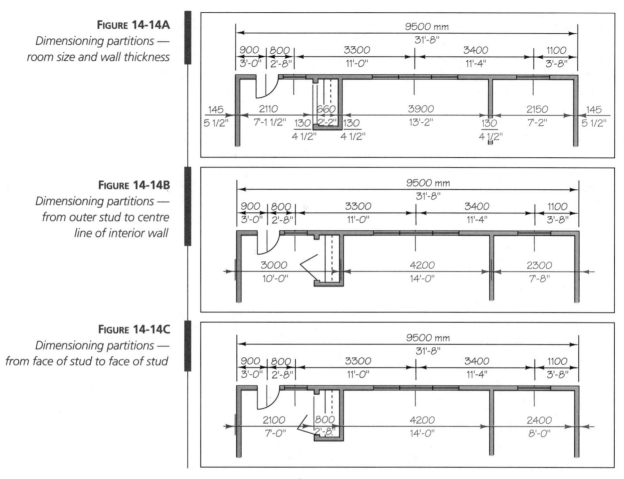

FIGURE **14-14A**
*Dimensioning partitions —
room size and wall thickness*

FIGURE **14-14B**
*Dimensioning partitions —
from outer stud to centre
line of interior wall*

FIGURE **14-14C**
*Dimensioning partitions —
from face of stud to face of stud*

Additional overall dimensions which include the wood siding and brick veneer, may be added to the floor plan if desired.

Various styles of line extends can be used in the dimensioning of drawings. Those used most frequently are shown in *Fig. 14-15.* The style selected must be used throughout the entire set of drawings.

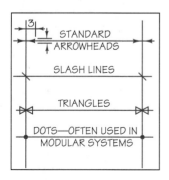

FIGURE **14-15**
*Styles of dimension
lines extends*

Each of the three dimension lines mentioned above may not be required on all sides of a floor plan. For instance, a basic rectangle-shaped house will need only the overall length and overall width of the house shown once on a drawing. Similarly, a house without doors or windows in an exterior wall will not require a line of dimensions for these items on that side. However, when an offset occurs on the outer wall of the structure, the lengths of the offset should include the thickness of the end wall.

Once the three lines of dimensions have been considered and applied to the floor plan, the majority of dimensioning will be in place. However, such dimensions as the length and depth of the closets, the width of the stairs, the number of stair risers, or the widths of passageways may not have been included in the three dimension lines and will have to be added independently. Careful scrutiny of a drawing will show which features of a structure will require additional dimensioning (*see Fig. 14-16*).

A designer assumes that the contractor who has been hired will be familiar with basic residential construction methods. For this reason, it is not usual to supply fully detailed measurements regarding the position of all studs and joists, the distance to the centre line of a door placed in the corner of a room, or the sizes of standard kitchen and bathroom equipment.

THE SUPPORT SYSTEM FOR A FLOOR

A series of horizontal wooden joists is used to support the floor and ceiling systems at each level of a house.

Information regarding the joist to be used is given on the floor plan by means of a special symbol that indicates the size, spacing, and direction of the joists (*see Fig. 14-17*). These joist symbols are shown on the plan of the floor that is below the ceiling in which the joists will be installed.

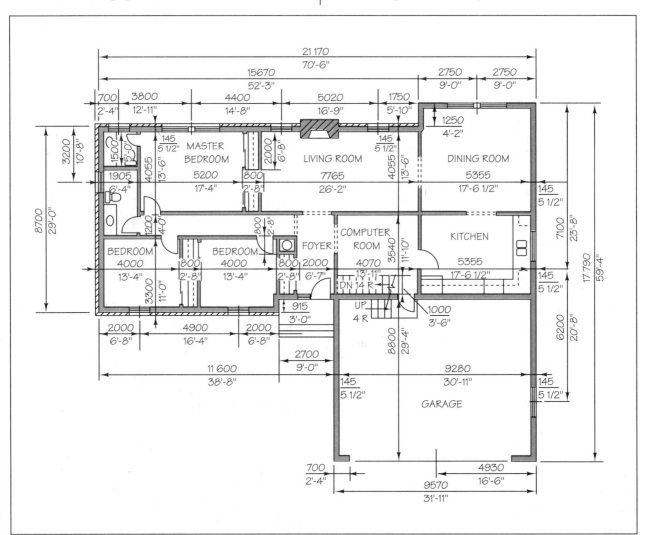

FIGURE 14-16 *Floor-plan dimensions for working drawings*

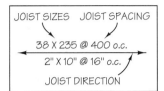

FIGURE 14-17
The joist symbol

In determining the appropriate joist sizes, the following factors must be considered:

1. The spacing of the joists: In most residential structures, the joists are spaced at 400 mm (16") on centres. The same sized joists placed closer together will span a greater distance and if placed further apart will span a lesser distance. Builders prefer to construct on 400 mm (16") centres so that the construction throughout the structure is assembled with the same size of spacing.

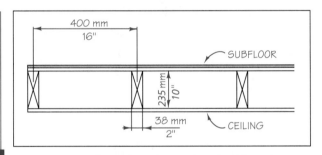

FIGURE 14-18 *Illustration of* $\frac{38 \times 235 @ 400 \text{ o.c.}}{2" \times 10" @ 16" \text{ o.c.}}$

2. The direction of the joists: It is preferable to have all the joists running in the same direction throughout one floor. Most residential rooms are rectangular. Joists that run parallel to the shorter or secondary dimensions of a room will probably require a smaller cross-section and will be less costly. Determine which way the joist will run in that particular floor level and use the same sized joists throughout.

3. The clear distance to be spanned: This distance is the inside measurement of a room, i.e., from the face of the partition to the face of the partition. So that the same sized joists may be used throughout one floor, the designer must determine the longest clear span for that particular floor level. This is done by finding the longest of the secondary dimensions for the rooms on the relevant floor plan.

4. Loading situations for joists: Government building code tables specify the correct joist sizes for any given span and location. The appropriate loading factors for each location are critical to the safety and stability of a structure.

The following are the loading situations that most frequently occur in house design. The joist tables referred to are provided in the *National and Provincial Building Codes* or in the *Canadian*

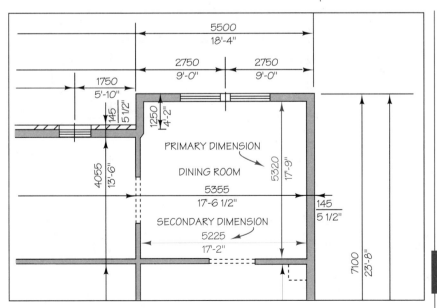

FIGURE 14-19
Primary and secondary dimensions

Wood Frame Construction book published by the Canada Mortgage and Housing Corporation and reproduced in the Appendix of this book for your convenience.

1. For a ceiling without a living area or bedroom above, use Table 7 (Table 11), Ceiling Joist – Attic Not Accessible by a Stairway in the Appendix. Indicate this joist by placing several symbols on the floor plan of a single-storey house or the upper-storey plan of a two-storey house.

2. For the upper floor system of a two-storey house, use Table 6 (Table 10), Floor Joists – Bedrooms and Attics Accessible by Stairway in the Appendix.

Indicate this joist by placing several symbols on the lower floor plan of a two-storey house.

3. For the floor system of the main living floor level, use Table 4 (Table 8), Floor Joist – Living Quarters. Indicate the joist by placing several symbols on the foundation plan.

A CEILING SUPPORT SYSTEM

The following is an example of how to select a joist size for the single-storey house for which working drawings are being developed in this chapter *(see Fig. 14-20).*

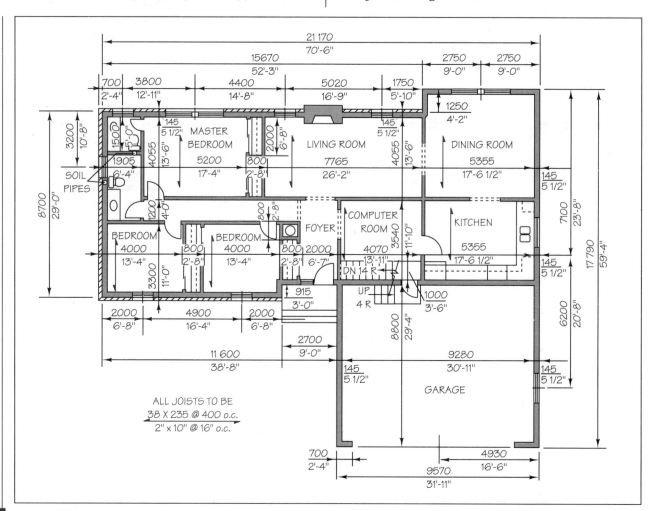

FIGURE 14-20 *Floor-plan dimensions with joists for working drawing*

The selection of joists for a two-storey house would involve a similar strategy using the appropriate table in the Appendix described on the previous page for various levels.

CALCULATIONS FOR SUPPORT SYSTEMS

Part A   Calculations to Determine Joist Size
When selecting the distance of clear span for ceiling joists to be used throughout the house, we find that the dining room has the largest secondary dimension of any room *(see Fig. 14-19)*.

Horizontal dimension
5355 mm – 130 mm (width of wall) (17'-6 1/2" – 4 1/2") = 5225 mm (17'-2") Secondary dimension

However, the joists in the remainder of the house will be best placed vertically on the plan. As it is preferable to have all the joists running in the same direction, check the primary dimension of the dining room.

Vertical dimension
4055 mm + 1250 mm (width of projection) + 145 mm – 130 mm (width of wall) (13'-6" + 4'-2" + 5 1/2" - 4 1/2") = 5320 mm (17'-9") Primary dimension

This appears to be the best span from which to base the joist size.

Determine the size of joist by using Table 7 (Table 11) in the Appendix of this book.

Column 1 – Select the type of wood generally used in your area, e.g., spruce, pine, etc.
Column 2 – Select the grade most often used in house construction, e.g., No. 2.
Columns 4 and 6 - Select spacing used in house construction, e.g., 400 o.c.
Column 5 – Select the first number in the column greater than the distance to be spanned by the joist. In the example shown above, the joist must span 5320 mm (17'-9"). 5620 mm (18'-7") is the next larger number in this column on the chart.

Column 3 – Read off the size of joist for the span that has been selected – 38 mm × 184 mm (2" × 8"). This is the largest joist size required for the support of a ceiling in this house, so it is the size of joist that should be used throughout the floor plan. In several convenient places on the plan, insert a joist symbol showing the size, spacing, and direction of the joists.

CHECKLIST FOR THE FLOOR PLAN

1. Is a ceiling joist symbol in each room?
2. Are the number of risers and direction of stairs given?
3. Are the location and width of the stairs dimensioned?
4. Does each of the complete lines of detail dimensions add up to the total?
5. Does the interior line of dimensioning give the location of all the partitions?
6. Are soil pipes shown from toilets on this floor and the other floor levels?
7. Are rods and shelves in closets shown and are other cupboards, such as broom and linen closets, marked?
8. Has a brick veneer or masonry finish been shown if desired?

REVIEW QUESTIONS

1. Why is it important today to draw a floor plan very accurately?
2. What three lines of dimensioning should be used when dimensioning a floor plan?
3. How do you determine the correct joist size?

WHAT DO YOU THINK?

1. Why were builders formerly advised not to measure a drawing?
2. Why is selecting the correct joist size so crucial?

ASSIGNMENTS

1. For this assignment, obtain a second copy of the basic floor plan supplied by the instructor in Chapter 9, Unit 4, Assignment 3 (Presentation Drawings).
   a. Dimension this copy as a working drawing, including the selection of a correct joist size.
   b. Using the second-storey floor plan you designed for this same house, dimension it as a working drawing. Include the selection of a correct joist size.

   OR
2. Complete the basic floor plan you have drawn for a magazine home in Chapter 9 by dimensioning it as a working drawing. Include the selection of a correct size joist.

UNIT 3 | Perimeter Foundation Plans

OBJECTIVES

- To understand the effect of soil conditions on a building
- To understand dead and live loads
- To understand all the factors that affect foundation design
- To draw peripheral foundations for a residence

SOIL CONDITIONS

In most areas of the world, today's population densities make it necessary to consider building on all types of land. The load-bearing capability can vary from very stable (rock) to an inability to bear any weight for very long (quicksand). When construction is to be undertaken on land that has not been previously built upon, soil borings must be made in various parts of the site. These soil samples are then tested to determine the maximum load that that specific soil can carry. Foundations will then be designed to compensate for any inadequacies in the load-bearing properties of the land.

The types of soil, and therefore their load-bearing capacities, can vary under a single structure so that the foundation design must ensure a firm, level platform under the entire building. Foundations built on the side of a steep hill are usually stepped to avoid digging out large quantities of earth.

LIVE AND DEAD LOADS

There are two types of loads transmitted by a building to the ground. The dead load is the weight of the construction materials and equipment in the building, and the live load is a variable load, such as that caused by cars in a garage,

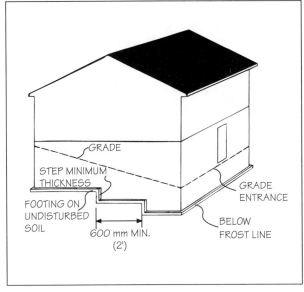

FIGURE 14-21 *Stepped footings*

Courtesy of CMHC: Canadian Wood Frame House Construction

by people in a theatre, or by snow or wind on a roof. Live and dead loads were discussed in more detail in Chapter 8.

THE FROST LINE

Besides the type of soil encountered and its load-bearing qualities, climate affects the construction of a foundation.

In a location where the ground does not freeze, it is possible to build a structure directly on grade using a concrete slab as the foundation. However, when the ground is subject to freezing, even intermittently, the foundations must be laid below the lowest level that is penetrated by frost. This level is called the **frost line**.

If the soil is permanently frozen, structures can be built directly on the **permafrost** because it will not heave.

FOUNDATION DESIGN FACTORS

The type of foundation depends on the type of construction design used for a building. A frame structure, such as that used in most residential houses, is usually supported by a continuous wall under the exterior wall of the **superstructure**, which is the portion of the building that is above the ground. This wall will enclose a space under the house that will form a basement or a heated crawl space *(see Fig. 14-22A)*. Some structures use the **post-and-beam** method of construction, where spaced columns transfer the roof load to the foundations. In this case, the exterior walls are non-load bearing, or curtain, walls. This type of construction is used when a building will have large areas of glass to make up the exterior walls. The foundation for this type of construction will consist of piers, which are placed directly under the columns. The weight of the building will be concentrated on those piers *(see Fig. 14-22B)*.

In summary, a foundation design must take into account the following factors:

1. the load-bearing capacities of the soil on which the structure is to be placed;
2. the total weight that the building will place on the soil, which will be a combination of the dead and live loads;
3. the effects of the climate, such as the depth of the frost line, snow loading, and wind conditions;
4. the method of construction to be used in the building.

THE FOOTINGS

Foundations are made up of two parts:

1. the foundation wall or the piers, which carry the load from the superstructure down into the earth, and
2. the footings, which form a stable platform under the foundation walls or piers and transmit the load directly to the soil.

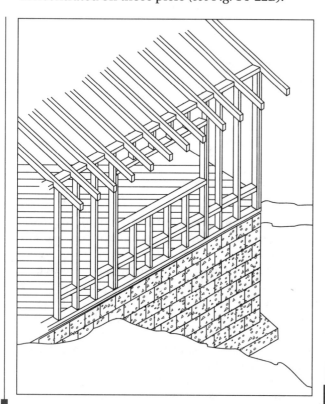

FIGURE 14-22A *Full foundation for conventional framing*

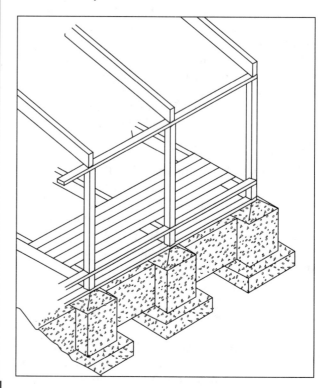

FIGURE 14-22B *Piers and curtain wall foundation for post-and-beam construction*

Footings are usually designed to cover a greater area than the foundation walls or piers so that the weight of the building is distributed over a larger area. The principle involved is the same as that which dictates that persons caught in quicksand should attempt to lie down full length on the surface so that their weight is distributed over the entire length of their body rather than directly over their feet alone.

The footings for a residential foundation are twice as wide as the foundation wall; therefore, the weight concentrated on each square metre or square foot of the soil is halved.

Footings must be placed below the frost line, which may vary from region to region. For example, the frost line is 1200 mm (4' -0") in southern regions of Canada. The frost line in your area can be obtained from the regional planning office or any local builder.

Concrete for footings can be poured directly into a trench or into forms made of wooden or metal shuttering. Footings must be **monolithic**; that is, they must be poured continuously so that there are no joins, and they must be allowed to cure or set gradually. This is done by preventing the exterior surface of the footings from drying rapidly before the centre core of the concrete begins to dry out, which would cause cracking of the footings' surface. The exterior surface is sprayed with water and then covered with burlap. This process cannot be hurried, so it is usually several weeks before anything can be built on the footings.

Standard proportions for footings are such that the thickness, or depth, of the footings has a ratio of 3:2 relative to the projection of the footings each side of the foundation wall. This projection must never be less than 100 mm (4"), and the width of the footings should always be twice the thickness of the wall that it supports.

Drain tile is placed around the perimeter of the footings at a level lower than that of the basement floor to facilitate drainage.

The purpose of footings is two-fold:

1. to distribute a building's weight over a larger area, and
2. to provide a firm, level platform for a structure.

FOUNDATION WALLS

Foundation walls can be made of either concrete blocks or of poured concrete. For poured concrete, forming must be put in place in order to shape and contain the concrete.

Poured concrete foundation walls are preferable to concrete blocks in areas where drainage might be a problem. Water can seep through the joints between blocks, but it is far less likely to gain entry into a basement through poured concrete.

The foundation walls are usually **keyed** to the footings as shown in *Fig. 14-23* to prevent earth pressure pushing them off the level footings.

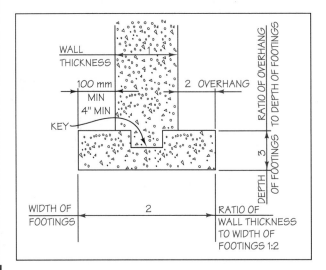

FIGURE 14-23 *Proportions of footings to the foundation wall*

Concrete blocks are laid by hand directly on the footings. They come in standard sizes. Most blocks are a nominal size of 200 mm × 400 mm (8" × 16"). In actual fact, the height and length is 10 mm (3/8") smaller than the nominal size to allow room for the mortar to bring the courses or rows of the blocks to a standard size. Blocks can be purchased in various widths from 150 mm (6") to 300 mm (1' -0") thick *(see Fig. 14-24)*.

To fasten the wooden superstructure of the house to the foundation, a series of anchor bolts is embedded into the top of the wall. When using concrete blocks, it is necessary to cap the top row with solid masonry to hold the bolts *(see Fig. 14-25)*.

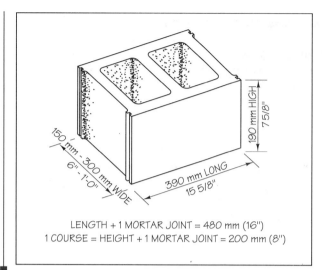

LENGTH + 1 MORTAR JOINT = 480 mm (16")
1 COURSE = HEIGHT + 1 MORTAR JOINT = 200 mm (8")

FIGURE 14-24 *Concrete block proportions*

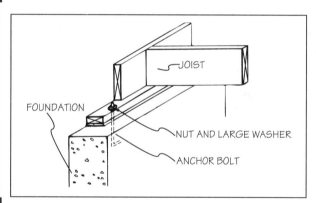

FIGURE 14-25 *Method of anchoring floor system to concrete walls, showing anchor bolt for wood sill*

Courtesy of CMHC: Canadian Wood Frame House Construction

Pilasters, or thickened portions of the wall, can be used to strengthen extra long portions of foundation walls or to provide support for beams. The pilaster must be an integral part of the wall; that is, it must be part of the poured concrete wall, or the concrete blocks that form it must be keyed into the wall. When foundation walls are over 250 mm (10") thick, pilasters are not usually necessary *(see Fig. 14-26).*

Reinforced Concrete

The compressive strength of concrete is very great, which means that it can carry heavy loads. Its tensile strength, or its ability to conform to any undulations caused by variations in the soil, is not as good. Reinforcing steel rods are often introduced to overcome the tensile pressure. Reinforcing rods can be placed in footings, as tie rods at the top and bottom of foundation walls, and in the form of a mesh throughout the basement floor. The correct placement of reinforcing steel is critical.

Other Materials

Foundations can be made of pressurized preserved woods. This type of wood has been chemically treated to make it decay-resistant and termite-resistant. Lumber that is suitable for this purpose bears the certification mark CSA STANDARD 050.15. Wooden footings are placed on granular fill. The bottom and top plates of the foundation wall, as well as the studs, are also made of pressure-treated wood and are clad with pressurized plywood. A sheet of **polyethylene** is used on the inside for damp-proofing, and the spaces between the studs can be filled with insulating material.

Residential foundations can also be made of special structural steel, which has been developed for this specific application. However, concrete is still the most common material used for constructing foundations and it has proven to be long lasting.

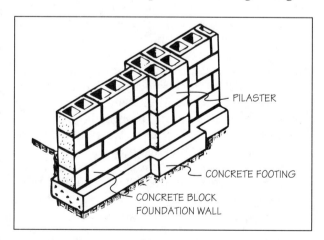

FIGURE 14-26 *Concrete block foundation pilaster*

Hepler/Wallach: *Architecture: Drafting and Design*, 5/e © 1987.
Reproduced by permission of Glencoe/McGraw-Hill Educational Division.

THE FOUNDATION AS A BASEMENT

Footings must be placed at a depth that is below the frost line. It is common practice to increase this depth so that an additional level of livable space can be created under the house. The cost of this additional level is minimal because excavating machinery has to be brought to the site anyway. This lower level can be used as a recreation room, a laundry room, and a furnace room. Contemporary houses tend to have family rooms and laundry rooms on the main level of the house as well as compact furnaces. However, the additional level is still valuable space for storage, work, and play, so the full-height basement is unlikely to disappear for some time to come.

A basement floor is usually made of concrete that is 75 mm (3") thick, poured on top of 150 mm (6") of granular fill that has been covered with a sheet of polyethylene 0.15 mm thick. The basement floor should not bear directly on the projection of the footings but should be cushioned by 25 mm (1") of sand. A perimeter joint should be placed between the foundation wall and the basement floor to form an expansion joint. This will prevent the floor from cracking as a result of temperature changes *(see Fig. 14-27)*.

THE FOUNDATION AS A CRAWL SPACE

It is possible to have a crawl space instead of a full height basement. Again, the footings will be taken down below the frost line. They must be deep enough to allow a minimum of 300 mm (1' -0") between the ground and the bottom of the joists and beams that will support the floor above. If this crawl space is less than 600 mm (2' -0"), trenches

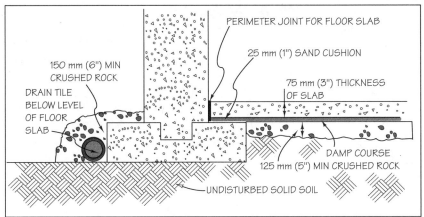

FIGURE 14-27
Drain tile and slab floor seating

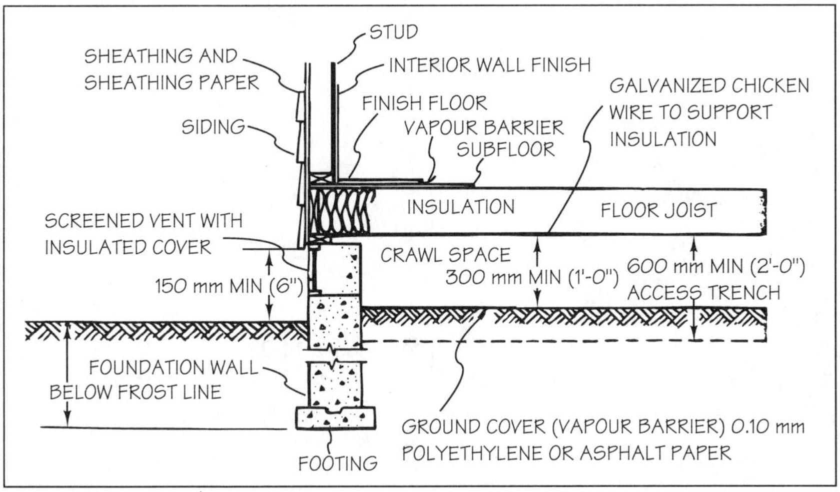

FIGURE 14-28
Unheated crawl space

Jensen: *Architectural Drawing and Design for Residential Construction* published by McGraw-Hill Ryerson

will be required to allow access to heating ducts, plumbing services, etc. The surface of the ground should be damp-proofed by covering it with a polyethylene sheet 0.10 mm thick, and the space should be heated and ventilated.

SLAB FOUNDATIONS

In areas where the frost does not penetrate the ground to any significant depth, a slab can be built on the grade to serve as a foundation or footings for a structure, provided that the soil conditions are suitable. The top of the slab should be a minimum of 150 mm (6") above grade and a layer of crushed rock 125 mm (5") thick should be placed under the slab, with a vapour barrier between the slab and the stones. The slab should also be reinforced with wire mesh.

UNEXCAVATED AND BACKFILLED FOUNDATIONS

The walls of a garage must be supported by foundation walls and footings that go below the frost line. It is unusual, however, to have a basement or crawl space under the garage because of the amount of reinforcement that would be necessary under this area. The space under the garage is usually unexcavated except where space is necessary to provide room to construct the perimeter

walls. Compacted granular fill is then used to fill up the spaces. The garage floor is sloped towards the entrance. If a floor drain is installed, the floor will slope in that direction. The floor of a garage is usually poured concrete 125 mm (5") thick when there is no granular base and 75 mm (3") thick when there is a compacted granular base. A perimeter joint should be installed around the edges of the floor.

Steps, decks, and other appendages to a structure are usually supported by a foundation wall, or are on piers, which will be specified on the foundation drawing.

For small or narrow areas such as flower planters, concrete decks, and steps supported by individual foundation walls, it will be necessary to excavate the earth and backfill after the job is completed.

WINDOW WELLS

When windows in the foundation wall are close to or below the grade level, window wells are used to protect the window from the earth. Window wells are usually made of galvanized steel, the base of which is filled with granular drainage chips. A drainage hole of 150 mm (6") diameter leading to the weeping tile ensures that rainwater will drain away rapidly *(see Fig. 14-29)*.

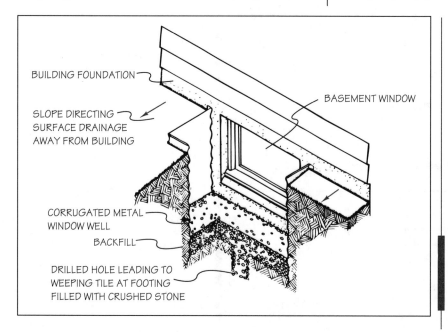

BUILDING FOUNDATION

BASEMENT WINDOW

SLOPE DIRECTING SURFACE DRAINAGE AWAY FROM BUILDING

CORRUGATED METAL WINDOW WELL

BACKFILL

DRILLED HOLE LEADING TO WEEPING TILE AT FOOTING FILLED WITH CRUSHED STONE

FIGURE 14-29
Window well at basement wall

Courtesy of CMHC: Canadian Wood Frame House Construction

DRAWING THE FOUNDATION PLAN

A working drawing must be made showing the foundation plan. This is a section looking down on the foundation taken at a point just below the sill that joins the foundation to the superstructure.

The foundation plan drawing, together with the plot plan, are the first drawings to be used at the site and should therefore be numbered as sheets one and two (or sheet one if they are combined on one sheet) of the set of working drawings.

The foundation plan and the plot plan should be drawn with the street side of the house placed at the base of the drawing paper. Because all the plan views of the house are oriented in the same direction on a sheet, the alignment of the various levels to one another is easily understood. This also minimizes the possibility of error at the building site.

To begin drawing the foundation plan, first place a fresh piece of vellum over the floor plan and trace the exterior line of the frame wall. The foundations for a house with wood siding will have the same dimensions as the overall first-storey dimensions (*see Fig. 14-30*).

However, when brick veneer is to be applied to the exterior of the first storey, the overall dimensions for the foundation plan must be 100 mm (4") greater on each of the sides that terminate in brick veneer. For example, if a house is bricked all the way around, then 200 mm (8") will be added

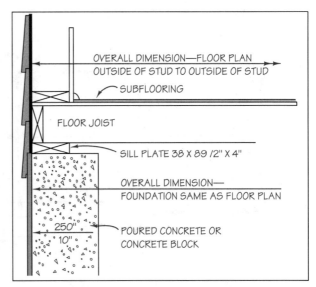

FIGURE 14-30 *Foundation for wood siding*

to the overall width and to the overall length of the house on the foundation plan. The extra 100 mm (4") on each side ensures that the foundation wall will form a ledge that will be wide enough to seat the brick veneer.

On houses with brick veneer, there will be a 25 mm (1") air space between the frame of the house and the bricks that are tied to the wooden structure, with metal ties placed at intervals throughout the wall. Because of the air space, the brick will protrude 25 mm (1") over the exterior of the foundation wall to form a drip ledge (*see Fig. 14-31*).

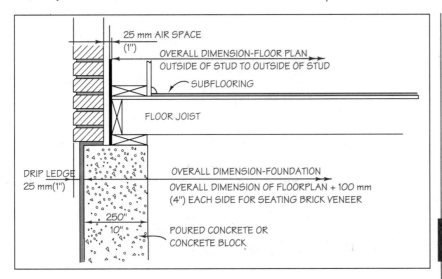

FIGURE 14-31
Foundation for brick veneer

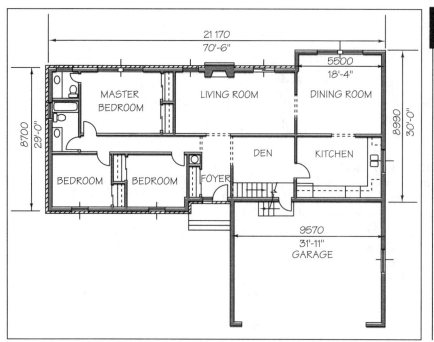

FIGURE 14-32A
Basic floor plan

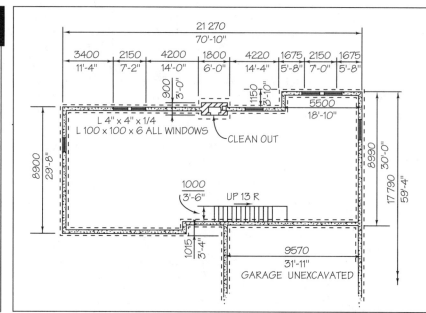

FIGURE 14-32B
Dimensioning the foundation wall

On the sample working drawing of a floor plan and foundation plan *(see Figs. 14-32A and 14-32B),* it can be seen that brick veneer has been added to the left-hand side of the house but not to the right-hand side. Accordingly, if the overall dimensions of the floor plan and of the foundation plan are compared, it will be noted that the overall width of the foundations is 200 mm (8") greater than the overall width of the floor plan on the left-hand side. The overall width of the foundation and of the floor plan is equal for the right-hand portion of the house that has wood siding. Also

100 mm (4") has been added to the left-hand side of the overall length of the foundations only *(see Fig. 14-33).*

After drawing a line to represent the exterior of the foundations, the next step is to draw in the thickness of the wall inside the line already drawn.

Thickness of Foundation Walls		*Width of Footings*
One-Storey	200 mm (8")	400 mm (16")
Two-Storey	250 mm (10")	500 mm (20")
Brick Veneer	250 mm (10")	500 mm (20")

Draw in the footings by placing a dashed line along each side of the foundation wall. The footings are twice as wide as the thickness of the foundation wall, so the dashed line will be half the width of the wall away from each of the lines.

Basement windows are usually added to the rear of the foundation except in the case of a split-entry house or a split-level design when it may be desirable to have the foundation windows placed at the front of the house.

DIMENSIONING THE FOUNDATION PLAN

Dimension the plan by giving overall dimensions for the length and width of the foundation and by showing the width of the foundation wall. The locations of the windows and their respective lengths must be shown by a complete row of dimensions that should equal the overall dimension of the house when all the dimensions are totalled. The method of dimensioning windows in a masonry wall is different from dimensioning windows in a frame wall *(see Fig. 14-32B).* To support the wall above the window opening, a lintel that is made of angle iron should be indicated over each window in the foundation. The size of this lintel is 100 mm × 100 mm × 6 mm (4" × 4" × 1/4").

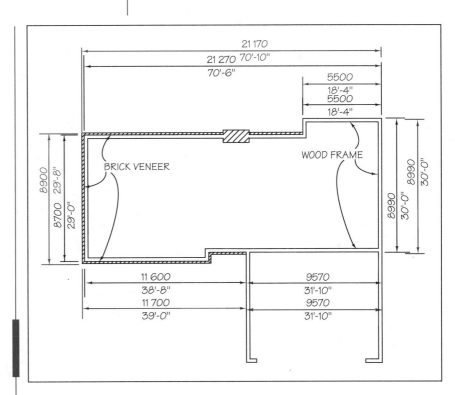

FIGURE 14-33

Comparison between foundation and floor plan sizes

REVIEW QUESTIONS

1. Why are footings built twice the width of the foundation walls?
2. What factors influence how a foundation is constructed?
3. Why is a 250 mm (10") foundation wall required for a one-storey brick veneer house?

WHAT DO YOU THINK?

1. If you were building in an area where external drainage could be a problem, what type of foundation would you select and why?
2. If you were building a house where the family room and laundry room were on the main floor, would you elect to place a crawl space under the house or a full-depth basement? State your reasons.

ASSIGNMENTS

1. On graph paper, using 5 squares = 1 m or 1 square = 1' - 0", draw a plan view of the basement of your home or a friend's home. Use the information that you have learned in this chapter to draw in the elements that you cannot see, such as footings. Don't forget to include the garage, any planters, or cold cellars.
2. Draw a perimeter foundation plan for the floor plan of the two-storey house that was supplied by your instructor and for which you have already made a working drawing in Unit 2, Assignment 1. Dimension the exterior of the foundations using the appropriate symbols for the walls and footings.

UNIT 4 | Internal Load Bearing Structures

OBJECTIVES

- To appreciate the need for an internal support for a house
- To plan an internal floor support system
- To calculate correct joist sizes, lally columns, and I beam spans
- To draw complete residential foundation plans

The provision of adequate perimeter support to convey the load of a roof and the exterior walls to the footings of a structure was covered in the preceding unit. Part of the roof load may be transmitted down through the internal members of the house. This load, together with the total weight of the various floors of a house and the furniture that will be carried by the floors, will make up an additional internal dead load.

The width of a house is usually such that it would not be practical to support the floors over the entire span because very large joists would be needed. As an alternative, a central support system is required to sustain the load that will be transmitted to the footings from the internal structure of a building.

THE FLOOR SUPPORT SYSTEM

The main floor support system in a long rectangular-shaped house usually runs lengthwise through the centre of the foundation area. If a house has a large square floor plan, two or even three floor support systems may be needed because of the wide spans involved.

A support system can be constructed in various ways. A commonly used method is to build a load-bearing wall, which will have its own footings in order to spread the load over a greater area. The bearing wall will stretch from the foundation wall on one side of the house to the oppo-

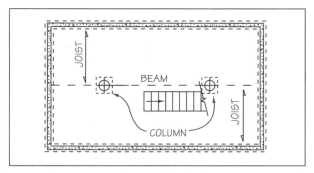

FIGURE 14-34A *Interior support system – rectangular structure*

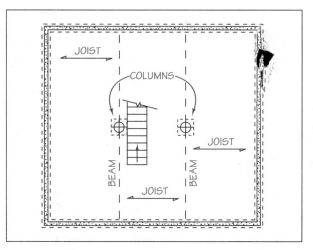

FIGURE 14-34B *Interior support system – square structure*

site side. The wall itself can be framed provided that at its base there is a row of concrete blocks that are the same width as the wall and that are laid directly on the footings *(see Fig. 14-35A)*. Alternatively, the wall can be constructed of concrete blocks *(see Fig. 14-35B)*.

The construction of a load-bearing wall will divide the foundation into two separate sections. Access is provided by means of an opening or a doorway in the wall. This will not diminish the load-bearing capabilities of the wall.

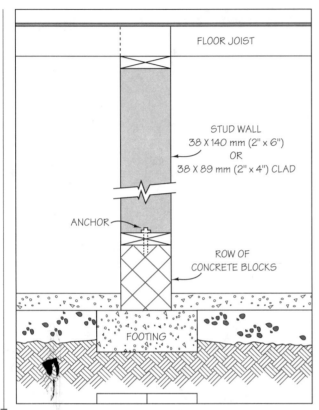

FIGURE 14-35A *Interior support systems –
Studwall support*

Jensen: *Architectural Drawing and Design for Residential Construction.*
Published by McGraw-Hill Ryerson

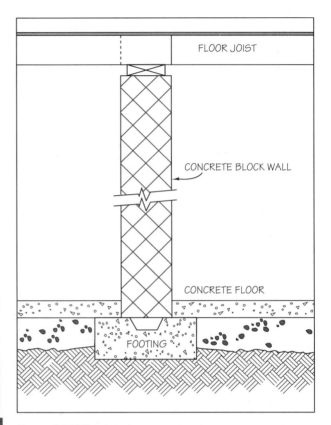

FIGURE 14-35B *Interior support systems –
Concrete block wall*

Jensen: *Architectural Drawing and Design for Residential Construction.*
Published by McGraw-Hill Ryerson

Another type of floor support system is that of a main beam supported at intervals by piers or **lally columns**, which are adjustable steel posts. This type of construction is the least costly, and it has the added advantage of providing greater flexibility for the eventual use of the area as a basement.

The main beam can be a built-up beam made of several pieces of lumber bolted together or it can be a single steel I beam or girder. The beam will be supported by piers (masonry columns), wooden columns, or lally (metal) columns, each of which will be seated on an individual footing *(see Figs. 14-35C and 14-35D).*

Care must be taken to ensure that the stairwell opening is clear of the beam and its supports. A centrally placed stairwell will often dictate the direction in which the beam will run and where it will be placed. A beam should not bear directly on a window, so the windows in the foundation walls must be positioned in order not to interfere with the floor support system.

A series of joists links the main beam or the bearing wall to the exterior walls. These joists carry the load of the living area to the footings in either direction, making a closed system of load-bearing members.

Because the same joist size should be used throughout any particular floor level, a designer must select the size of joist that is needed to support the widest clear span of the foundation plan. This is usually the distance from the inner edge of the foundation wall or sill to the beam or bearing wall. The joist size selected will support the first-

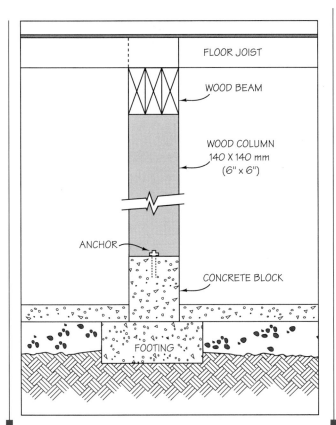

FIGURE 14-35C *Interior support systems –*
Wood column and wood beam

Jensen: *Architectural Drawing and Design for Residential Construction.*
Published by McGraw-Hill Ryerson

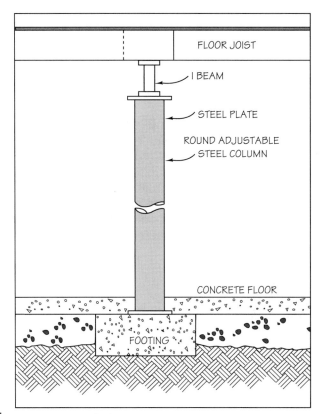

FIGURE 14-35D *Interior support systems –*
Steel column and I beam

Jensen: *Architectural Drawing and Design for Residential Construction.*
Published by McGraw-Hill Ryerson

floor level and will be shown on the foundation plan by a joist symbol.

The size of joists and of I beams and the number of support columns used are critical factors. In this regard, special tables are provided in the *National and Provincial Building Codes*. The dimensions stipulated in the tables must be adhered to strictly. The tables are reproduced in the book *Canadian Wood Frame Construction* published by the Canada Mortgage and Housing Corporation. For your convenience, selected tables are reprinted at the back of this textbook.

It is important to note that the spacing and sizes of the joists and I beams and the number of supports required for a crawl space are the same as those used for a full-sized basement.

INTERNAL FLOOR SUPPORT SYSTEM CALCULATIONS

The first step in the calculations is to determine the size of the joists that will support the first-floor level. The size depends on:

1. the spacing of the joists (which is usually 400 mm [16"] on centres),
2. the direction of the joists,
3. the clear distance to be spanned,
4. the appropriate loading.

Shown below are sample calculations for a floor support system relevant to the one-storey house for which working drawings are developed throughout this chapter. Follow these calculations by referring to the floor plans and to the foundation plans shown in *Figures 14-36A, 14-36B, 14-36C, 14-37A and 14-37B* and to the appropriate tables in the Appendix. The calculations are typical of those necessary for designing a house with a rectangular plan.

A steel I beam will be used to carry the internal load of the house. It will be supported by lally columns placed lengthwise through the centre of the structure.

The difference in width of the left-hand and the right-hand ends of the house cause us to consider several optional methods of calculating the span distance for joists and therefore how the support system will be designed.

PART A
CALCULATIONS TO
DETERMINE JOIST SIZE

Option 1 – For the left-hand (brick veneer-faced) side of the house

	Metric	Imperial
Width of LHS of house:	8900 mm	29'-8"
Less 2 × width of foundation wall:	500 mm	1'-8"
Total span	= 8400 mm	= 28'-0"
Span either side of I beam	$=\dfrac{8400 \text{ mm}}{2}$	$=\dfrac{28'\text{-}0"}{2}$
	= 4200 mm	= 14"-0"

Determine the size of joist by using Table 4 (Table 8) at the end of this book.

Column 1 – Select the type of wood generally used in your area, e.g., spruce, pine, etc.

Column 2 – Select the grade most often used in house construction, e.g. No. 2.

Columns 4-7 – Select the spacing used in house construction, e.g., 400 mm (16") o.c.

Column 5 – Select the first number in the column that is greater than the distance to be spanned by the joist. In the example shown above, the joist must span 4200 mm (14"-0"). The next larger number in this column is 4460 mm (14'-6").

Column 3 – Read off the size of joist for the span that has been selected – 38 mm × 235 mm (2" × 10").

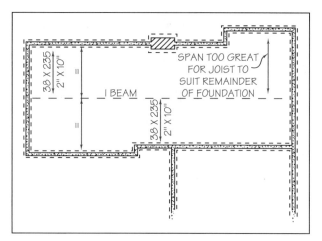

FIGURE 14-36A *Floor support system – Option 1 Location of I beam*

Note that there is a projection at the rear of the house, towards the right-hand side, which is 1250 mm (4'-2") wide. In this area of the house, the joist must span 4200 mm + 1150 mm = 5350 mm (14'-0" + 3'-10" = 17'-10").

It is possible to use closer spacing for joists over a short distance so that the area that can be spanned is greater.

Consulting Table 4 (Table 8)
38 mm × 235 mm (2" × 10") joists spaced at 400 mm (16") o.c. will span 4460 mm (14'-6")
38 mm × 235 mm (2" × 10") joists spaced at 300 mm (12") o.c. will span 5050 mm (16'-5")
In neither of these cases will a 38 mm × 235 mm (2" × 10") joist support the additional width of the projection.

Option 2 – For right-hand (wood siding) side of house

	Metric	Imperial
Total span = Width of RHS of house:	8990 mm	30'-0"
Less 2 × width of sill plate:	300 mm	1'-0"
Total span	= 8690 mm	= 29'-0"
Span either side of I beam	$=\dfrac{8690 \text{ mm}}{2}$	$=\dfrac{29'\text{-}0"}{2}$
	= 4345 mm	= 14'-6"

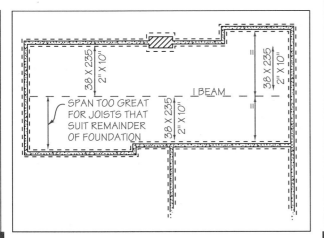

Figure 14-36B *Floor support system – Option 2 Location of I beam*

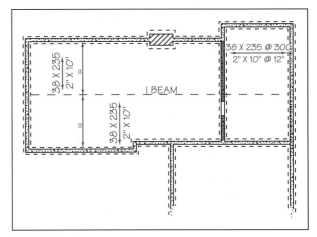

Figure 14-36C *Floor support system – Option 3 Bearing wall and I beam location*

From Table 4 (Table 8), the 38 mm × 235 mm (2" × 10") joist is suitable for this span. Note that there is a projection at the front of the house, towards the left-hand side, which is 1015 mm (3'-4") wide. In this area of the house, the joist must span 4345 mm + 1015 mm = 5360 mm (14'-6" + 3'-4" = 17'-10").

Consulting Table 4 (Table 8)
A 38 mm × 235 mm (2" × 10") joist, whether it is spaced at 400 mm (16") or 300 mm (12"), will not span the additional width.

Option 3
Divide the basement by placing a bearing wall in line with the rear projection. The right-hand end of the foundation will be separated from the remainder of the area and will have joists running from left to right of this area that can be the same size as those shown elsewhere on the foundation plan if spaced at 300 mm (12") o.c. See the following calculation.

	Metric	Imperial
Width from end of foundation to bearing wall	5500 mm	18'-0"
Less 2 × width of foundation wall	– 500 mm	– 1'-8"
Total span	= 5000 mm	= 16'-4"

A joist 38 mm × 235 mm (2" × 10") at 300 (12") o.c. will span 5050 mm (16'-5"); therefore this joist is suitable.

The calculations made in Option 1 established that a 38 mm × 235 mm (2" × 10") joist will span the 4200 mm (14'-0") distance from the exterior walls to a central I beam. This method of internal support system will be used by placing the I beam through the left-hand side of the structure.

**PART B
CALCULATIONS TO DETERMINE THE SIZE OF THE I BEAM AND THE NUMBER OF LALLY COLUMNS TO BE USED**

	Metric	Imperial
Distance to be spanned = length of house	21 270 mm	70'-10"
Less distance from bearing wall:	– 5500 mm	– 18'-0"
	= 15 770 mm	= 52'-10"
Less width of one foundation wall:	– 250 mm	– 10"
	= 15 520 mm	= 52'-0"

Distance to be spanned if three lally columns are used:

Number of columns + 1 = 4

Span either side of I beam:

$$= \frac{15\ 520\ \text{mm}}{4} \qquad = \frac{52'\text{-}0''}{4}$$
$$= 3880\ \text{mm} \qquad = 13'\text{-}0''$$

Select the size of I beam by using Table 5 (Table 9) at the end of this book.

Column 1 – Select the number of storeys (one).

Columns 4-8 – Select the column for width (2) of the floor to be supported = 4200 mm (14'-0"); therefore select column 7.

Column 7 – Select the first number in that column that is greater than the distance to be spanned. In the above example, using three lally columns, the I beam must span 3880 mm (13'-0"). The next larger number is 3890 mm (15'-0").

Columns 2-3 – Read off along the same line the size of the I beam for the span that has been selected.

Answer: I 127 @ 14.88 kg/m (I 7" @ 15.3 ft/lbs)

ALTERNATIVE

Distance to be spanned if two lally columns are used:

Number of columns + 1 = 3

Span either side of I beam $= \dfrac{15\ 520\ \text{mm}}{3} = \dfrac{52'\text{-}0''}{3}$
$$= 5173\ \text{mm} \quad = 17'\text{-}4''$$

According to Table 5 (Table 9), Column 7, to use the lally columns, the I beams must span 5173 mm (17'-4"). The next larger number on the chart is 5380 mm (17'-6").

Columns 2-3 – Read off along the same line the size of the I beam for the span that has been selected.

Answer: I 152 @ 23.07 kg/m (I 8" @ 18.4 ft/lbs)

Either of these I beams and the number of lally columns is suitable. The choice will depend on the current cost of steel and the way in which the basement might ultimately be divided. In the example, three lally columns have been selected.

TO CONTINUE DRAWING THE FOUNDATION PLAN

Additional symbols must be added to the foundation plan to show where the I beam, lally columns, and joists are to be located.

Draw in the I beam using long dashes (10 mm [1/2"]), and divide the span of the I beam so that the desired number of lally columns is shown with the correct-sized footing pads for the number of storeys of the house.

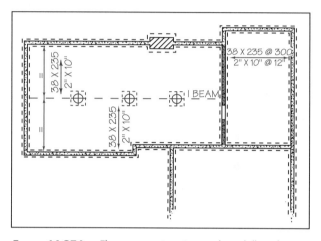

FIGURE 14-37A *Floor support system – three lally columns*

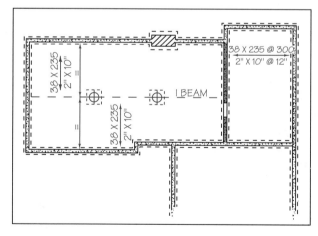

FIGURE 14-37B *Floor support system – two lally columns*

Size of Footing Pads	Metric	Imperial
One-storey	650 mm	2' - 2"
Two-storey	860 mm	2' -10"

TO CONTINUE DIMENSIONING THE FOUNDATION PLAN

Locate the I beam or bearing wall by placing dimensions through the width of the foundation. Give the size of the I beam directly on top of the dashed line that represents it *(see Fig. 14-38)*.

With a complete row of dimensions across the foundation, locate each of the lally columns and show the size of the footings required to support them.

Next, in several convenient places, insert the symbol showing the size and direction of the joists on the plan.

To complete the foundation plan, an electrical plan, a furnace, and plumbing must be added. Refer to the next unit of this chapter.

Foundation Plan Checklist

	Thickness of Foundation Walls	Thickness of Footings	Size of Pads for Lally Columns
One-Storey	200 mm (8")	150 mm (6")	650 mm (2' - 0")
Two-Storey	250 mm (10")	200 mm (8")	860 mm (2' -10")

1. Is the foundation plan on sheet one of the working drawings and is the plot plan on the same sheet?
2. Is the foundation plan drawn to the same scale and oriented on the sheet the same way as the floor plan?
3. Are the correct symbols shown for poured concrete, concrete blocks, and footings?
4. Has the foundation wall thickness been shown?
5. Does the overall size of the foundation relate to the size of the floor plan according to whether brick veneer or wood siding is used?
6. Are the direction, size, and spacing of floor joists shown in each area of the basement?
7. Is the main beam size shown and its location dimensioned?
8. Is the beam supported by lally columns or piers that have individual footings for which the sizes are given?
9. Are the lally columns or pier locations dimensioned?
10. Are the stairs clear of foundation supports and of the I beam?
11. Does the location of the stairs relate to the floor plan and have the stairs been dimensioned on the foundation plan?
12. Have the foundation windows been shown and have lintels for support of the wall above the windows been indicated?
13. Has the garage been shown supported by a foundation wall and footings and is it marked *unexcavated* in the centre?
14. Has the chimney been extended to the foundations and are the footings 300 mm (12") thick?
15. Does the dimensioning correspond to that shown in the diagram on page 332?

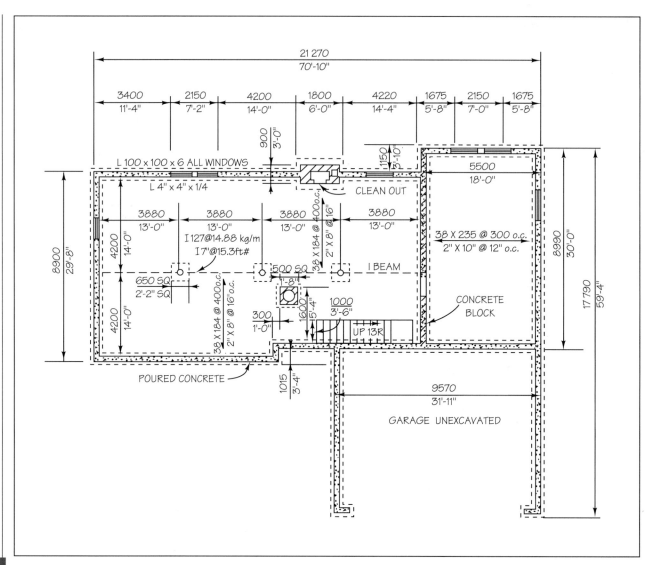

FIGURE 14-38 *Dimensioning the complete foundation plan*

REVIEW QUESTIONS

1. What are some alternative ways of providing an internal support system for the floors and furniture of a house?
2. Why must load-bearing walls, piers, and lally columns have footings?
3. Describe how the foundations for a crawl space would differ from those required for a full-depth foundation.

WHAT DO YOU THINK?

1. Why must the spans given in the *National and Provincial Building Codes* be adhered to rigidly?
2. Why would you prefer to put an I beam supported by lally columns in the foundation of a new house instead of building a bearing wall?

ASSIGNMENTS

1. For Chapter 14, Unit 3, Assignment 1, you drew a perimeter foundation plan of your house or a friend's house. Review that plan and add any further information regarding the foundation that you have acquired from this chapter. Complete this foundation plan.
2. For the foundation plan provided by your instructor, determine the correct sizes of the I beam, lally column spacing, and joists or use a bearing wall as a floor support system.
   Completely dimension the plan as for a working drawing. Use the checklist at the end of this chapter.
3. Complete the foundation plan for the two-storey house supplied for Chapter 14, Unit 2, Assignment 1 and used for Chapter 14, Unit 3, Assignment 2 by selecting the correct I beam, lally columns, and joist sizes or by using a bearing wall as a floor support system for this structure. Add any other details that are necessary. Use the checklist at the end of this chapter.

UNIT 5

Electrical Heating and Plumbing Plans

OBJECTIVES

- To understand the various uses of electricity in modern homes
- To learn basic electrical terms
- To become familiar with the electrical symbols used in drafting
- To design an electrical plan for working drawings
- To understand the residential plumbing system and how it relates to working drawings
- To be able to compare various heating and cooling systems

During the last decade, the role of electricity in contemporary households has expanded dramatically. Lighting, cooking, and heating are no longer the only domestic applications using electrical current. Electronic equipment, intercom systems, central vacuum systems, and central air-conditioning are common features in some modern houses. The number of small household electrical appliances has increased considerably. Naturally, these changes have increased the demand for the generation and distribution of more electrical power.

FIGURE 14-39 *A modern kitchen*

Idea Place, Pickering Home and Design Centre; Wares & Wares; Photo: Gwen Williams

RESIDENTIAL ELECTRICAL SERVICE

The electrical service entry is the point at which a power supply enters a house from the transmission line, and it is also the location for the utility company's meter that measures the consumption of electricity by the household. These meters are placed outside the house on the driveway side for easy reading by utility officials and must be within 3000 mm (10' -0") of the front of a house.

Inside the house, the bulk power supply panel, which is located near the service entry and should be in a position that is readily accessible in an emergency, is separated into a number of branches or circuits.

These circuits are controlled by fuses or circuit breakers, which are an integral part of the service panel. Other special service circuits service higher-rated electrical equipment such as a stove, a freezer, or a central air-conditioning system. These special service circuits can be controlled by sub-panels which are located near the equipment that they serve. It is not unusual to have as many as six sub-panels linked to the main panel.

A house designer does not have to detail the circuits and how they fit into the overall electrical system. However, a designer should have a knowledge of the power consumption or rating of various standard appliances and be familiar with the more common electrical terms.

COMMON ELECTRICAL TERMS

There are three different types of measurement applied to electrical current.

Voltage is the pressure applied to electrons in order to cause electrical motion in a circuit (similar to the pressure found in a water supply system). The SI symbol for volt is V.

Amperage is used to specify the rate of flow (similar to the amount of water that passes through the water system when a tap is turned on). The SI symbol for ampere is A.

Wattage combines the measurements of voltage and amperage, thus establishing the amount of electricity used. That is:

$1 \text{ A} \times 1 \text{ V}$ = 1 W
1 W used for 1 h = 1 W·h
1000 W used for 1 h = 1 kW·h

A meter records the number of kilowatt hours consumed over a set period of time, and the householder is billed accordingly by the utility company. The SI symbol for watt is W.

NECESSARY CHARACTERISTICS OF AN ELECTRICAL WIRING SYSTEM

SAFETY

Familiarity with the use of domestic electricity on a daily basis causes many people to forget that electricity can be lethal, in much the same way as we forget the family car can be lethal.

When planning a residential electrical system, great care must be taken to ensure that the system will be as safe and as child-proof as possible. All installations must comply with the government electrical code, and all work should be completed by a reputable licensed electrical contractor whose work must be inspected and approved by a government or utility company inspector. The electrical outlets in hazardous areas, such as near a swimming pool or a bathroom, require special attention to avoid the possibility that water, which is an excellent conductor of electricity, does not come in contact with live wires. To this end, outlets and appliances must be located well away from both water- and steam-laden areas, and **ground fault interrupters** must be used in outdoor and bathroom circuits. Ground fault interrupters react instantaneously to electrical leaks and prevent shocks that could cause personal injury or death. They can be inserted in a circuit either at the service panel or at specific outlets. These outlets should be marked on an electrical plan with the subscript lettering G.F.I.

CAPACITY

Collectively, residential circuits should be able to carry 50% of the full load or twice the load that is used by the household at peak power consumption times, such as early evening when stoves, hot water supplies, and various other appliances may be in use at the same time.

Special electrical circuits, such as those serving major appliances, should be served by a circuit at the voltage for which the appliance is designed and with sufficient amperage to maintain the appliance at *full efficiency* when it is operating at maximum usage.

CONTROL

Switches and outlets should be positioned so that they are within easy reach of adults yet not accessible to small children. Outlets should be sufficiently numerous that lamps and appliances can be operated with minimal use of extension cords.

ISOLATION

Automatically switched and motor-driven appliances should be served by individual circuits so that lights, television, and computerized equipment, which are all very sensitive to fluctuations in electrical current, will not be affected.

TYPES OF CIRCUITS

There should be approximately 24 general purpose circuits in an average house, plus six special circuits. The electrician will wire the house in accordance with standard practices and will determine which circuits will control the various appliances and outlets in the house. The designer should be aware of the various types of circuits that are used in case of special design requirements.

General-purpose residential circuits in North America are usually wired for 110/120 V and 15 A and are designed to serve lighting fixtures and convenience outlets to which small appliances such as lamps, radios, and clocks can be connected. A general-purpose circuit is constructed of 14 B and S gauge wire and has a 1800 W rating.

Appliance circuits have 120 V and 15 A ratings and serve **split receptacle** outlets, which are used mainly for kitchen applications. Usually they serve two outlets only. Split receptacles have separate circuits running to each of the dual sockets in each outlet so that the sockets are isolated from each other electrically. This arrangement will allow two heating elements, which are high energy-consuming appliances, to be operated from the same receptacle simultaneously. A kitchen will normally have at least three split receptacle outlets installed 150 mm (6") above counter height. This type of circuit uses a 3-wire 14-gauge cable that will be grounded.

Circuits with high ratings must be provided for appliances such as stoves, dishwashers, and central air conditioners. These circuits will be wired for 220 V with amperages varying to suit particular requirements. Refrigerators and microwave ovens do not usually require special circuits.

PARTS OF THE ELECTRICAL SYSTEM

LIGHTING

The prime use for electricity in a home is to provide illumination. General lighting is required in all areas of the house to allow good visual control throughout.

Additional area lighting must be available for special tasks such as cooking, reading, craftwork, or using a computer. The range of lighting includes non-glare, fluorescent, indirect, and spot lighting. The most affordable type of fixture that will provide the required amount of lighting for the task should be selected to illuminate all major work sites.

SWITCHES

Wall switches are mostly used to control the area lighting in the house. Wall switches are usually placed at a height of 1200 mm (4' -0") above the floor level and are on the latch side of the door for ease of use. Exterior lights should be controlled from the inside of the house.

Any area that has two or more entrances should have a switch at each entrance, so that one does not have to retrace one's steps to turn out a light. These switches are called three-way switches and are found in garages, on stairways, and in kitchens. Any number of four-way switches can be placed between the first and last three-way switch *(see Figs. 14-40A, 14-40B, and 14-40C).*

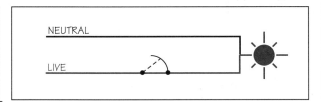

FIGURE 14-40A   *Single switch*

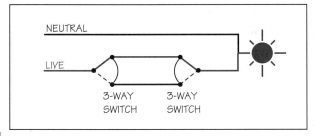

FIGURE 14-40B   *Dual switches*

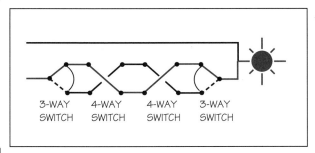

FIGURE 14-40C   *Multiple switches*

CONVENIENCE OF OUTLETS

Outlets should be placed so that no point along a wall is a greater distance than 1800 mm (6'-0") from an outlet. This means that there will be 3600 mm (12'-0") maximum between outlets. There should be one convenience outlet for every 1.4 m^2 (15 sq. ft.) of room area. Large items of furniture are usually placed centrally on long walls in a house; therefore outlets should be installed towards corners of the rooms so that they will not

be awkward to reach. Any wall that is wider than 600 mm (2'-0") should have an outlet. Convenience outlets are placed 300 mm (1'-0") above floor level except in kitchens, dining areas, and bathrooms, in which case the outlets will be above counter height.

DRAWING THE ELECTRICAL PLAN

The location of switches, lights, and convenience outlets must be shown on the working drawing for the guidance of the electrician. Standard symbols have been developed and the most used residential symbols are shown in *Fig. 14-41*. Most symbols use an 8 mm (3/16") diameter circle and are linked to the wall by perpendicular short lines. The electrical plans do not show the circuits but do show the connection between switches and lights or outlets by a fine line as shown in *Fig. 14-41*. Special convenience outlets should have sub-

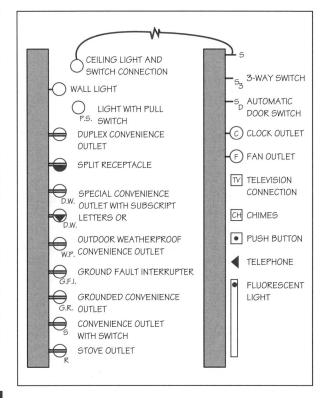

FIGURE 14-41   *Electrical symbols*

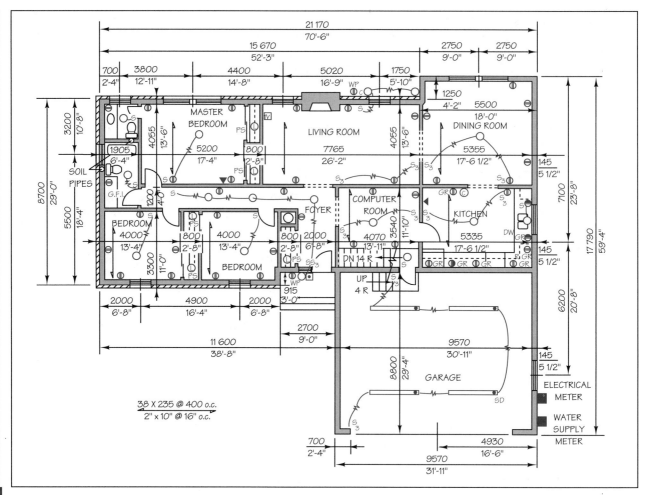

FIGURE 14-42A *Floor plan with electrical plan and plumbing features shown*

script letters to indicate their type or specific use. Electrical plans should be shown on each floor plan of the house *(see Fig. 14-42A)* including the foundation plan *(see Fig. 14-42B)*. The height of convenience outlets can be shown on interior elevation drawings when available or stated in a note *(see Fig. 14-43)*.

PLUMBING

Plumbing is another utility service, similar to the electrical system, that must be included on the floor plan drawing. However, it does not require

that the draftsperson show detailed drawings of the hook-up of pipes as the plumber will have much better knowledge of how the system should be installed. Nevertheless, the designer should have an elementary knowledge of how the plumbing system works in case special conditions necessitate specific drawings. Vertical pipes in the system are referred to as stacks and horizontal pipes as branches.

Residential plumbing consists of two separate systems:

1. the water supply system, and
2. the waste removal system.

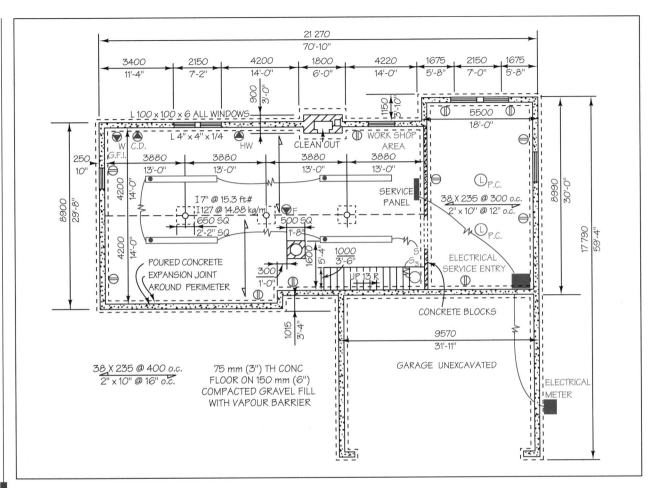

FIGURE 14-42B *Foundation plan with electrical plan*

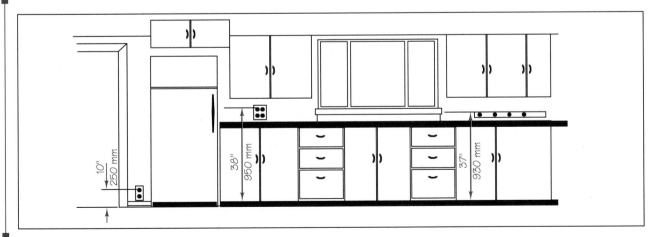

FIGURE 14-43 *The height of all outlets should be noted on wall elevations or in the specifications.*

Hepler/Wallach: *Architecture: Drafting and Design*, 5/e © 1987. Reproduced by permission of Glencoe/McGraw-Hill Educational Division.

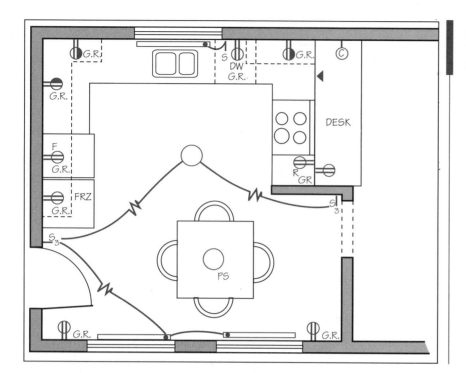

FIGURE **14-44**

Typical electrical plan for a kitchen with eating area

THE WATER SUPPLY SYSTEM

Fresh water is supplied to a house either from a public supply system or from a private well. In either case, the water is fed through the lines under pressure. It is possible to run the pipes in any direction although it is unwise to create too many bends in the pipes as this will reduce the pressure of water at the tap.

A shut-off valve is introduced where the public water supply crosses the property line and an additional shut-off valve and meter are required where the water supply enters the building.

Branch lines, which supply cold water, are routed to the appropriate kitchen, laundry, and bathroom fixtures throughout the house. An additional branch of the water supply is diverted through the hot water heater so that all sinks can be supplied with hot water. It is customary to place the hot water faucet on the left side of each fixture. Shut-off valves are located close to each fixture so that repairs can be facilitated when necessary *(see Fig. 14-45A)*.

The water supply pipes are the smallest pipes and are usually 20 mm to 25 mm (3/4" to 1") in diameter.

THE WASTE REMOVAL SYSTEM

The waste-water lines in the system consist of drainage from all sinks and baths and soil lines, which remove waste from each toilet. All drainage is by gravity into the public sewers. The lines in the waste removal system must therefore slant downwards. Soil lines are bigger in size than any of the other lines and should have as straight a run as possible to the house sewer to prevent clogging. All waste lines should be concealed in the floors and walls.

Vents are a necessary part of the waste system. Vent stacks run to the roof and allow gases to escape into the air; they also provide air circulation and help to equalize the pressure in the drainage system. Fixture traps are also necessary to prevent a backflow of sewer gas from entering the house and are exposed to allow for ease of maintenance. Toilets have a trap with a water seal built into the actual fixture *(see Fig. 14-45B)*.

Septic Tank Systems

When a house is a great distance from the public sewer system, a septic tank is used. A septic tank system consists of a container, in which the solid

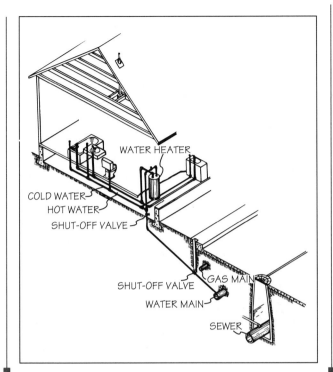

FIGURE 14-45A *Water supply system*

Hepler/Wallach: *Architecture: Drafting and Design*, 5/e © 1987.
Reproduced by permission of Glencoe/McGraw-Hill Educational Division.

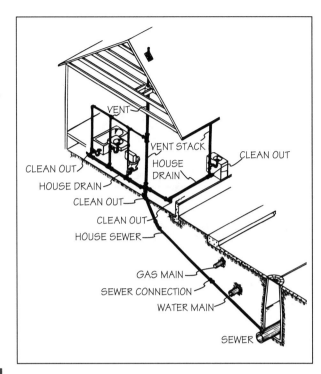

FIGURE 14-45B *Waste removal system*

Hepler/Wallach: *Architecture: Drafting and Design*, 5/e © 1987.
Reproduced by permission of Glencoe/McGraw-Hill Educational Division.

matter is converted into a liquid by bacterial action, and a pattern of pipes, which discharges the waste liquid over a wide area called an absorption field. A septic tank must be positioned some distance from the dwelling as is specified in the building code. The location of the tank and the area of drainage should be shown on the plot plan (*see Fig. 14-46*).

PLUMBING ON THE FLOOR PLAN

It is usually unnecessary to show the plumbing system in detail on the working drawing of the floor plan, but the location of all kitchen and bathroom sinks, baths, and any other water supply outlets such as exterior hose bibs and roughed-in plumbing should be shown. Soil pipes will go from behind each toilet and be shown going through all floor levels to the basement. Soil pipes are drawn as circles in the walls and labelled.

Occasionally because of special conditions, it may be necessary to make a schematic drawing of a run of pipes. See *Fig. 14-47* for symbols to be used on the drawing and for line styles associated with the system.

HEATING AND COOLING SYSTEMS

The air inside most houses completely changes approximately ten times a day. This is caused by the opening of doors and windows and by infiltration, which is air coming in through various cracks in the structure. Cold air is therefore constantly entering the house during the winter, and hot air is entering during the summer. Caulking can slow down this process but does not retard it altogether.

As well as heat loss or gain from infiltration, the temperature of the air inside the house will change because of heat being lost through the materials that the house is made of. Insulation

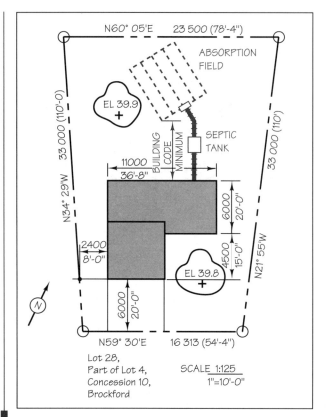

FIGURE 14-46 *Plot plan showing septic tank system*

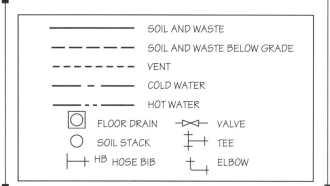

FIGURE 14-47 *Plumbing symbols*

can be added to diminish the rate that heat is lost to the outside, but it would be too costly to provide sufficient insulation to prevent heat loss in a house altogether. Therefore, it is necessary in most areas to have a heating and/or a cooling system to ensure that the temperature in the house remains at a comfortable level.

TYPES OF HEATING SYSTEMS

Various types of furnaces can be used to produce heat by burning such fuels as natural gas, oil, wood, or coal; some furnaces heat by electricity. The major types of heating systems are listed.

Warm-Air Heating

Warm air is distributed to the house by means of metal or plastic ducts that run between the studs in the walls or the joists in the floor. Warm air enters the rooms through air registers placed in the floor or walls. Some air units are operated by gravity. The warm air that is lighter rises and the cold air descends to be drawn into the furnace and reheated. This action tends to move the warm air around the house. Most contemporary houses use a forced-air system. In these units, a fan in the furnace blows air into the ducts for distribution *(see Figs. 14-48A and 14-48B)*. This method is very popular because a central air-conditioning unit can use the same ducts and fan unit to distribute cool air. However, for cooling it is preferable to have air registers higher in the wall. Cold air will flow downwards whereas hot air will rise. However, few people wish to have two sets of duct work installed in their home.

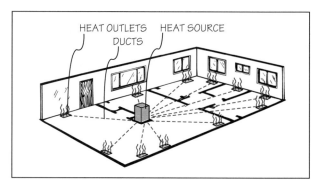

FIGURE 14-48A *Warm-air perimeter heating*

Hepler/Wallach: *Architecture: Drafting and Design*, 5/e © 1987.
Reproduced by permission of Glencoe/McGraw-Hill Educational Division.

Hot-Water Heating

The heat from the furnace is used to heat a boiler. The hot water is conveyed by a pump to radiators or baseboard outlets located throughout the house *(see Fig. 14-48C)*. Although this system is

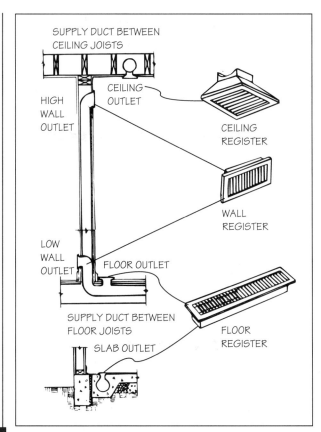

FIGURE 14-48B *Warm-air outlets*

Hepler/Wallach: *Architecture: Drafting and Design*, 5/e © 1987.
Reproduced by permission of Glencoe/McGraw-Hill Educational Division.

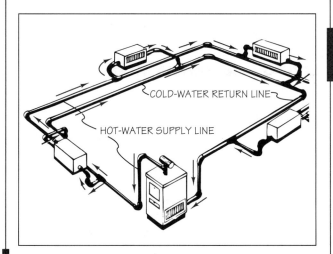

FIGURE 14-48C *Two-pipe hot-water series loop system*

Hepler/Wallach: *Architecture: Drafting and Design*, 5/e © 1987.
Reproduced by permission of Glencoe/McGraw-Hill Educational Division.

easier to install because of the small size of the pipes compared to the size of the ducting required for air systems, it is not generally as popular for residential houses because it is not compatible with air conditioning.

Electrical Radiant Heating

An electrical current is passed through resistant wires so that heat is produced. These wires can be placed in ceilings, walls, or floors or can be contained in individual units such as baseboard heaters. Electrical radiant heating is quiet, clean, and safe. However, it does tend to dry the atmosphere so good ventilation must be provided. One of the major advantages of electrical radiant heating is that it can be controlled by a separate thermostat in each room and therefore is completely flexible and conserves energy *(see Fig. 14-48D)*.

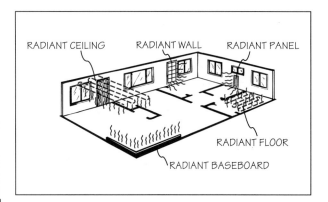

FIGURE 14-48D *Electrical radiant heating*

Hepler/Wallach: *Architecture: Drafting and Design*, 5/e © 1987.
Reproduced by permission of Glencoe/McGraw-Hill Educational Division.

A heat pump, another device that is operated electrically, can be used to bring heat in from the outside in the winter and reversed to cool the house in the summer. This device uses the same technology as used in a refrigerator for cooling and is explained in Chapter 3, Unit 2.

Solar Heating and Cooling Systems

Methods of active and passive solar heating were also discussed in Chapter 3, Unit 2. However, in climates where there is a large proportion of below-freezing days, a back-up heating unit is necessary.

Thermostat Controls

A thermostat is used with all the systems that have been outlined. The thermostat activates and controls the amount of heating or cooling required. Thermostat controls should always be placed on interior walls well away from heating outlets, windows, or fireplaces.

ADDING A HEATING SYSTEM TO FLOOR PLANS

Experience is required to correctly place ducts and registers in order that a house be heated uniformly. Because of this, it is left to the heating and ventilating professionals to install the system. The draftsperson is not required to indicate how the heating system will be installed. The heating system should be specified in a note on the drawing or as part of the general specifications.

COMPLETING THE FOUNDATION PLAN

Add the following items to the dimensioned foundation plan.

1. A complete electrical plan with adequate lighting over the stairs. Three-way switches should be installed to control this light from the upper and lower floors. Also show the electrical service entry and panel.
2. A plumbing plan that indicates tubs, a hot water tank, roughed-in plumbing, laundry facilities, if required, plus a floor drain and sump pump to remove water that may have seeped into the foundation. Also show the water service entry. *Note:* All plumbing should be concentrated in one area of the foundation, if possible, to avoid costly runs of piping and ensure the efficiency of the water-supply system.
3. The heating system – a furnace located on a footing pad that is in close proximity to a flue.
4. Details of floor construction, such as thickness of gravel bed and concrete floor, added as a note. An expansion joint around the perimeter of the floor should also be indicated *(see Fig. 14-49)*.

CHECKLIST FOR ELECTRICAL, PLUMBING, AND HEATING PLAN

You may not wish to incorporate all the features mentioned but the checklist will prevent unnecessary omissions.

ENTRY AND EXTERIOR OUTLETS

1. Is there sufficient general illumination at the front and rear doors for people arriving in the dark and as security lighting?
2. Is the number of the house clearly illuminated as well as the lock and doorbell?
3. Are all the outside lights controlled from the interior?
4. Are there convenience outlets at the front and rear doors? Are the outlets waterproof and do they have a ground fault interrupter?
5. Is there a hose bib located at the front of the house and at the rear?

HALLWAYS AND STAIRS

1. Are the switches for the hallway lighting and the exterior lighting close to the entry and on the latch side of the doorway?
2. Is there good lighting over the stairs and is this controlled by a three-way switch at the top and bottom of the stairway?
3. Is there a convenience outlet for each 4500 mm (15' -0") length of hallway and on any landing for use of a vacuum cleaner and a night light?
4. Is there a concealed outlet for a fire and smoke detector?

LIVING AND FAMILY ROOM

1. Is there a switch located at the main entrance for the room that will control an outlet for a lamp?
2. Are there sufficient outlets to provide general illumination or has indirect ceiling or valance lighting been suggested?
3. Is there electrical provision for local spot lighting for reading or other activities?
4. Are there concealed outlets for decorative lighting, for wall units, or picture illumination?
5. Are dimmer switches being used to control the lighting effects?
6. Are there convenient outlets for a vacuum cleaner, television, or other appropriate appliances?

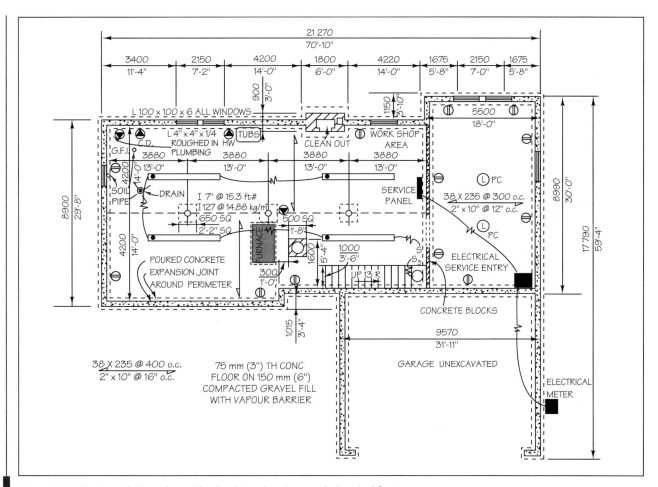

Figure 14-49 *Foundation plan with plumbing, heating, and electrical features*

DINING AREA

1. Is there a permanent lighting fixture over the eating area and appropriate switches at the entries?
2. Are there sufficient outlets for a vacuum cleaner and other appliances?
3. Is there a table-height split receptacle outlet for heating trays, a coffee maker, etc.?
4. Are there concealed outlets for cabinet and picture illumination?

KITCHEN

1. Is general illumination provided by a central fixture or lighting panels and is this lighting controlled by a three-way switch at each entry?
2. Is there local lighting over the sink, work areas, etc.?

3. Are there local convenience outlets for the refrigerator and microwave oven?
4. Is there a concealed outlet for a clock?
5. Have special-purpose outlets been added for the stove, dishwasher, etc.?
6. Have split receptacles been provided for every 1200 mm (4' -0") of counter top? Are there a minimum of three split receptacles?
7. Is the plumbing for a dishwasher located close to the main sink area?

BATHROOMS

1. Is there adequate lighting on the same wall as the mirror?

2. Is there an electrical outlet that is rated at 15 A suitably positioned for the use of a hairdryer or an electric razor?
3. Are all convenience outlets some distance from the bath for safety reasons and have they a ground fault interrupter?
4. Is there a ventilating fan, particularly if there is no exterior window?
5. Is there an access panel for plumbing behind the bath?

BASEMENT, LAUNDRY ROOM, UTILITY AREAS

1. Is there sufficient area lighting?
2. Are the furnace and water heater wired directly into the system?
3. Are there special-purpose outlets for the washer and dryer?
4. Is there a ventilating fan, particularly if there is no exterior window?

5. Are there sufficient electrical receptacles available?
6. Is there roughed-in plumbing in the basement for a future washroom?
7. Is all the plumbing located in one area?
8. Are the furnace and flue in close proximity to each other?

GARAGE

1. Are there three-way switches controlling the lighting at all doors?
2. Is there good area lighting?
3. Is there at least one convenience outlet and more if a workshop is planned in this area?
4. Has an automatic door opener been planned?

Is there an adequate supply of electricity into the house so that additional equipment can be added in the future?

REVIEW QUESTIONS

1. What is a kilowatt-hour and what connection does it have with amps and volts?
2. What symbols should be shown on an electrical plan?
3. What are the two main parts of a plumbing system?
4. Name three types of heating systems.

WHAT DO YOU THINK?

1. How many electrical outlets are installed in the modern contemporary house?
2. What safety devices would you incorporate into an electrical system?
3. Why are detailed drawings of electrical, plumbing, and heating systems not usually required on floor plans?
4. Why is a forced-air system becoming popular in modern houses?

ASSIGNMENTS

1. On the floor plan of your own home or a friend's home drawn for Chapter 9, Unit 5, Assignment 2,
   a. add the electrical system as it exists;
   b. add the plumbing and heating systems as they exist.
2. On the floor plan of the main floor, upper storey, and foundation plan developed during this chapter from a floor plan supplied by the instructor, add an electrical plan and show the necessary symbols for the plumbing and heating systems. Check your drawing against the checklist contained in this unit.

WORKING DRAWINGS

THE PROJECT

By this time you will have made a formal presentation to the clients and should have come to a final agreement regarding the design of the house. Changes should not be anticipated after this stage.

Now you are ready to begin the set of working drawings from which the builder will construct the building.

Step 20 – Making a plot plan:

Carefully check the survey drawing with the site plan. Check any revisions to see that they are compatible with the available building space. The plot plan is primarily to show the location of the house on the lot. If the lot is an average size, it should be drawn to a scale of 1:250 or 1:125 (1" = 20' - 0" or 1" = 10' - 0").

Step 21 – Drawing the ground floor plan:

a. If there are a limited number of changes requested by the client, alter the basic floor plan for use as the working drawing. If there are a number of constructional changes, redraw the floor plan accurately to incorporate these changes.

b. Fully dimension the floor plan using the three-line system and add other dimensions as required.

c. Calculate the joist sizes using Table 6 (Table 10) in the Appendix and add joist symbols in appropriate areas.

Step 22 – Drawing the upper-storey and floor plan:

a. The upper storey can be drawn by tracing over the major features of the floor plan such as the exterior walls, chimneys, stairways, and major partitions. When these are in the correct position, complete the upper-storey floor plan.

b. Dimension the upper storey using the three-line dimension system and add other dimensions as required.

c. Calculate the joist sizes using Table 7 (Table 11) in the Appendix and add in the appropriate places.

Step 23 – Drawing the foundation plan:

a. The foundation plan should now be traced from the floor plan, taking care to enlarge the sides of the foundation by 100 mm (4") on each side where there is to be brick veneer applied to the superstructure. Add footings in hidden lines on either side of the foundation wall.

Dimension the plan by placing overall dimensions and the size and location of windows outside the drawing. Also locate the stairway and give the wall thickness.

b. Calculate the size of joists, I beams, and lally columns that will support the interior of the house using Tables 4 and 5 (Tables 8 and 9) in the Appendix.

Dimension the interior supports to complete the working foundation plan.

c. Add heating and plumbing equipment.

Step 24 – Addition to floor plans:

a. Add electrical outlets and switches as required to each floor plan. Check that three-way switches and split receptacles are used in appropriate places. Exterior electrical connections should be included.

b. All plumbing features should have been designed to be in one area of the house and vertically above each other. Check that all soil stacks are shown running vertically down to the basement.

| Sections and
Elevations for
Working Drawings

A SECTION THAT SHOWS the construction details of a typical wall is a necessary part of the working drawings. Other sections, such as door jamb details, a section through a fireplace, or through the entire house, can be incorporated as needed.

The elevations, which also form part of the working drawings, must be consistent with both the wall section and the floor plan design. The purpose of the working drawing elevations is different from the elevations drawn for the presentation drawings, which was to indicate the style of the building to the clients. The elevations that form part of the working drawings not only will show the exterior materials and the specific types of windows, doors, and roofs to be used in the structure but will also provide dimensions for the roof and relative heights of the various elements that make up the structure, including the foundation. All four elevations will be required for a set of working drawings.

Window and door schedules are a vital part of the working drawings as they chart the sizes, type, and manufacturers who will supply these items and are a quick reference when ordering.

UNIT 1 | Wall Sections and Roof Trusses

OBJECTIVES

- To identify the common methods of house construction
- To understand the purpose of a wall section
- To know how a house is constructed
- To draw a wall section
- To recognize the advantages and disadvantages of roof trusses

There are several methods of constructing a house, such as building one of solid masonry or using either concrete blocks, cinder blocks, poured concrete, or bricks. Houses can also be constructed of wood. In North America, the most frequently used material is wood, as it is an easy material to work with, it absorbs moisture, and it is in relatively good supply.

TYPES OF WOOD CONSTRUCTION

There are three major methods of wood house construction.

Platform framing is the most frequently used. On each floor level, a platform is constructed consisting of horizontal pieces of lumber called joists; each wall is a framework made of vertical pieces of lumber called studs. Because platforms are constructed at each floor level, the building is less hazardous to work on than those with other types of construction *(see Fig. 15-1A)*. The studs frame only one storey at a time so the frames can be usually put together on the platform and then raised into a vertical position. This type of framing is less costly and easier to make than balloon framing.

Balloon framing requires studs that are long enough to frame two storeys at the same time. In this type of construction, the walls are built in the vertical position, which is more difficult than assembling them on the ground.

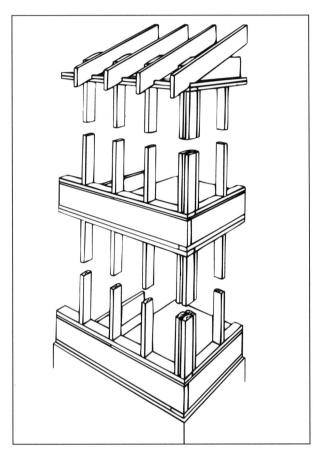

FIGURE 15-1A *Platform construction*

From Ernest R. Weidhaas, *Architectural Drafting and Design*, Sixth Edition, Copyright © 1989 by Allyn and Bacon. Reprinted with permission.

If a building is to be faced with stucco, balloon framing should be used, because the long studs will expand consistently *(see Fig. 15-1B)*. Platform framing expands irregularly because it is made up of several lengths of lumber positioned both lengthways and crossways *(see Fig. 15-1A)*.

Post-and-beam construction is used when curtain walls are to form the exterior of a building. Curtain walls are not intended to carry loads. An example of this is a building where large areas

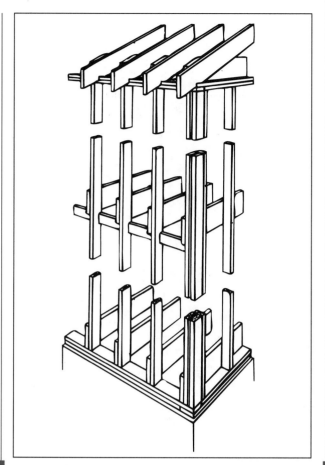

FIGURE 15-1B *Balloon (or platform) construction*

From Ernest R. Weidhaas, *Architectural Drafting and Design*, Sixth Edition, Copyright © 1989 by Allyn and Bacon. Reprinted with permission.

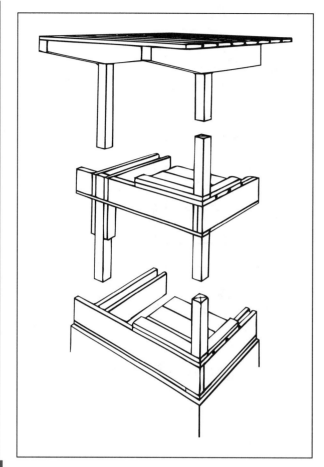

FIGURE 15-1C *Post-and-beam construction*

From Ernest R. Weidhaas, *Architectural Drafting and Design*, Sixth Edition, Copyright © 1989 by Allyn and Bacon. Reprinted with permission.

of glass are used on the exterior. In this case, the load of the roof must be carried by columns that are placed at regular intervals along the wall *(see Fig. 15-1C).*

Post-and-beam construction can be combined with platform or balloon framing.

In this text we shall deal with platform framing only.

THE WALL SECTION

All sets of working drawings should include a typical wall section, which is an imaginary cut made through a wall to show how all the various ele-

ments of the wall fit together. *Figs. 15-2A and 15-2B* show simple wall sections, with minimal notation, which will enable you to identify the various elements.

In section drawing, special symbols are used to identify various materials. These symbols are illustrated in *Fig. 15-3.*

Initially, wall sections may appear to be very complicated, but if they are studied a portion at a time, they are not difficult to understand.

Because wall sections are drawn at a comparatively large scale so that all the elements can be identified clearly, the drawing is apt to be very long and narrow. Break lines are used to reduce the height of the drawing to avoid an awkward

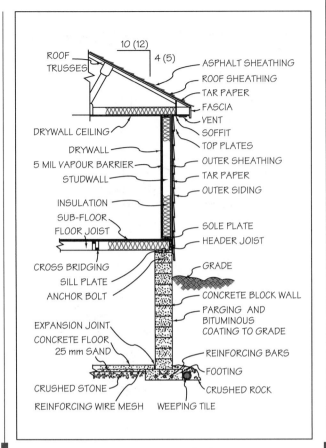

FIGURE 15-2A *Wall section, wood siding, one storey with truss roof*

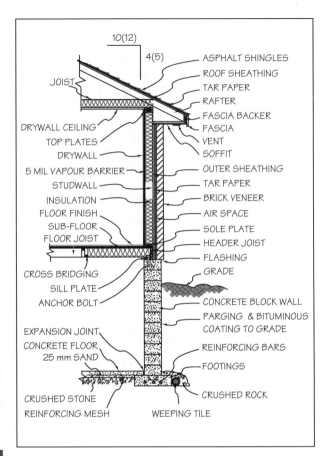

FIGURE 15-2B *Wall section, brick veneer, one storey with rafters forming roof*

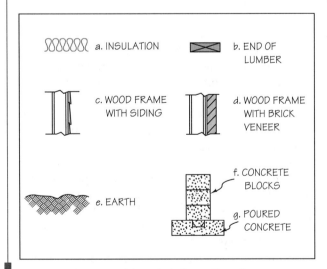

FIGURE 15-3 *Material symbols for wall sections*

arrangement of the section on the sheet. The break lines are placed where there is no change of materials, for example, half-way up the foundation wall or the first storey wall *(see Fig. 15-4)*.

The most vital parts of a wall section are those where changes do occur, such as at the footings, the sill, the second-storey platform, and the cornice. Two types of wall sections are shown in this chapter, a single storey *(see Figs. 15-2A and 15-2B)* and a two storey *(see Figs. 15-5A and 15-5B)*.

The **footing section** shows how the foundation wall is keyed to the footings. Footings are monolithic, that is, they are made of poured concrete with no joins. The footings are twice the width of the foundation wall and are one-and-a-half times the size of the projection either side of the wall, in depth.

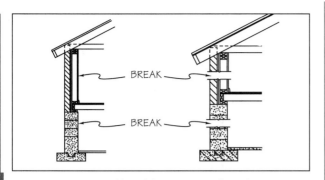

FIGURE 15-4   *Use of break lines on a wall section*

Courtesy of CMHC: Canadian Wood Frame House Construction

The foundation wall can be made of concrete blocks or of poured concrete. For a two-storey house or a house with a brick veneer exterior, the foundation walls must be 250 mm (10") thick. For a single-storey house with wood siding, the concrete wall need only be 200 mm (8") thick.

Concrete block foundation walls are parged to provide a smooth surface by coating the outside with a 6 mm (1/4") thick mixture of Portland cement plaster. This coating is then scratched so that an additional layer of bituminous damp-proofing material can be applied. This coating

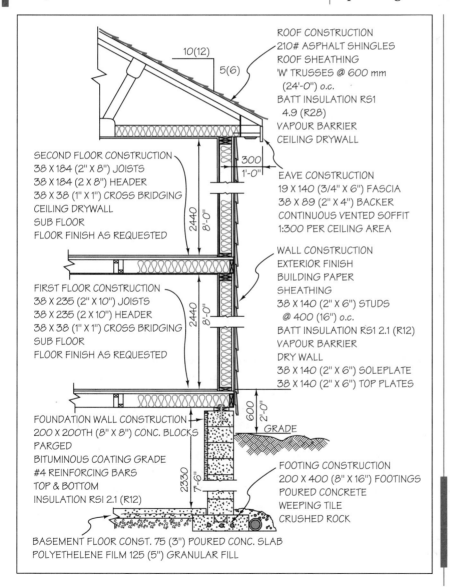

FIGURE 15-5A

Wall section, wood siding, two storey, platform construction with wood siding showing material and sizes

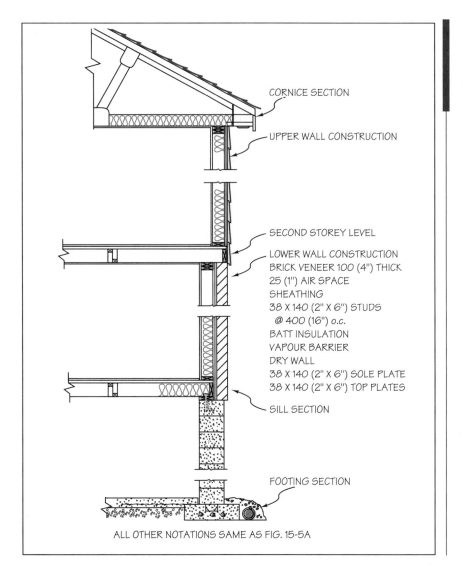

FIGURE 15-5B

Wall section two storey platform construction with brick veneer and wood siding, showing material and sizes

CORNICE SECTION

UPPER WALL CONSTRUCTION

SECOND STOREY LEVEL

LOWER WALL CONSTRUCTION
BRICK VENEER 100 (4") THICK
25 (1") AIR SPACE
SHEATHING
38 X 140 (2" X 6") STUDS
@ 400 (16") o.c.
BATT INSULATION
VAPOUR BARRIER
DRY WALL
38 X 140 (2" X 6") SOLE PLATE
38 X 140 (2" X 6") TOP PLATES

SILL SECTION

FOOTING SECTION

ALL OTHER NOTATIONS SAME AS FIG. 15-5A

extends from the footings to the grade level. Poured concrete walls are similarly damp-proofed with bituminous material.

The drain tiles and gravel bed that surround the perimeter of a foundation are shown at the base of a wall section drawing. Drain tile usually takes the form of a plastic tube 100 mm (4") in diameter; it is perforated so that water can seep into it. Drawings should not show gravel in place under the footings as they must always be constructed on undisturbed ground.

A concrete basement floor is supported by the footings but rests on a cushion of sand 25 mm (1")

all around the inner edge of the footing projection. The floor is usually made of poured concrete and is bordered by an expansion joint, which helps to prevent cracking of the concrete as a result of temperature changes. A basement floor slab is a minimum of 75 mm (3") thick, and it is reinforced with steel mesh that is placed one-third from the bottom when the concrete is poured. The slab is supported underneath by 125 mm (5") of coarse fill with a 0.10 mm polyethylene film between the slab and the fill to ensure that the floor will be damp-proof. All the elements mentioned can be identified in *Figs. 15-2A and 15-2B*.

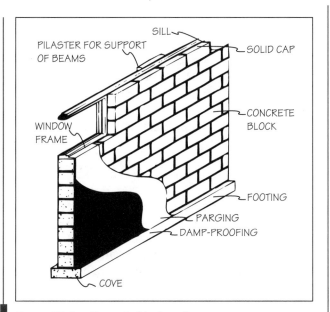

FIGURE 15-6   *Concrete block walls*

Courtesy of CMHC: Canadian Wood Frame House Construction

The **sill section** shows how the foundation wall supports and intersects the floor system.

To fasten the wooden superstructure of a house to the foundation, a series of anchor bolts 12.7 mm (3/8") diameter is embedded into the top of the wall, spaced at 2400 mm (8'-0") intervals. When using concrete blocks that have large airholes in them, it is necessary to cap the top row with 60 mm (2 1/2") of solid masonry. To achieve this, the air spaces in the blocks must be filled with concrete to hold the bolts. The joists that support a first-storey floor are shown lengthwise together with the header, which is the same size but which runs perpendicularly to the joists along the outer edge of the wall. A sub-floor is installed on top of the joists and extends under the sole plate, which is the bottom member of the wall frame.

The wall itself consists of studs that are usually 38 mm × 89 mm (2" × 4") and are spaced at 400 mm (16") on centres. When an extra thickness of insulation is to be installed, the studs are increased to 38 mm × 140 mm (2" × 6") thick. In *Fig. 15-2A*, the wall is shown as being faced with building paper and sheathing under wood siding.

A brick veneer-faced wall is shown in *Fig. 15-2B*. Note that there is a 25 mm (1") gap between the bricks and the frame wall. This gap allows moisture to dissipate over a period of time. Also, the foundation wall is extended beyond the frame wall at the foundation level to allow the bricks to be seated on the top edge of the wall.

On the interior side of the walls, studs are covered with a vapour barrier and then drywall or plaster is applied. The spaces between the studs are filled with insulation. All these elements can be identified on the wall section.

Fig. 15-5A shows a two-storey wall section with joists that form the ceiling for the first floor and that also support the floor for the second storey. Joists can vary in depth from 140 mm to 286 mm (6" to 12"), according to the sizes of the rooms that they must span. The joist is shown in the diagram lengthwise with the header on the outside. The joists are supported at the ends by the two top plates, which are part of the wall framing. The ceiling finish is shown on the underside of the joists. The sub-flooring and sole plate are located in a similar manner to those on the first floor. In *Fig. 15-5B*, the wall frame has been moved out at the second-storey level so that the wood siding can overlap the brick veneer below. This means that the second storey will be 125 mm (5") larger than the first floor wherever the first storey is brick veneer and the second storey is faced with wood siding.

The **cornice** shows the relationship of the roof overhang to the outer wall.

Ceiling joists may vary in depth and are covered on the underside with dry wall. The rafters that form the roof are usually 38 mm × 89 mm (2" × 4"). They have bird's mouth-shaped recesses cut into them, which enables them to rest on the top plate.

There are several ways of dealing with the overhang or soffit portion of a roof. In *Fig. 15-7*, various treatments are illustrated. Also the wall section shown in *Fig. 15-2A* for wood siding shows a truss roof and *Fig. 15-2B* for brick veneer shows a plywood soffit. A fascia board trims the edge so that eavestroughs may be installed. The size of the fascia board is 25 mm × 140 mm (1" × 6").

The rafters or trusses are covered with plywood sheathing that is protected from the weather by roof shingles. The roof pitch symbol should also be shown *(see Figs. 15-2A and 15-2B)*.

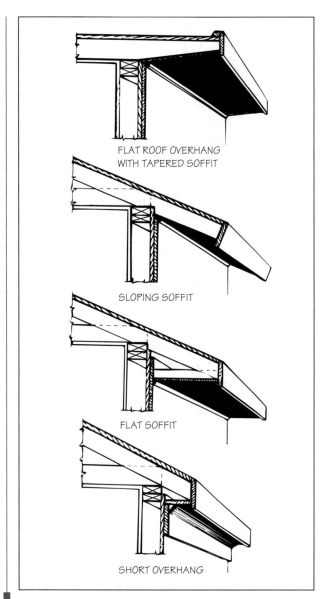

FLAT ROOF OVERHANG
WITH TAPERED SOFFIT

SLOPING SOFFIT

FLAT SOFFIT

SHORT OVERHANG

FIGURE 15-7 *Types of soffit design*

Hepler/Wallach: *Architecture: Drafting and Design*, 5/e © 1987.
Reproduced by permission of Glencoe/McGraw-Hill Educational Division.

DRAWING A WALL SECTION

The scale most often used for a wall section is 1:20 (3/4" = 1' -0"). If the drawing is to be done on a separate sheet of vellum, the most suitable size is A3/B placed upright. The drawing should be posi-

tioned in the centre of the sheet so there will be room for notes on both sides.

When drafting a wall section, keep your linework light until the complete drawing has been outlined. Then add the material symbols in dark, medium-weight lines. Darken the entire outline after the symbols are in place.

DIMENSIONING A WALL SECTION

A great deal of information appears on a wall section as details of all materials and their respective sizes must be included. To ensure a neat drawing, make a print of your drawing before any notations are added. Use this print to plan the best location for the notes. This will save you much time and will prevent possible dissatisfaction with the finished results.

The first dimensions that should be put on a drawing are the room heights, the widths of the overhangs, and the distance of the sub-floor above the grade. Set these dimensions away from the drawing, but allow space for those notations which must be placed outside of these dimensions.

To ensure a neat-looking drawing, use a lettering guide for all blocks of lettering and leave a space between each row. Draw a few vertical or sloping guidelines, as well, to ensure that all the lettering is uniform in appearance.

Notations must be placed adjacent to the area to which each note refers. Place all the information regarding the exterior of the house on the outer side of the wall, and the notes that relate to the interior on the inner side.

Full sections are those that are taken right through the entire house. This type of section is generally reserved for a situation involving an unusual arrangement of floor levels, such as in a split-level or a split-entry house. Those that run parallel to the front of the house are called **longitudinal sections**; if the cutting plane line goes from the front to the back of the building, they are called **transverse**. The relationship of the various levels can be dimensioned clearly on a full-section drawing.

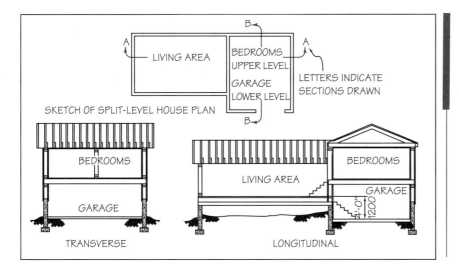

FIGURE 15-8

Typical transverse and longitudinal sections of a residence

Hepler/Wallach: *Architecture: Drafting and Design,* 5/e © 1987. Reproduced by permission of Glencoe/McGraw-Hill Educational Division.

Because of the scope of this type of drawing, a scale of 1:50 (1/4" = 1' -0") must be used. Naturally, not as much detail can be shown as in a wall section drawn at a larger scale, but showing the individual elements is not the purpose of this section rather, it is used to show the difference in floor levels. See *Fig. 15-8* for an example of transverse and longitudinal sections. These sections are additional and do not replace the wall section.

ROOF TRUSSES

Trusses are prefabricated units that can be used for either roof or floor support. In residential construction, they are used mainly in the fabrication of roofs.

A truss is a carefully engineered system of triangles that results in a very strong structural shape and has several advantages over conventional roof framing.

A truss can be designed to span the entire width of a house with no intermediate support required. This allows a designer great flexibility when planning the floor level immediately under the roof. Trusses are both quicker and safer to erect than conventional roof framing as fewer hours are required in a hazardous location at roof height.

As smaller and lighter pieces of lumber are used in truss construction and because they need

only be spaced 600 mm (24") apart instead of the usual 400 mm (16") on centres, approximately 30 to 35% less material is used. These factors result in a considerable overall saving in materials and labour costs *(see Fig. 15-9A and B)*.

Trusses that are to be used in house construction are usually designed with a W plan. A variety of configurations is available but all include webs, which will reduce the amount of attic space in a house.

The best application for trusses is in simple gable roofs. When used in a hip roof or other non-standard roof styles, trusses are much more difficult to design and therefore are more expensive.

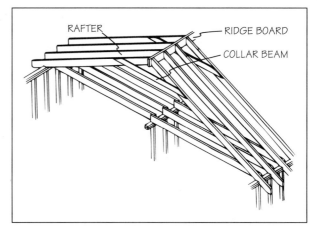

FIGURE 15-9A   *Roof framing with ceiling joists parallel to rafters*

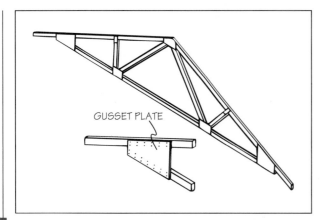

GUSSET PLATE

FIGURE 15-9B *Trussed rafter assembled with plywood gusset plates*

Trusses must be designed by a professional engineer who is experienced in that field. As trusses are usually factory made, they must be ordered well ahead of the date on which they are required, especially if that date falls in the busy period of the year.

REVIEW QUESTIONS

1. What is the purpose of a wall section?
2. What are the most significant parts of a wall section?
3. What dimensions are required on a wall section?

WHAT DO YOU THINK?

1. What type of building would require that a full section be drawn?
2. What are the advantages and disadvantages of using trusses in the roof of a house?

ASSIGNMENTS

1. On the undimensioned drawing of the wood siding or brick veneer wall section provided by your instructor, label as many parts as possible from memory.
2. Draw a wall section for a single-storey or a two-storey house using a scale of 1:20 (3/4" = 1' -0"). Label all the parts and dimension as for a working drawing.

UNIT 2 | **Elevations**

OBJECTIVES

- To accurately determine the height of the ridge
- To know how to draw and dimension elevation drawings
- To appreciate the purpose of the working drawing elevations

The elevation drawings that form part of the working drawings need to be drawn with greater accuracy and attention to detail than the pictorial elevations that were used during the design process in Chapter 10. However, they are similar, and in order to draw both types of elevations the same series of construction guidelines should be drawn across the page to relate the elements of the exterior to the interior construction. In addition to the above guidelines on working drawings, the depth of the foundations must be shown.

TO DETERMINE THE HEIGHT OF THE RIDGE

The first step in drawing these elevations is to properly determine the height of the ridge of the roof. In order to do this, a layout must be made. A layout is a very accurate drawing at a fairly large scale that is used by the designer to determine dimensions that are otherwise not easy to calculate.

In Chapter 9, Unit 3, Assignment 2, you made a layout of the stairway in order to obtain the size of the stairwell opening. You will now make a roof layout to determine three dimensions that will vary according to the slope selected for the roof.

X – the height of the ridge above the eave line
Y – the height of the eave line above the window line
Z – the width of the overhang

Follow this step-by-step method of making a layout, which will, for drawing purposes, be related to a house that is 10 000 mm (30'- 0") wide. Later the drawing can be adapted to the corresponding size for your own house design. Make the layout on an A3/B sheet of vellum at a scale of 1:20 (3/4" = 1'- 0"). Use construction lines for the layout and label all the lines neatly as you draw them *(see Fig. 15-10).*

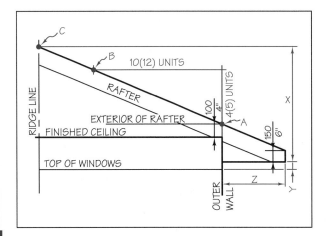

FIGURE 15-10 *Roof layout, not to scale (N.T.S.)*

1. Draw in a line that represents the top of the windows, about 1000 mm (3'- 6") in scale from the bottom of the sheet. This window line is normally 2050 mm (6'- 8") above the sub-floor. As roof construction is not required below the top of the windows, this line will be used as a datum line so that other measurements can be made from it.

2. Draw in the finished ceiling line 400 mm (16") in scale above the top of the windows. The finished ceiling line is usually 2440 mm (8'- 0") above the sub-floor.

3. Assume a house width of 10 000 mm (30'- 0") and a ridge line that is central to the structure. Starting 1500 mm (5'- 0") in scale from the right-hand side of the sheet, draw in a vertical line to

represent the outer wall of the house. Draw a second vertical line to represent the centre or the ridge line, which will be 5000 mm (15'- 0") to the left of the outer wall.

4. Establish the external face of the rafter vertically above the outer wall by measuring 100 mm (4") above the ceiling line. This is point A on the diagram.

5. From point A, extend the vertical line upwards.

6. Measure five units along this line (or whatever ratio number you have selected for the slope of the roof). The unit can be of any convenient size. Units on the 1:50 (3/4" = 1'- 0") scale are suggested as being a convenient size for this purpose.

7. Draw a horizontal line from the extent of the five-unit measurement and measure 10 (12) units along this line to the left using the same sized units. This is point B on the diagram.

8. Join point A to point B to establish the slope of the roof.

9. Extend the slope to the left-hand side until it touches the ridge line. This is the height of the ridge and is point C on the diagram.

10. Extend the slope line to the right to form the overhang.

11. Decide on a suitable width for the overhang and draw a perpendicular line through the slope at this point.

12. A fascia board 150 mm (6") wide must be measured downward from the slope of the overhang. From this point, a line will be drawn that will represent the bottom of the eaves or the soffit. This line must not come below the top of the window line. If it does, you must correct this by making the overhang narrower, which will raise the soffit line.

13. Darken in the outline of the roof, the eaves, and the outer wall for clarity.

14. Measure X, Y, and Z, and record the dimensions on the drawing.

This drawing can now be adapted to fit any house width that has the same roof slope. Merely draw in a new ridge line at the correct distance from the outer wall and remeasure X. Retain the layout for reference.

ARRANGEMENT OF THE ELEVATIONS

When planning the elevations for a one-storey house on A2/C sheets, it should be possible to place the four views on one sheet in the correct orthographic alignment, that is the rear view below the front view and the left-hand side under the right-hand side *(see Fig 15-11A)*. Simple foun-

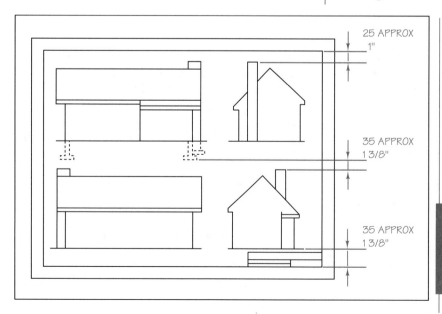

25 APPROX
1"

35 APPROX
1 3/8"

35 APPROX
1 3/8"

FIGURE 15-11A

Orthographic arrangement of elevations for a one-storey house showing foundation on front elevation only, on A2/C sheet

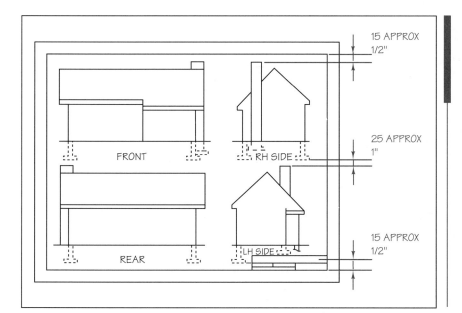

FIGURE 15-11B
Orthographic arrangement of elevations for a one-storey house showing foundation on all elevations on an A2/C sheet

dations are shown on the front view only, but if the foundation is complicated, it must be shown in each view. The additional space required to get them all on one sheet *(see Fig. 15-11B)* will mean that the views will have to be positioned a little more carefully.

Because of the extra height of the elevations for a two-storey house, one or two views placed side-by-side only can be placed on each sheet *(see Fig. 15-12).*

DRAWING THE ELEVATION GUIDELINES

Make the necessary series of guidelines for drawing the elevation as shown in *Figs. 15-13A and 15-13B* and incorporate the height of the ridge determined by the roof layout. If the foundation is a simple one, the hidden lines, which will show the depth of the footings and the thickness of the walls, need be shown only on the front elevation.

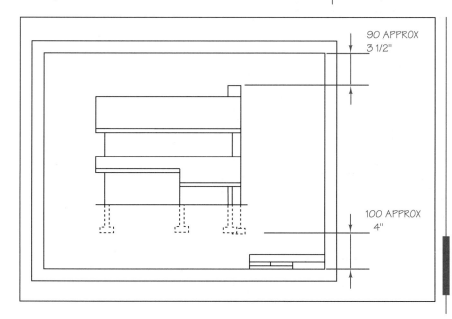

FIGURE 15-12
Two-storey house elevations, one view per A2/C sheet

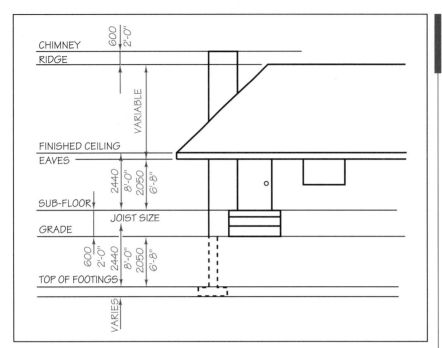

FIGURE 15-13A

Construction lines for a one-storey house

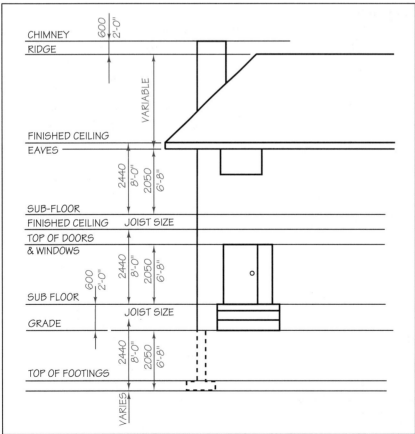

FIGURE 15-13B

Construction lines for a two-storey house

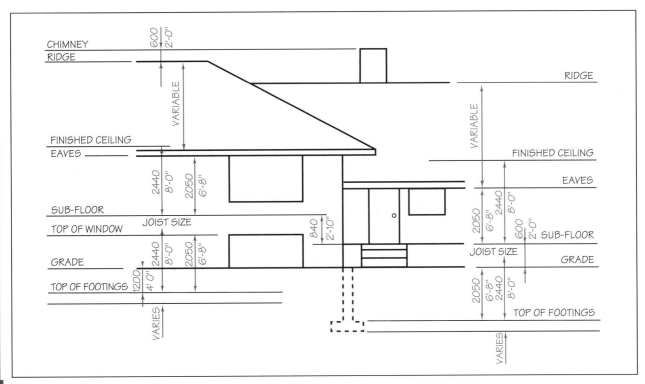

FIGURE 15-13C *Construction lines for a split-level house*

However, if the foundation is composed of different levels, then it should be shown in all four views for clarity.

Compare the grade level at the front and the rear of the building and revise the guideline on the rear elevation accordingly. In most cases, the grade will be lower at the rear to accommodate the windows in the foundation. The grade level on the side views will naturally show a sloping line to accommodate the change in levels from front to back.

To allow for the difference in levels for the elevations of a split-level house, the construction guidelines for the portion of the building related to the front entrance should be drawn in first and should extend to a vertical line that represents the wall that divides the two sections of the split *(see Fig. 15-13C)*. Then a second series of guidelines, showing the change in floor levels, should be drawn in on the other side of the division line. This will occur on the front and rear elevation for a side-split and on the side elevations for a back-to-front split. Naturally, con-

struction lines for the other two views in each case will be drawn in line with the end of the split-level that the elevation represents. It will be possible to draw only one of these elevations per sheet as the foundation will need to be shown on each view in this case.

USING THE FLOOR PLAN

The floor plan can be used to assist in drafting the elevations. Place the floor plan above the paper on which you have drawn the construction guide lines so that the front wall of the floor plan is parallel to the lines you are now going to use for the front elevation. Project the edges of all the salient features such as the length of the house, the doors and windows, and the overhangs, to the appropriate construction line so that these items can be correctly located *(see Fig. 15-14)*. This method saves a lot of time in transferring measurements from one drawing to another.

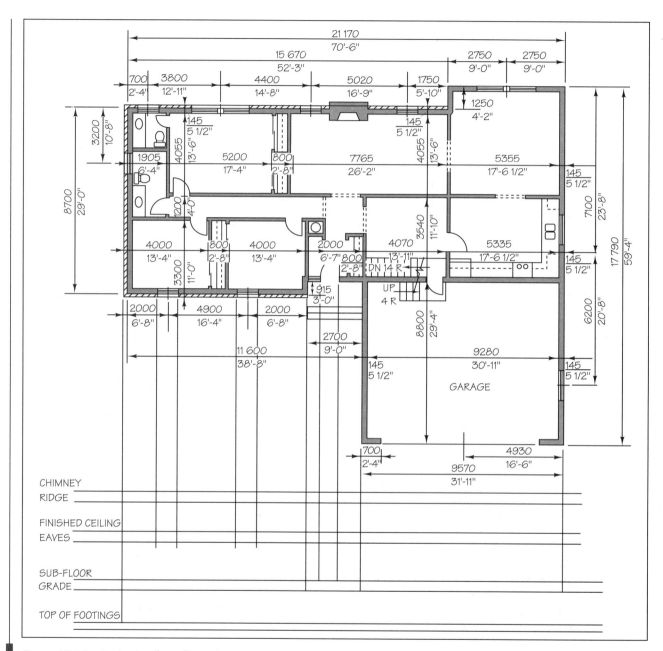

FIGURE 15-14   *Projection from floor plan*

After the front elevation is drawn, the floor plan can be turned around so that the features of each side can be projected when drawing the other elevations.

Before drawing in the doors and windows, consult a manufacturer's catalogue to ensure that the types and sizes of items being proposed are available. Information regarding windows and doors such as the manufacturer's name, the size and type, and any other relevant data should be noted on a separate sheet of paper. These notes will be useful when making up the schedules (see

Chapter 15, Unit 4) and will save time as the research will not have to be done twice.

MATERIAL SYMBOLS

The symbols for materials to be used on elevation drawings were shown in *Fig. 10-12*. The front view should show complete material representation. In the other elevations, the material symbols used need only be drawn partially on the appropriate surfaces.

ADDITIONAL ITEMS

Downspouts should be added from the eave line in the relevant locations *(see Fig. 15-15A)*.

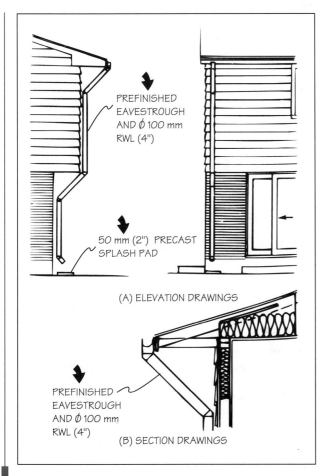

FIGURE 15-15A *Drawing requirement for gutters and downspouts*

Jensen: *Architectural Drawing and Design For Residential Construction*
published by McGraw-Hill Ryerson

Sheet metal flashing should be shown where breaks in the roof structure occur, such as dormers and chimneys. It is installed in order to prevent leakage *(see Fig. 15-15B)*.

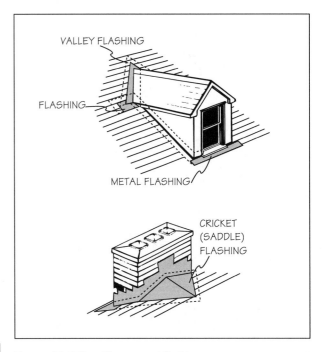

FIGURE 15-15B *Sheet metal flashing*

Jensen: *Architectural Drawing and Design For Residential Construction*
published by McGraw-Hill Ryerson

Continuous screened vents are usually put in under the soffits and are indicated by a note that states that 1 m² (1'- 0" sq. ft.) of venting is required for each 300 m² (300 sq. ft.) of insulated ceiling area. Louvred vents at the gabled ends of roofs can also be used *(see Fig. 15-15C)*.

A carport roof will be supported by columns that are 150 mm (6") square and are spaced approximately 2400 mm (8'- 0") apart. These columns will have corresponding foundation piers installed to a depth of 1200 mm (4'- 0"), which must be shown on both the elevation and the foundation plan *(see Fig. 15-15D)*. If there is a chimney included in the plan, see Chapter 15, Unit 3 for details pertaining to the elevations.

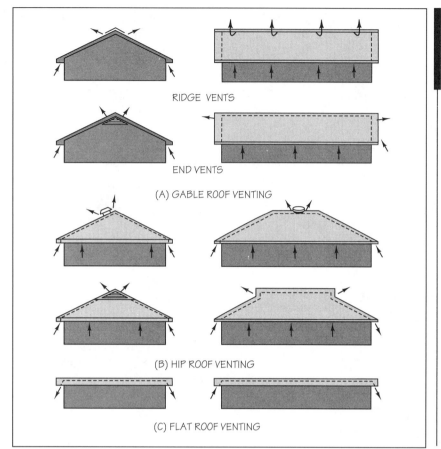

RIDGE VENTS

END VENTS

(A) GABLE ROOF VENTING

(B) HIP ROOF VENTING

(C) FLAT ROOF VENTING

FIGURE 15-15C

Methods of ventilating roof spaces

Jensen: *Architectural Drawing and Design For Residential Construction*
published by McGraw-Hill Ryerson

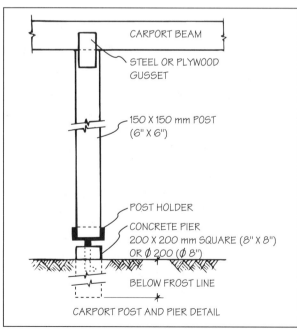

CARPORT BEAM

STEEL OR PLYWOOD GUSSET

150 X 150 mm POST (6" X 6")

POST HOLDER

CONCRETE PIER 200 X 200 mm SQUARE (8" X 8") OR Ø 200 (Ø 8")

BELOW FROST LINE

CARPORT POST AND PIER DETAIL

DIMENSIONING THE ELEVATIONS

Add the following groups of dimensions to the elevations:

1. The construction guidelines should now be darkened on one side of the drawing for use as dimension lines. These lines should be labelled and dimensioned as shown on *Fig. 15-16*. The height of the ridge dimension should not be included, and the line showing the ceiling level should be dimensioned and extended to the side of the drawing only. The room height is an important construction dimension although it is not a feature of the exterior of the building.

FIGURE 15-15D *Carport post and pier detail*

Jensen: *Architectural Drawing and Design For Residential Construction*
published by McGraw-Hill Ryerson

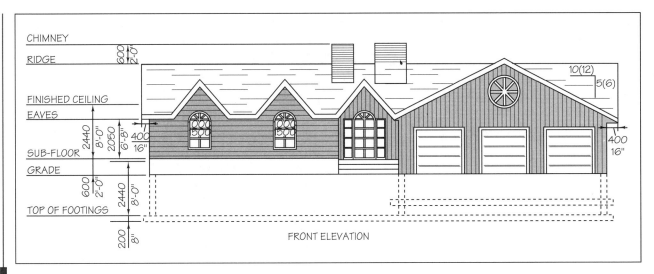

CHIMNEY

RIDGE

FINISHED CEILING

EAVES

SUB-FLOOR

GRADE

TOP OF FOOTINGS

600
2'-0"

2440
8'-0"

2050
6'-8"

400
16"

600
2'-0"

2440
8'-0"

200
8"

10(12)

5(6)

400
16"

FRONT ELEVATION

FIGURE 15-16   *Dimensioning and labelling an elevation*

2. Any changes in grade level should be dimensioned on the view that shows the change in the grade line most clearly.
3. The size of each window sash should be shown in the top right-hand corner as in *Fig. 15-17*. If the window is to be divided into small panes of glass, do not dimension each of these. Modern windows are made with removable inserts; therefore this is not a structural feature.
4. The roof pitch symbol should be noted above the roof slope, and the overhangs should be dimensioned on the front and on one side view.
5. Each elevation must be titled. These can be called *Front Elevation*, *Rear Elevation*, *Right-hand Elevation*, and *Left-hand Elevation*. If the house design is to apply to a house built on a specific lot only, the elevations can be specified as *North*, *South*, *East*, and *West* if desired.

All other dimensions are optional but no length dimensions are required on the elevations.

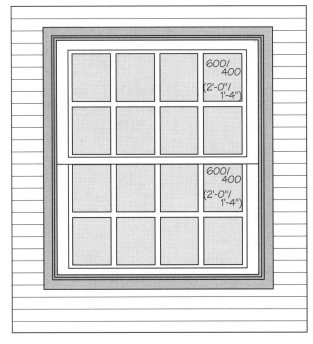

600/
400

(2'-0"/
1'-4")

600/
400

(2'-0"/
1'-4")

FIGURE 15-17   *Dimensioning a double-hung window for an elevation*

REVIEW QUESTIONS

1. What additional horizontal construction guidelines are required in order to draw the elevations for the working drawings that were not needed on the presentation elevations?
2. How do you determine the height of the ridge?
3. What is the correct orthographic arrangement when four elevations are drawn on one sheet?

WHAT DO YOU THINK?

1. What factors would cause you to show the foundations on each elevation?
2. Why might it be unwise to title elevations *North*, *West*, etc. for a house plan that was going to be built on several different lots?

ASSIGNMENTS

1. For the two-storey house developed in Chapter 14, make four elevation drawings suitable for a set of working drawings at a scale of 1:50 (1/4" = 1'- 0") in a specific style. Use the elevation drawings made in Chapter 10 for reference.

UNIT 3 | Chimneys and Fireplaces

OBJECTIVES

- To understand the purpose of a chimney
- To design a chimney
- To appreciate various types of fireplaces and stoves
- To design and draw a fireplace

Although a fireplace is not an efficient method of heating and is also a costly item to build, some people who are building a new house incorporate it into the design. Most houses will require a chimney so that the fumes from the furnace can be dispersed unless they are to be heated by solar or electrical heating and do not have any major gas appliances in the house.

THE CHIMNEY

A chimney is a masonry support for the flue, which is a vertical vent from a fireplace, a furnace, or a gas-burning appliance; its purpose is to remove fumes and smoke from the house. The flue also produces a draft that will draw in the necessary supply of oxygen for combustion.

The flue itself is made up of ceramic tile, which can be cylindrical, square, or rectangular in shape. The tile is usually in 600 mm (2'- 0") lengths and is approximately 200 mm (8") in diameter or 200 mm (8") square. The cylindrical-shaped flue is the most efficient as smoke spirals as it rises up the flue. However, a square flue is much easier to brick around and so this shape tends to be favoured by builders.

The tile is glazed on the inside surface in order to prohibit the adhesion of soot to the sides of the flue. The sections of tile must be set close to and flush with each other in order to protect the masonry of the chimney from the heat. Factory-built chimneys have metal flues and are discussed later in the chapter.

DESIGN CRITERIA IN CHIMNEYS

The chimney not only supports the flue but serves as protection for the wooden frame of the building so that it will not become overheated, causing it to catch fire or the wood to deteriorate. The house framing should not come in contact with the chimney, which should be at least 50 mm (2") away from any structural elements. The space between the structure and the masonry may be filled with incombustible material. Joist, rafters, or beams should never be supported by the chimney. However, sub-flooring and roof sheathing may come to within 20 mm (3/4") of the chimney.

Metal flashing is used around the chimney where it breaks through the roof to prevent leakage between the masonry chimney and the roofing materials *(see Fig. 15-18)*.

The chimney is free-standing and is tied to the house frame by metal rods that are attached to the wood frame and anchored into the masonry. The chimney extends from the foundation to the roof. This column of masonry must be supported by footings, which are placed below the frost line. As the weight of the masonry exceeds the weight of the frame structure, the footings will have to be larger than for the rest of the house. They are usually 300 mm (1'- 0") thick and project 300 mm (1'- 0") around the chimney itself. A clean-out is usually formed at the base of the fireplace flue so that soot and ashes can be removed easily. At the top, the chimney should protrude not less than 900 mm (3'- 0") from the highest point of intersection with the roof and must be a minimum of 600 mm (2'- 0") above the ridge or any other obstruction within 3000 mm (10'- 0"). In this way, down drafts caused by wind turbulence, which tends to cling to roof slopes, will be inhibited from entering the top of the flue *(see Fig. 15-19)*.

The top of the chimney is capped with concrete to protect the masonry from the weather. The cap is approximately 75 mm (3") thick and

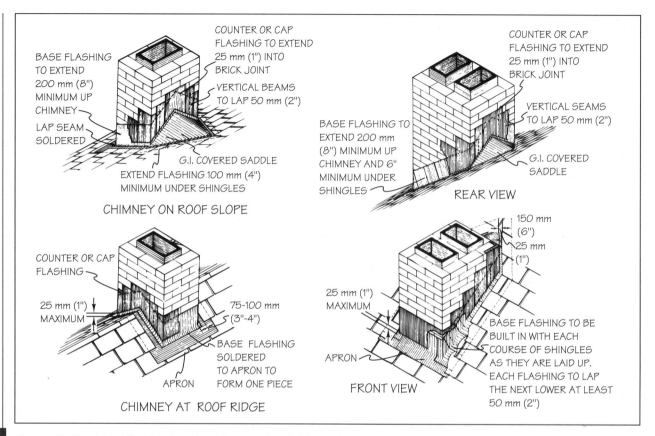

FIGURE 15-18 *Metal flashing is critical where roof and chimney intersect*

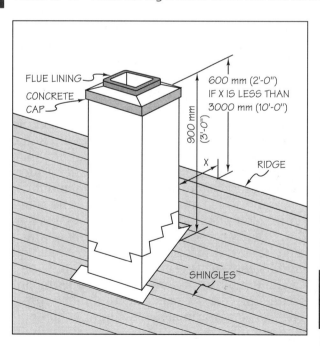

should be 25 mm (1") larger on all sides to form a drip ledge around the chimney. The cap is made to slope away from the flue, which extends 100 mm (4") above it.

A chimney can incorporate several flues in order to accommodate fireplaces, the furnace, and any other gas-burning appliance *(see Fig. 15-20)*. Each fireplace must have a separate flue; however, two appliances may be vented into one flue provided they are in the same storey of the building. When there is more than one flue in a chimney, each of the flues must be surrounded with 75 mm (3") minimum of masonry. Some gas equipment is provided with special vents and therefore does not require a built-in chimney. If all the appliances

FIGURE 15-19 *Chimney height above ridge and intersection with roof*

Courtesy of CMHC: Canadian Wood Frame House Construction

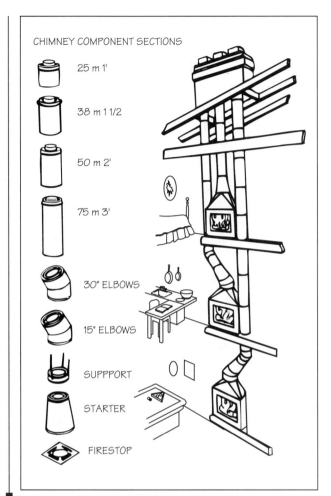

FIGURE 15-20 *Multiple-flue design using metal flues*

Hepler/Wallach: *Architecture: Drafting and Design*, 5/e © 1987.
Reproduced by permission of Glencoe/McGraw-Hill Educational Division.

requiring a chimney are not close together, then two chimneys may have to be built.

A fireplace chimney is best located inside the structure so that heat that would be lost to the outside can be absorbed into the house. If a chimney is located on a northwest outside wall, the cold air will cause the flue gas to condense and eventually the masonry will deteriorate. A chimney can be located on the south wall of a house so that the masonry mass will absorb the heat of the day and release it during the night. This method of heat conservation has been discussed in Chapter 3, Unit 2, which deals with passive solar energy.

Factory-built chimneys have become more acceptable recently. They are lightweight and do not need masonry support. These chimneys are encased in metal and have a terra cotta flue lining. They are easily assembled in sections. The chimney may be left exposed or can be concealed in the structure. However, the installation of these chimneys must always be approved by the Underwriters Laboratory *(see Fig. 15-21)*.

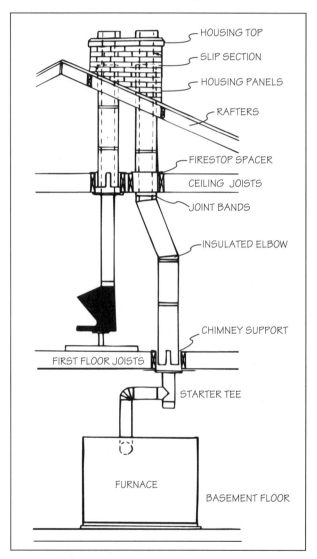

FIGURE 15-21 *Factory-built chimneys*

Jensen: *Architectural Drawing and Design For Residential Construction*
published by McGraw-Hill Ryerson

THE FIREPLACE

The fireplace consists of a firebox, where the fire will actually be set; a damper above it, which will encourage a draft; and the flue, which will expel the smoke. The structure is a complicated one and should be carefully designed and constructed by an experienced builder.

The firebox must be lined with fire bricks 50 mm (2") thick, which are laid with fire clay mortar, or the firebox can be lined with material that has a high resistance to heat. The masonry that surrounds the firebox should be a minimum of 190 mm (8") thick, including the fire brick, or 140 mm (6") thick where the chimney is on an outside wall. Metal firebox units are often designed to circulate the heat, which would otherwise be lost up the chimney. These units will usually have fans and grills built in, which will assist the discharge of the warm air into the room *(see Figs. 15-22A and 15-22B).*

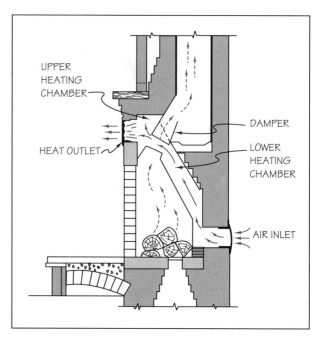

FIGURE 15-22B *Section through welded-steel, prefabricated fireplace. The fire warms the air in the lower heating chamber; the warm air rises, drawing in cool air at the air inlet and discharging warm air at the heat outlet. Electric fans can be used to increase the circulation of warm air.*

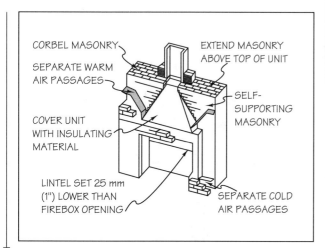

FIGURE 15-22A *A steel prefabricated heat-circulating fireplace with unit partially bricked up. Note cold-air intakes at the floor and the hot-air ejection registers above them.*

A fire will require oxygen in order to burn, so cold air is drawn in from the floor of the room. To prevent the draft this creates, air inlets can be inserted in the back of a chimney if it is on an external wall.

DESIGN FEATURES FOR A FIREPLACE

1. To encourage heat to be projected into the room, the front of the firebox is made wider than the back at a ratio of 3:2. The back wall should tilt forward from a distance equal to half the height of the front opening.

2. To inhibit smoke from entering the room, a long narrow throat opening that will encourage drafts must be constructed at the top of the firebox. The throat should have the same area, although it is not the same shape as the flue and will have a damper or metal door that can be closed when no fire is burning to prevent cold air from entering the room. The damper is made to be adjustable in order to control the amount of draft that the fire requires to keep it burning. A smoke shelf and chamber are hollowed out immediately above the throat so that any down draft will not send smoke into the room.

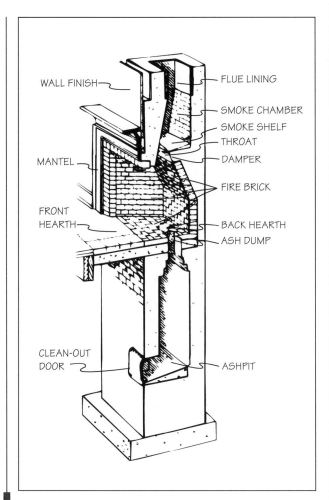

FIGURE 15-23 *Terms used in fireplace construction*

Courtesy of CMHC: Canadian Wood Frame House Construction

3. To form a smooth connection with the flue, the sides of the smoke chamber are drawn together at the top. The slope of the walls should not exceed 45° or the smoke and soot will be hindered in escaping up the flue. The cross-section area of the flue should equal one-tenth of the fireplace opening.

4. The front of the fireplace is covered by a decorative mantel and the wall above the firebox opening is supported by a lintel, which is usually a length of angle iron. To aid in preventing heat loss up the chimney when there is no fire and as a safety device when there is, it is advisable to have a glass screen fixed to the fireplace opening.

5. The floor in front of the fireplace is protected by the hearth, which can be raised, made flush with the floor, or sunken. This hearth is made of incombustible materials and is supported underneath the floor by a concrete arch. The hearth projects a minimum of 400 mm (16") in front of the firebox and extends 200 mm (8") on either side.

6. For easy removal of ashes, an ash dump is built into the floor of the firebox. An ash pit at the base of the chimney in the basement will collect the ashes and needs to be cleared out periodically. This ash pit should have a close-fitting door so that fine particles of dust will not escape or be drawn back up into the room by a draft created from an ill-fitting door.

Many types of factory-built fireboxes or stoves can be purchased that are made of welded metal. These can be designed to fit into an existing fireplace or they can be placed in an alcove made of fire-resistant material. Frequently, it is possible to use a factory-built chimney with these types of units and a large structural adaptation to the house is not required. Gas fires that can be built into the firebox or that are free-standing have been revived with the availability of more modern designs.

TO DRAW A FIREPLACE AND CHIMNEY IN SECTION

In order to show the design of the fireplace and chimney, a separate drawing is usually necessary. This drawing should include a vertical section through the chimney from the roof to the foundation and an additional plan view of the chimney taken through the firebox. A view of the front of the firebox and mantle should also be shown.

Proportions for the size of the firebox, flue, etc. can be obtained from construction manuals and a set of sizes for an average fireplace have been provided *(see Figs. 15-24A and 15-24B)*.

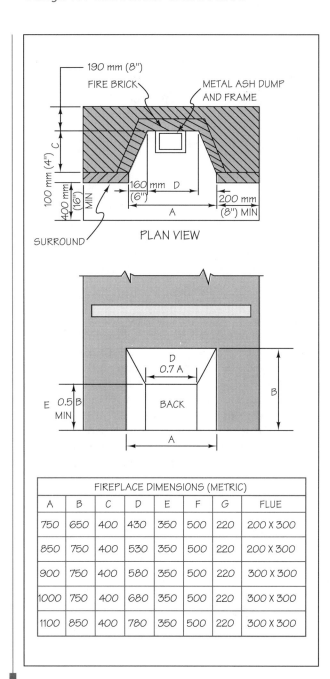

FIGURE 15-24A *Fireplace sizes*

Jensen: *Architectural Drawing and Design For Residential Construction*
published by McGraw-Hill Ryerson

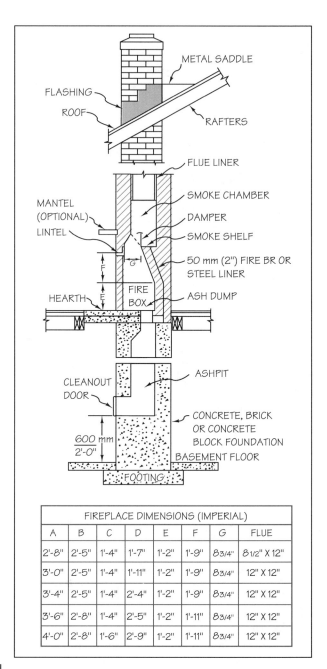

FIGURE 15-24B *Section through fireplace and chimney*

Jensen: *Architectural Drawing and Design For Residential Construction*
published by McGraw-Hill Ryerson

FIREPLACE DIMENSIONS (METRIC)							
A	B	C	D	E	F	G	FLUE
750	650	400	430	350	500	220	200 X 300
850	750	400	530	350	500	220	200 X 300
900	750	400	580	350	500	220	300 X 300
1000	750	400	680	350	500	220	300 X 300
1100	850	400	780	350	500	220	300 X 300

FIREPLACE DIMENSIONS (IMPERIAL)							
A	B	C	D	E	F	G	FLUE
2'-8"	2'-5"	1'-4"	1'-7"	1'-2"	1'-9"	8 3/4"	8 1/2" X 12"
3'-0"	2'-5"	1'-4"	1'-11"	1'-2"	1'-9"	8 3/4"	12" X 12"
3'-4"	2'-5"	1'-4"	2'-4"	1'-2"	1'-9"	8 3/4"	12" X 12"
3'-6"	2'-8"	1'-4"	2'-5"	1'-2"	1'-11"	8 3/4"	12" X 12"
4'-0"	2'-8"	1'-6"	2'-9"	1'-2"	1'-11"	8 3/4"	12" X 12"

REVIEW QUESTIONS

1. How many flues are required in a house with two fireplaces, a gas furnace, and a gas hot-water heater? Both of the latter are in the basement.
2. How far should a chimney extend above the roof?
3. What safety features are used in the design of a fireplace and chimney?

WHAT DO YOU THINK?

1. What is the reason that people often wish to have a fireplace incorporated into their house designs?
2. How can the draft required for combustion be controlled and down drafts inhibited in fireplace and chimney construction?

ASSIGNMENTS

1. On an A3/B sheet of vellum used upright, draw a fireplace and chimney design at a scale of 1:20 (3/4" = 1'- 0") using the chart provided in *Fig. 15-24A* for firebox sizes.
   a. Draw front and plan views of the firebox. See *Fig. 15-24A* on the left-hand side of the sheet. Dimension appropriately.
   b. Draw a vertical section through the fireplace and chimney on the right-hand side of the sheet *(see Fig. 15-24B)*. Label appropriately.

UNIT 4

Sections, Schedules, and Collating the Drawings

OBJECTIVES

- To understand how doors and windows are built into frame or masonry structures
- To draw sections through windows and doors
- To use manufacturers' brochures for ordering doors and windows and compiling schedules
- To collate the working drawings and issue a set of prints

Most door and window manufacturers include in their sales brochures instructions regarding the installation of their products. Included with these instructions are illustrations of the door or window sections. This has made the drafting of these sections optional for working drawings. The following unit briefly outlines how windows and doors are installed and shows typical sections.

WINDOW SECTIONS

In order to insert windows into a frame wall, it is necessary to cut away a portion of some studs to provide a rough opening to take the window frame. Because windows should not be subjected to the dead load of the building, the ends of the studs that have been cut must be framed with horizontal double headers that will form lintels over the opening to support the weight of the wall above it. Double headers are also required to join the cut-off studs below the window. These lower headers will support the weight of the window itself.

In order to transmit the dead load of the building to the foundation, the studs on either side of the windows are doubled and the headers are fastened to them. In this way, the frame of the wall will not be weakened by having a hole cut in it.

When windows are placed in a masonry wall, a piece of angle iron or channel will be used as a lintel to support the wall above a window or door in a similar way to that used above a fireplace opening.

The rough stud or masonry opening in the wall is usually a little longer than the exterior of the frame of the window that is to fit into it. This allows the frame of the window to be shimmed to ensure correct alignment, which is essential for the installation of modern precision-built windows. Insulation is then put into the remaining space to lessen the amount of air infiltration through the space created around the windows. Infiltration from cracks around the windows and doors can cause considerable heat loss if they are not insulated and then caulked.

Exterior and interior trim is placed around the windows so that a neat appearance is given to the installation of the windows. Much of the actual construction is hidden by the trim; therefore section drawings are necessary if one wishes to show details of how the windows are set into the wall *(see Fig. 15-25)*.

The base of the window is usually fitted with a wooden sill, which forms a drip ledge for water run-off. However, if the wall has a brick veneer finish, then a course of bricks is fitted under the wooden sill and a lintel of angle iron is used above the window to support the brickwork over the opening.

The sections showing details of the installation of a window are usually drawn at a scale of 1:20 (3/4" = 1'- 0"). The head and sill details as well as the meeting rail details for a double- or single-hung window are developed from a cutting plane line taken vertically through the window. The jamb details, which are sections resulting from a horizontal cutting plane line, are the same on either side of the window, so normally only one jamb detail is shown.

FIGURE 15-25
*Double-hung window in
wood frame wall*

From Ernest R. Weidhaas,
Architectural Drafting and Design, Sixth Edition,
Copyright © 1989 by Allyn and Bacon.
Reprinted with permission.

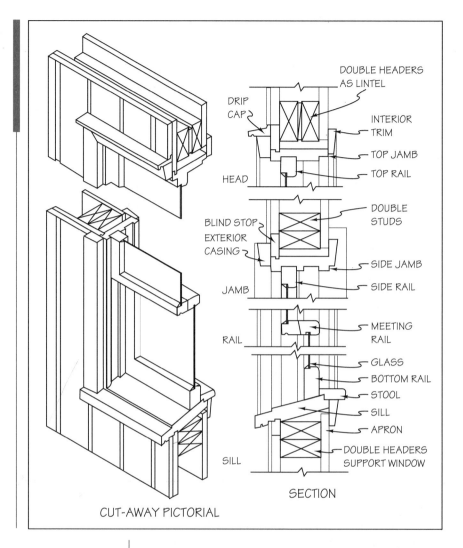

DOOR SECTIONS

The swing door is the type of door most widely used for entrances. These doors are hinged on one side and swing into the house or into rooms. The traffic pattern will determine on which side the door is hinged. As with the windows, a rough frame or masonry opening is required that is larger than the door frame. A double header is placed horizontally over the door and the full-length studs on both sides are reinforced with shorter studs extending down to the floor which are framed under the lintel formed by the double header.

An exterior door is usually 44 mm (1 3/4") thick and a minimum of 810 mm (3'-4") wide by 2030 mm (6'- 8") in height. The exterior frame, which is rabbetted or cut away to form the door stop, is 35 mm (1 3/8") thick at the side and head jamb and 44 mm (1 3/4") thick. The sill is made of hardwood or softwood with a metal-covered threshold. Exterior doors are weather stripped all around.

An interior door is usually 35 mm (1 3/8") thick and 750 mm (2'- 6") wide by 2030 mm (6'- 8") in height. The door frames, which are also rabbetted, are usually 32 mm (1 1/4") thick.

Sections are usually drawn of the head and sill of the door, which are taken from a vertical cutting

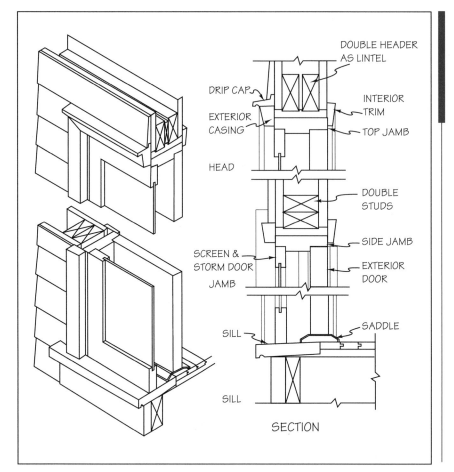

FIGURE 15-26A

An exterior door in a wood frame wall

From Ernest R. Weidhaas,
Architectural Drafting and Design, Sixth Edition,
Copyright © 1989 by Allyn and Bacon.
Reprinted with permission.

Labels in figure: DOUBLE HEADER AS LINTEL, DRIP CAP, INTERIOR TRIM, EXTERIOR CASING, TOP JAMB, HEAD, DOUBLE STUDS, SCREEN & STORM DOOR JAMB, SIDE JAMB, EXTERIOR DOOR, SILL, SADDLE, SILL, SECTION

plane line, and a jamb section from a horizontal cutting plane line *(see Figs. 15-26A and 15-26B)*. These sections are drawn at a scale of 1:20 (3/4" = 1'-0") so that all details can be clearly identified.

OTHER OPTIONAL DETAILS

Elevations and sections of the interior such as kitchen cupboards, a workshop, or other specific design details can be included in the set of working drawings *(see Figs. 15-27A and 15-27B)*. As this type of work will usually be completed either after the house is built or elsewhere by a cabinet maker, it is advisable to draw these details on a separate sheet of the working drawings.

These drawings should be drawn at a scale of 1:20 (3/4" = 1'-0") and dimensioned so that the items can be readily made. Label these drawings carefully and relate them to the working drawings by symbols that pinpoint the specific area where they are to be installed.

SCHEDULES

A contractor needs to be able to take the specifications for doors and windows from the working drawing before commencing work on the building. Factory-made products, such as doors and windows, often take a long time to be delivered because factories make their various products in rotation, so you may have to wait some time for a specific item to get into production again. The schedules that are part of the working drawings facilitate ordering.

FIGURE 15-26B

An exterior door in siding and brick veneer walls

Architectural Drafting by Herbert F. Bellis and Walter A. Schmidt © 1961. Reprinted by permission of Glencoe/McGraw-Hill Educational Division

FIGURE 15-27A *(bottom left)*

Details for wardrobe closets

Hepler/Wallach: *Architecture: Drafting and Design,* 5/e © 1987. Reproduced by permission of Glencoe/McGraw-Hill Educational Division.

FIGURE 15-27B *(bottom right)*

Wall storage

Hepler/Wallach: *Architecture: Drafting and Design,* 5/e © 1987. Reproduced by permission of Glencoe/McGraw-Hill Educational Division.

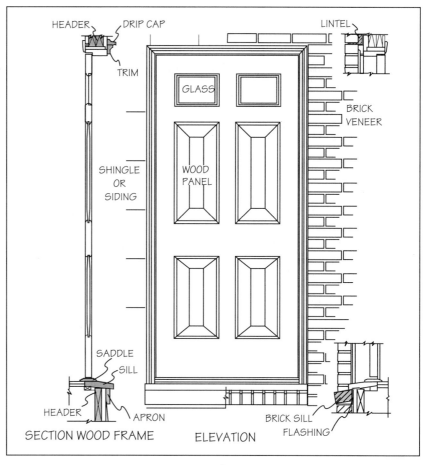

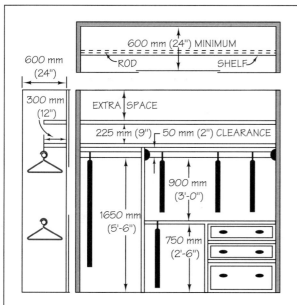

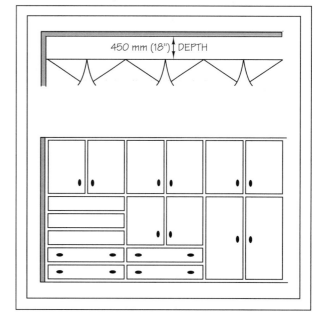

Two separate schedules are compiled listing the windows, which are identified by number, and the doors, which are identified by letter. The items that are usually included in door schedules are:

Example

Identification letter	A
Quantity	6
Type	Interior
Size	750 mm x 2030 mm
	(2'- 6" x 6'- 4")
Material	Mahogany
Manufacturer	Lloyd

The items that are usually included in window schedules are:

Example

Identification number	1
Quantity	2
Type of window	Double hung
Size (width x height)	700 mm x 1500 mm
	(2'- 4" x 5'- 0")
Materials	Extended aluminum
Remarks	Screens included
Manufacturer	Dashwood

Information similar to that shown above is compiled on the drawing in the form of a chart *(see Fig. 15-28)*. Other optional items can be added as desired. The schedules will contain a great deal of data that would otherwise clutter up the drawings. The schedules are related to the drawings by symbols placed on the floor plan *(see Fig. 15-29)*.

DOOR SCHEDULE

Symbol	Width	Height	Thickness	Material	Type	Screen	Quantity	Threshold
A	3'- 0"	7'- 0"	1 3/4"	Wood – Ash	Slab core	No	1	Oak
B	2'- 6"	7'- 0"	1 3/4"	Wood – Ash	Slab core	Yes	1	Oak
C	2'- 3"	6'- 8"	1 3/8"	Wood – Oak	Hollow core	No	3	None
D	2'- 0"	6'- 8"	1 3/8"	Wood – Ash	Hollow core	No	2	None
E	2'- 3"	6'- 8"	1 1/4"	Wood – Fir	Plywood	No	1	None
F	1'- 9"	5'- 6"	1/2"	Glass & Metal	Shower door	No	1	None
G	4'- 6"	6'- 6"	1/2"	Glass & Metal	Sliding	Yes	2	Metal

WINDOW SCHEDULE

Symbol	Width	Height	Material	Type	Screen	Quantity	Remarks	Manufacturer
1	5'- 0"	4'- 0"	Aluminum	Stationary	No	2		Dashwood
2	2'- 9"	3'- 0"	Aluminum	Louvre	Yes	1		Dashwood
3	2'- 6"	3'- 0"	Wood	Double Hung	Yes	2	4 Lites-2 High	Dashwood
4	1'- 6"	1'- 6"	Aluminum	Louvre	Yes	1		Dashwood
5	6'- 0"	3'- 6"	Aluminum	Louvred Sides	Yes	1		Dashwood
6	4'- 0"	6'- 6"	Aluminum	Stationary	No	1		Dashwood
7	5'- 0"	3'- 6"	Aluminum	Sliding	Yes	2	Frosted Glass	Dashwood
8	1'- 9"	3'- 0"	Aluminum	Awning	Yes	1		Dashwood

FIGURE 15-28 *Door and window schedules*

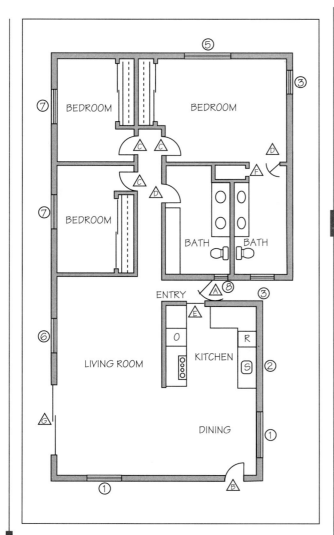

FIGURE 15-29 *Symbols indexed to floor plan*

Hepler/Wallach: *Architecture: Drafting and Design*, 5/e © 1987.
Reproduced by permission of Glencoe/McGraw-Hill Educational Division.

COLLATING THE DRAWINGS

The construction details of the design are now complete. It is necessary to see that all the drawings that comprise the set of working drawings are finished off with a border 10 mm (3/8") from the edge of the sheet and a title block *(see Fig. 15-30)*.

The title block for each sheet should contain the following items:

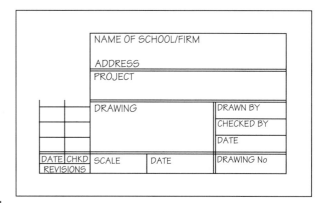

FIGURE 15-30 *Sample title block*

1. the identification of the project. For example, *A One-Storey House for Mr. and Mrs. Pinto, Dolbeau* plus a project number if the work is to be done for a large organization;
2. the name of each drawing, that is, *Foundation Plan*, *Elevations*, etc.;
3. the scale of the drawings;
4. the name of the draftspersons;
5. the date the drawings were completed;
6. the name of the firm responsible for the drawings.

Collating the drawing means numbering the sheets in the order in which they are to be used. The total number of sheets should also be stated because, if one of the drawings is missing and this fact was overlooked, it could mean that the work would not be carried out according to the contract.

An example of how drawings for a one-storey house would be collated is shown below:

Plot Plan and Foundation Plan	1 of 5
Floor Plan	2 of 5
Front and Rear Elevations	3 of 5
Right-hand and Left-hand Elevations	
Plus Wall Section	4 of 5
Schedules and Optional Details	5 of 5

When all the drawings have been assembled, go over the checklist that follows to ensure that all necessary details have been included.

CHECKLIST FOR A SET OF WORKING DRAWINGS

GENERAL

1. Are there completed title blocks and borders on all sheets?
2. Are all sheets collated?
3. Is all line work and lettering dark enough to print well?
4. Are the drawings uncluttered and attractive to look at?

PLOT PLAN

1. Are the north symbol and identification of the lot clearly shown?
2. Is the scale indicated?
3. Are the size and location of the building on the lot adequately shown?
4. Does each side of the lot have a bearing and length readable from the bottom right-hand corner of the drawing?
5. Has the driveway been dimensioned?

FOUNDATION

1. Are the overall sizes and the thickness of the walls given?
2. Are footings shown as dotted lines on either side of the foundation wall?
3. Have sizes of joists, lally columns, and I beams been correctly located?
4. Are sizes of windows and lintel L's over windows given?
5. Has the location of the start of the stairway been given by dimensions?
6. Have the chimneys and flues been correctly shown and dimensioned and a furnace included?
7. Are soil pipes, water heater, laundry tubs, and roughed-in plumbing shown?

FLOOR PLAN

1. Are the overall dimensions given?
2. Do all lines of detail dimensions add up to the overall dimensions?
3. Are additional interior dimensions required to locate offset walls and lengths of closets, width of passages, etc.?
4. Are the ceiling joists' symbols shown in several locations?
5. Are the number of risers and location of the stairs dimensioned?
6. Are rods and shelves in closets shown and broom and linen cupboards marked?
7. Are split receptacles indicated in the kitchen and electrical outlets for the stove and fridge shown?
8. Is the electrical plan complete, including exterior lighting and outlets?
9. Are soil pipes and access to plumbing in the bathroom shown?
10. Are access to the attic and a smoke warning device shown?

ELEVATIONS

1. Are all four elevations shown?
2. Are the floor and finished ceiling marked and heights given?
3. Is the pitch of the roof shown correctly?
4. Are footing depths given and the height of the floor above grade shown?
5. Is the size of each sash shown in the top right-hand corner of the windows?
6. Is the chimney shown in all views with a dimension from the break in the roof?
7. Are window and door schedules complete and has each item been related to the floor plan?

TECHNICAL CHECKING

After applying the checklist given in this chapter or, if you are working professionally, a checklist devised by that organization, a print of the drawings should be passed over to another draftsperson or checker who will scrutinize it for dimensional accuracy and the correctness of symbols.

The checker should go systematically through each print of the set of working drawings marking the approved dimensions in yellow and any errors in red. The prints with errors or omissions marked on them are returned to the draftsperson to be corrected on the original, reprinted, and, together with the marked-up print, resubmitted to the checker for approval. The checker should sign the original of each drawing he or she finally approves.

The time spent checking for accuracy more than compensates for the time that could be wasted at the site correcting errors made from faulty dimensioning.

ISSUING THE DRAWINGS

After the set of drawings is approved, prints can be made and issued to the contractor. The date of issue and the number of prints made should be recorded. In the event of changes, new sets of prints are issued and all the old prints retrieved.

The originals should always be retained by the draftsperson to facilitate changes that may occur during construction; to correct errors; to use as reference in the case of a dispute; or to assist in making other designs.

REVIEW QUESTIONS

1. How is the wall above a window or door opening supported?
2. What enlarged sections should be shown
   a. for a window?
   b. for a door?
3. What data would you expect to find on a schedule?
4. What is the correct order for a set of working drawings?

WHAT DO YOU THINK?

1. Where would you find details on how to install a window?
2. What is the purpose of schedules?
3. What problems might occur if it went unrecognized that a sheet was missing from a set of working drawings?

ASSIGNMENTS

1. Draw the appropriate sections for either a standard door or window placed in a typical frame wall. These sections should be drawn to a scale of 1:20 (3/4" = 1'- 0").
2. Make orthographic drawings of the door sections shown on the assignment sheet provided by the instructor.
3. On an A3/B sheet of vellum, make door and window schedules for the two-storey design you have developed as assignments during this chapter.
4. Collate all the drawings you have made as assignments during this chapter and check the drawings with the checklist provided for a set of working drawings. Then, print a complete set of drawings.

SECTIONS AND ELEVATIONS

THE PROJECT

You have now reached the final stage of the preparation of the working drawings. This phase of the work will require knowledge of how a house is constructed.

Step 25:
Make a wall section at a scale of 1:20 (1/2" = 1'-0") suitable for the house that you have designed. This drawing should be drawn on an A2/C sheet of vellum and other drawings, possibly the elevations, may eventually be drawn on the same sheet.

Dimension the drawing and include as many details of the materials to be used as possible. Care must be taken in lettering this section.

Step 26:
Draw the four elevations required to show the style and materials used on each exterior side of the house. These drawings should be made at a scale of 1:50 (1/4" = 1'-0").

Step 27:
If a chimney and fireplace are included in the design, make the following drawings at a scale of 1:20 (1/2" = 1'-0") on an A2/C sheet of vellum. It would be appropriate to place the fireplace section and wall sections on one sheet.
a. Draw a front and a plan view of the firebox. Dimension all these drawings fully.
b. Draw a section taken vertically through the chimney. Label and add the height dimensions required.

Step 28:
Compile window and door schedules for the set of house plans and identify each of these items on the floor plans. Data from manufacturers' catalogues should be incorporated into the charts. Other schedules for materials, fixtures, etc. may be added.

It is a good idea to have all schedules contained on one sheet to facilitate ordering.

Step 29:
The drawing of the window and door sections is optional. Details of interior woodwork can also be shown if desired. The usual scale for these drawings is 1:20 (1/2" = 1'-0").

Step 30:
a. Check all the sheets that will make up the set of working drawings and see that the title blocks are complete.
b. Collate all the sheets and number them according to the order in which they will be used.

c. Compare with the checklist provided and print a complete set of working drawings.

The project, which was to design and draw a set of presentation and working drawings, has now been completed. As you move into your future career, you will recognize the value of completing this work.

Career Information

ARCHITECTURAL TECHNOLOGIST

An architectural technologist works as a skilled technical assistant to an architect. Your work is done primarily at a drafting desk during working hours, but you may also be required to occasionally do some outside work at the site of the project. You must understand construction methods and materials and be able to supervise construction.

To do the job successfully, you should have the ability to make precise drawings that pay attention to detail and enjoy working on projects alone. Because being able to do mathematical calculations is another important skill, you should have a Secondary School Graduation Diploma that emphasizes your strength in mathematics. It's usually desirable to have a knowledge of computer-aided design.

Most employers will expect you to have successfully completed a three-year program in architectural technology at a community college. A two-year course as a technician is also available, but the three-year program is the most advisable.

ARCHITECT

An architect is involved in all stages of construction work from discussing the concept with the client to overseeing the execution of the project. An architect's job can be a demanding and stressful one. A great deal of your day will be spent in the office, but you must periodically visit the construction site. Creating drawings with precision is a solitary aspect of the job, but you must also be able to work with the clients and the construction team. Architects can choose from a wide range of specialties within the field — city planning, industrial complexes, individual homes, etc.

Your Secondary School Honours Graduation Diploma should demonstrate a good standing in mathematics and science. It is a benefit to be familiar with computer-aided design. It is important to have an artistic imagination and good spatial perception.

In order to become an architect, you should follow your secondary education with the completion of an architectural degree program at a university and several years of internship with an established firm before you can become a registered professional.

CARTOGRAPHER

Most cartographers are hired by governments, municipalities, and land survey companies. There is a limited demand for cartographers.

A cartographer makes topographical maps and geophysics sections, which can include navigational weather forecasting, geographical exploration, traffic studies, and town planning. You would also gather map information, select scales, and design maps, sometimes in four colour. Because of this, it is necessary to be familiar with the graphic arts, lithography, and photographic processes. The job requires that you have the ability to concentrate and are patient; that you have good eyesight; that you are neat, accurate, and good at drawing.

You will need to take courses that show your strength in mathematics and physical sciences; a knowledge of computers is an asset. After you have successfully completed the requirements for your Secondary School Graduation Diploma, it is possible to find a job that will give you on-the-job training for about two years. It is preferable, however, to take a two-years' technician's course in cartography at a community college. Universities sometimes offer cartography as a related subject in the geography department.

CIVIL ENGINEER

A civil engineer may work for an engineering consulting firm or for a government office. If you are a civil engineer, you design and supervise the construction of all kinds of public structures, working with many different types of specialists. You may work outdoors for part of the time.

A civil engineer is the kind of person who likes solving technical and scientific problems. Your high school Graduation Diploma will have Ontario Academic Credits in mathematics, physics, and chemistry. To become a registered professional civil engineer, you will take a four-year degree program in engineering offered at several universities, followed by two years of work on related jobs. There are a limited number of jobs in the field, but they are well paid.

DRAFTSPERSON

A drafting job requires you to prepare architectural drawings. You may often work alone, but must be able to integrate your work with that of other technicians. Neatness, accuracy, and attention to detail are important. You must be flexible and able to adjust to changing parameters. You will be interested in creative computer work and have confidence in your mathematical ability.

Your education should include courses in architectural or mechanical drafting and some mathematics, leading to your Secondary School Graduation Diploma. A knowledge of computers is desirable. It is often possible to find a job after high school that will provide you with training, but it is advisable to take a college course of one or two years' length. Evening courses in drafting are also available.

INTERIOR DESIGNER AND DECORATOR

The responsibilities of an interior designer or decorator vary according to the stage of your career and the branch of occupation chosen. You can expect to develop decorating plans using sketches, photographs, and models; present plans to clients; and make estimations of costs. Your working hours are likely to be irregular as you go on field trips to offices, homes, or stores.

You must have a good colour sense, be sensitive to line and texture, and able to create three-dimensional drawings. An ability to express ideas with sketches or drawings and some interest in the history of design, furniture, and architecture are also important. You must be good at dealing with people. It's advisable to have some knowledge of computers.

There are several ways to enter this profession and there are various levels at which you can enter. You can receive a Bachelor of Interior Design by completing your Secondary School Graduation Diploma and a three- or four-year university program. Another route is to complete a community college program. This will equip you to work as an assistant to a designer or as a salesperson in furniture and decorating stores. Having completed a degree program, you may find employment with a firm of designers or architects, in contract sales, department stores, and planning offices of hotels and restaurant chains. It is possible to undertake freelance work as well.

REAL ESTATE APPRAISER

A real estate appraiser assesses the value of property, taking into account location, depreciation, and impending changes that could influence future market values. The job includes some travelling but is mainly indoor work with regular office hours. Occasionally you may be asked to do some overtime. You must enjoy business contact with people, be good at arithmetical calculations, and be confident in business transactions.

To enter the field, you need a Secondary School Graduation Diploma with a good standing in mathematics. Then you must complete a real estate appraisers' program, usually available in the evenings. It includes specific university-level courses. You also need three years of practical experience before you are accredited. The Appraisal Institute of Canada grants two designations: (1) the Accredited Appraiser, Canadian Institute (AACI) may be used by the holder in connection with all types of property, both residential and commercial; (2) the Canadian Residential Appraiser (CRA) is an intermediate designation that may be used by the holder only in connection with individual undeveloped residential site dwellings.

REAL ESTATE SALES REPRESENTATIVE

A real estate sales representative acts as an agent for people who sell, buy, and lease land, houses, apartments, and commercial buildings. The job involves outdoor and indoor work with some travelling. The hours are irregular and there is evening and weekend work. Payment is by commission only (you are not on a regular salary). You must enjoy business contact with a variety of people, have good sales initiative, and the ability to influence others.

You must be over the age of 18 and a permanent resident of your province. You must also have a potential position with a registered real estate broker. Several community colleges offer a pre-licensing course that you must take. It is 150 hours long and is usually available in the evenings. You must also register with the registrar of real estate and business brokers.

SET DESIGNER

Set designers are hired by theatres, so you will probably have to move around to various theatres in different cities to develop experience. The work is almost always indoor. The work is well paid, but frequently seasonal.

Your visual sense of structure and colour must be above average. You must be able to mentally picture shapes and positions of objects in space and have some feeling for the historical design of furniture and costumes. Artistic ability, especially in model making, is important. You will be working with other creative individuals and must be sensitive to their ideas.

Once you have complete your Secondary School Graduation Diploma, you can take a one- or two-year college course or a three- or four-year university degree program in production. This will usually be followed by a two-year training as an assistant set designer.

SURVEYOR

A surveyor measures the elevation, location, and shape of specific areas of land. These surveys are used in map making, exploration, and town planning. You would also prepare land descriptions and plans. Surveyors often specialize in areas such as geodetic surveying, topographical surveying, hydrographical surveying, and mine work, as well as land surveying.

The work is undertaken at all times of the year, both indoor and outdoor, and can be physically demanding but also often involves team work. You must be able to measure, calculate, and draft with care and precision. A knowledge of computers is useful, as well as an ability to work with electronic equipment.

To become a surveyor, you need a Secondary School Graduation Diploma. Your high school credits should be in physics, geography, and chemistry. You would then take a four-year university course in survey science, leading to a bachelor of science degree. To work as a surveyor, you must be registered with the Ontario Land Surveyors' Association, which governs the profession.

SURVEY TECHNOLOGIST

An assistant to a surveyor on the work site is called a survey technologist. In this job, you study aerial photographs, search legal titles, prepare plans, operate survey equipment, and maintain files. Most of the work is outside at the site and can be physically demanding, so it is important to be in good physical condition. A great deal of the work is team work, and you may be called upon to do some supervisory work.

You need to be able to make careful, accurate measurements and calculations, have some skill in drafting and sketching, and have an interest in computer work.

You will need Grade 12 high school credits in english and mathematics. A Secondary School Graduation Diploma is an asset. You can take a three-year program in Survey Technology at a community college. This, with two years' work experience, will lead to certification by the Association of Certified Survey Technologists. A two-year technicians' program is also available. This qualification requires two years of experience to become qualified.

TABLE 1 — NATURAL SINES

Deg	0'	6'	12'	18'	24'	30'	36'	42'	48'	54'	1	2	3	4	5
											Mean Difference				
0	.00000	00175	00349	00524	00698	00873	01047	01222	01396	01571	29	58	87	117	145
1	.01745	01920	02094	02269	02443	02618	02792	02967	03141	03316	29	58	87	117	145
2	.03490	03664	03839	04013	04188	04362	04536	04711	04885	05059	29	58	87	116	145
3	.05234	05408	05582	05756	05931	06105	06279	06453	06627	06802	29	58	87	116	145
4	.06976	07150	07324	07498	07672	07846	08020	08194	08368	08542	29	58	87	116	145
5	.08716	08889	09063	09237	09411	09585	09758	09932	10106	10279	29	58	87	116	145
6	.10453	10626	10800	10973	11147	11320	11494	11667	11840	12014	29	58	87	116	145
7	.12187	12360	12533	12706	12880	13053	13226	13399	13572	13744	29	58	87	115	144
8	.13917	14090	14263	14436	14608	14781	14954	15126	15299	15471	29	58	86	115	144
9	.15643	15816	15988	16160	16333	16505	16677	16849	17021	17193	29	57	86	115	144
10	.17365	17537	17708	17880	18052	18224	18395	18567	18738	18910	29	57	86	114	143
11	.19081	19252	19423	19595	19766	19937	20108	20279	20450	20620	29	57	86	114	143
12	.20791	20962	21132	21303	21474	21644	21814	21985	22155	22325	28	57	85	114	142
13	.22495	22665	22835	23005	23175	23345	23514	23684	23853	24023	28	57	85	113	141
14	.24192	24362	24531	24700	24869	25038	25207	25376	25545	25713	28	56	85	113	141
15	.25882	26050	26219	26387	26556	26724	26892	27060	27228	27396	28	56	84	112	140
16	.27564	27731	27899	28067	28234	28402	28569	28736	28903	29070	28	56	84	112	139
17	.29237	29404	29571	29737	29904	30071	30237	30403	30570	30736	28	56	83	111	139
18	.30902	31068	31233	31399	31565	31730	31896	32061	32227	32392	28	55	83	110	138
19	.32557	32722	32887	33051	33216	33381	33545	33710	33874	34038	27	55	82	110	137
20	.34202	34366	34530	34694	34857	35021	35184	35347	35511	35674	27	55	82	109	136
21	.35837	36000	36162	36325	36488	36650	36812	36975	37137	37299	27	54	81	108	135
22	.37461	37622	37784	37946	38107	38268	38430	38591	38752	38912	27	54	81	107	134
23	.39073	39234	39394	39555	39715	39875	40035	40195	40355	40514	27	53	80	107	133
24	.40674	40833	40992	41151	41310	41469	41628	41787	41945	42104	27	53	79	106	132
25	.42262	42420	42578	42736	42894	43051	43209	43366	43523	43680	26	53	79	105	131
26	.43837	43994	44151	44307	44464	44620	44776	44932	45088	45243	26	52	78	104	130
27	.45399	45554	45710	45865	46020	46175	46330	46484	46639	46793	26	52	77	103	129
28	.46947	47101	47255	47409	47562	47716	47869	48022	48175	48328	26	51	77	102	128
29	.48481	48634	48786	48938	49090	49242	49394	49546	49697	49849	25	51	76	101	126
30	.50000	50151	50302	50453	50603	50754	50904	51054	51204	51354	25	50	75	100	125
31	.51504	51653	51803	51952	52101	52250	52399	52547	52696	52844	25	50	74	99	124
32	.52992	53140	53288	53435	53583	53730	53877	54024	54171	54317	25	49	74	98	123
33	.54464	54610	54756	54902	55048	55194	55339	55484	55630	55775	24	49	73	97	121
34	.55919	56064	56208	56353	56497	56641	56784	56928	57071	57215	24	48	72	96	120
35	.57358	57501	57643	57786	57928	58070	58212	58354	58496	58637	24	48	71	95	118
36	.58778	58920	59061	59201	59342	59482	59622	59763	59902	60042	23	47	70	94	117
37	.60181	60321	60460	60599	60738	60876	61015	61153	61291	61429	23	46	69	92	115
38	.61566	61704	61841	61978	62115	62251	62388	62524	62660	62796	23	46	68	91	114
39	.62932	63068	63203	63338	63473	63608	63742	63877	64011	64145	23	45	67	90	112
40	.64279	64412	64546	64679	64812	64945	65077	65210	65342	65474	22	44	66	88	111
41	.65606	65738	65869	66000	66131	66262	66393	66523	66653	66783	22	44	65	87	109
42	.66913	67043	67172	67301	67430	67559	67688	67816	67944	68072	22	43	64	86	107
43	.68200	68327	68455	68582	68709	68835	68962	69088	69214	69340	21	42	63	84	106
44	.69466	69591	69717	69842	69966	70091	70215	70339	70463	70587	21	41	62	83	104
45	.70711	70834	70957	71080	71203	71325	71447	71569	71691	71813	20	41	61	82	102
46	.71934	72055	72176	72297	72417	72537	72657	72777	72897	73016	20	40	60	80	100
47	.73135	73254	73373	73491	73610	73728	73846	73963	74080	74198	20	39	59	79	98
48	.74314	74431	74548	74664	74780	74896	75011	75126	75241	75356	20	39	58	77	96
49	.75471	75585	75700	75813	75927	76041	76154	76267	76380	76492	19	38	57	76	94
50	.76604	76717	76828	76940	77051	77162	77273	77384	77494	77605	19	37	56	74	93
51	.77715	77824	77934	78043	78152	78261	78369	78478	78586	78694	18	36	54	72	91
52	.78801	78908	79015	79122	79229	79335	79441	79547	79653	79758	18	35	53	71	89
53	.79864	79968	80073	80178	80282	80386	80489	80593	80696	80799	17	35	52	69	87
54	.80902	81004	81106	81208	81310	81412	81513	81614	81714	81815	17	34	51	68	84
55	.81915	82015	82115	82214	82314	82413	82511	82610	82708	82806	16	33	49	66	82
56	.82904	83001	83098	83195	83292	83389	83485	83581	83676	83772	16	32	48	64	80
57	.83867	83962	84057	84151	84245	84339	84433	84526	84619	84712	16	31	47	62	78
58	.84805	84897	84987	85081	85173	85264	85355	85446	85536	85627	15	31	46	61	76
59	.85717	85806	85896	85985	86074	86163	86251	86340	86427	86515	15	30	44	59	74
60	.86603	86690	86777	86863	86949	87036	87121	87207	87292	87377	14	29	43	57	72
61	.87462	87546	87631	87715	87798	87882	87965	88048	88130	88213	14	28	42	56	69
62	.88295	88377	88458	88539	88620	88701	88782	88862	88942	89021	14	27	40	54	67
63	.89101	89180	89259	89337	89415	89493	89571	89649	89726	89803	13	26	39	52	65
64	.89879	89956	90032	90108	90183	90259	90334	90408	90483	90557	13	25	38	50	63
65	.90631	90704	90778	90851	90924	90996	91068	91140	91212	91283	12	24	36	48	60
66	.91355	91425	91496	91566	91636	91706	91775	91845	91914	91982	12	23	35	46	58
67	.92050	92119	92186	92254	92321	92388	92455	92521	92587	92653	11	22	33	45	56
68	.92718	92784	92849	92913	92978	93042	93106	93169	93232	93295	11	21	32	43	54
69	.93358	93420	93483	93544	93606	93667	93728	93789	93849	93909	10	20	31	41	51
70	.93969	94029	94088	94147	94206	94264	94322	94380	94438	94495	10	19	29	39	49
71	.94552	94609	94665	94721	94777	94832	94888	94943	94997	95052	9	18	28	37	46
72	.95106	95159	95213	95266	95319	95372	95424	95476	95528	95579	9	17	26	35	44
73	.95630	95681	95732	95782	95832	95882	95931	95981	96029	96078	8	17	25	33	41
74	.96126	96174	96222	96269	96316	96363	96410	96456	96502	96547	8	16	23	31	39
75	.96593	96638	96682	96727	96771	96815	96858	96902	96945	96987	7	16	22	29	36
76	.97030	97072	97113	97155	97196	97237	97278	97318	97358	97398	7	14	20	27	34
77	.97437	97476	97515	97553	97592	97630	97667	97705	97742	97778	6	13	19	25	32
78	.97815	97851	97887	97922	97958	97992	98027	98061	98096	98129	6	12	17	23	29
79	.98163	98196	98229	98261	98294	98325	98357	98388	98420	98450	5	11	16	21	27
80	.98481	98511	98541	98570	98600	98629	98657	98686	98714	98741	5	10	14	19	24
81	.98769	98796	98823	98849	98876	98902	98927	98953	98978	99002	4	9	13	17	22
82	.99027	99051	99075	99098	99122	99144	99167	99189	99211	99233	4	8	11	15	19
83	.99255	99276	99297	99317	99337	99357	99377	99396	99415	99434	3	7	10	13	16
84	.99452	99470	99488	99506	99523	99540	99556	99572	99588	99604	3	6	8	11	14
85	.99619	99635	99649	99664	99678	99692	99705	99719	99731	99744	2	5	7	9	11
86	.99756	99768	99780	99792	99803	99813	99824	99834	99844	99854	2	4	5	7	9
87	.99863	99872	99881	99889	99897	99905	99912	99919	99926	99933	1	3	4	5	6
88	.99939	99945	99951	99956	99961	99966	99970	99974	99978	99982	1	2	2	3	4
89	.99985	99988	99990	99993	99995	99996	99998	99999	99999	99999	0	1	1	1	1
90	1.00000														

TABLE 2 NATURAL COSINES

Deg	0'	6'	12'	18'	24'	30'	36'	42'	48'	54'	Mean Difference 1	2	3	4	5
0	1.00000	99999	99999	99999	99998	99996	99995	99993	99990	99988	0	1	1	1	1
1	.99985	99982	99978	99974	99970	99966	99961	99956	99951	99945	1	2	2	3	4
2	.99939	99933	99926	99919	99912	99905	99897	99889	99881	99872	1	3	4	5	6
3	.99863	99854	99844	99834	99824	99813	99803	99792	99780	99768	2	4	5	7	9
4	.99756	99744	99731	99719	99705	99692	99678	99664	99649	99635	2	5	7	9	11
5	.99619	99604	99588	99572	99556	99540	99523	99506	99488	99470	3	6	8	11	14
6	.99452	99434	99415	99396	99377	99357	99337	99317	99297	99276	3	7	10	13	16
7	.99255	99233	99211	99189	99167	99144	99122	99098	99075	99051	4	8	11	15	19
8	.99027	99002	98978	98953	98927	98902	98876	98849	98823	98796	4	9	13	17	22
9	.98769	98741	98714	98686	98657	98629	98600	98570	98541	98511	5	10	14	19	24
10	.98481	98450	98420	98388	98357	98325	98294	98261	98229	98196	5	11	16	21	27
11	.98163	98129	98096	98061	98027	97992	97958	97922	97887	97851	6	12	17	23	29
12	.97815	97778	97742	97705	97667	97630	97592	97553	97515	97476	6	13	19	25	32
13	.97437	97398	97358	97318	97278	97237	97196	97155	97113	97072	7	14	20	27	34
14	.97030	96987	96945	96902	96858	96815	96771	96727	96682	96638	7	16	22	29	36
15	.96593	96547	96502	96456	96410	96363	96316	96269	96222	96174	8	16	23	31	39
16	.96126	96078	96029	95981	95931	95882	95832	95782	95732	95681	8	17	25	33	41
17	.95630	95579	95528	95476	95424	95372	95319	95266	95213	95159	9	17	26	35	44
18	.95106	95052	94997	94943	94888	94832	94777	94721	94665	94609	9	18	28	37	46
19	.94552	94495	94438	94380	94322	94264	94206	94147	94088	94029	10	19	29	39	49
20	.93969	93909	93849	93789	93728	93667	93606	93544	93483	93420	10	20	31	41	51
21	.93358	93295	93232	93169	93106	93042	92978	92913	92849	92784	10	21	32	43	54
22	.92718	92653	92587	92521	92455	92388	92321	92254	92186	92119	11	22	33	45	56
23	.92050	91982	91914	91845	91775	91706	91636	91566	91496	91425	11	23	35	46	58
24	.91355	91283	91212	91140	91068	90996	90924	90851	90778	90704	12	24	36	48	60
25	.90631	90557	90483	90408	90334	90259	90183	90108	90032	89956	13	25	38	50	63
26	.89879	89803	89726	89649	89571	89493	89415	89337	89259	89180	13	26	39	52	65
27	.89101	89021	88942	88862	88782	88701	88620	88539	88458	88377	13	27	40	54	67
28	.88295	88213	88130	88048	87965	87882	87798	87715	87631	87546	14	28	42	56	69
29	.87462	87377	87292	87207	87121	87036	86949	86863	86777	86690	14	29	43	57	72
30	.86603	86515	86427	86340	86251	86163	86074	85985	85896	85806	15	30	44	59	74
31	.85717	85627	85536	85446	85355	85264	85173	85081	84989	84897	16	30	46	61	76
32	.84805	84712	84619	84526	84433	84339	84245	84151	84057	83962	16	31	47	62	78
33	.83867	83772	83676	83581	83485	83389	83292	83195	83098	83001	16	32	48	64	80
34	.82904	82806	82708	82610	82511	82413	82314	82214	82115	82015	16	33	49	66	82
35	.81915	81815	81714	81614	81513	81412	81310	81208	81106	81004	17	34	51	68	84
36	.80902	80799	80696	80593	80489	80386	80282	80178	80073	79968	17	35	52	69	87
37	.79864	79758	79653	79547	79441	79335	79229	79122	79015	78908	18	35	53	71	89
38	.78801	78693	78586	78478	78369	78261	78152	78043	77934	77824	18	36	54	72	91
39	.77715	77605	77494	77384	77273	77162	77051	76940	76828	76717	18	37	56	74	93
40	.76604	76492	76380	76267	76154	76041	75927	75813	75700	75585	19	38	57	76	94
41	.75471	75356	75241	75126	75011	74896	74780	74664	74548	74431	19	39	58	77	96
42	.74314	74198	74080	73963	73846	73728	73610	73491	73373	73254	20	39	59	79	98
43	.73135	73016	72897	72777	72657	72537	72417	72297	72176	72055	20	40	60	80	100
44	.71934	71813	71691	71569	71447	71325	71203	71080	70957	70834	20	41	61	82	102
45	.70711	70587	70463	70339	70215	70091	69966	69842	69717	69591	21	41	62	83	104
46	.69466	69340	69214	69088	68962	68835	68709	68582	68455	68327	21	42	63	84	106
47	.68200	68072	67944	67816	67688	67559	67430	67301	67172	67043	21	43	64	86	107
48	.66913	66783	66653	66523	66393	66262	66131	66000	65869	65738	22	44	65	87	109
49	.65606	65474	65342	65210	65077	64945	64812	64679	64546	64412	22	44	66	88	111
50	.64279	64145	64011	63877	63742	63608	63473	63338	63203	63068	22	45	67	90	112
51	.62932	62796	62660	62524	62388	62251	62115	61978	61841	61704	23	45	68	91	114
52	.61566	61429	61291	61153	61015	60876	60738	60599	60460	60321	23	46	69	92	115
53	.60181	60042	59902	59763	59622	59482	59342	59201	59061	58920	23	47	70	94	117
54	.58779	58637	58496	58354	58212	58070	57928	57786	57643	57501	24	47	71	95	118
55	.57358	57215	57071	56928	56784	56641	56497	56353	56208	56064	24	48	72	96	120
56	.55919	55775	55630	55484	55339	55194	55048	54902	54756	54610	24	49	73	97	121
57	.54464	54317	54171	54024	53877	53730	53583	53435	53288	53140	24	49	74	98	123
58	.52992	52844	52696	52547	52399	52250	52101	51952	51803	51653	25	50	74	99	124
59	51504	51354	51204	51054	50904	50754	50603	50453	50302	50151	25	50	75	100	125
60	.50000	49849	49697	49546	49394	49242	49090	48938	48786	48634	25	51	76	101	126
61	.48481	48328	48175	48022	47869	47716	47562	47409	47255	47101	26	51	77	102	128
62	.46947	46793	46639	46484	46330	46175	46020	45865	45710	45554	26	52	77	103	129
63	.45399	45243	45088	44932	44776	44620	44464	44307	44151	43994	26	52	78	104	130
64	.43837	43680	43523	43366	43209	43051	42894	42736	42578	42420	26	53	79	105	131
65	.42262	42104	41945	41787	41628	41469	41310	41151	40992	40833	26	53	79	106	132
66	.40674	40514	40355	40195	40035	39875	39715	39555	39394	39234	27	53	80	107	133
67	.39073	38912	38752	38591	38430	38268	38107	37946	37784	37622	27	54	81	107	134
68	.37461	37299	37137	36975	36812	36650	36488	36325	36162	36000	27	54	81	108	135
69	.35837	35674	35511	35347	35184	35021	34857	34694	34530	34366	27	54	82	109	136
70	.34202	34038	33874	33710	33545	33381	33216	33051	32887	32722	27	55	82	110	137
71	.32557	32392	32227	32061	31896	31730	31565	31399	31233	31068	28	55	83	110	138
72	.30902	30736	30570	30403	30237	30071	29904	29737	29571	29404	28	56	83	111	139
73	.29237	29070	28903	28736	28569	28402	28234	28067	27899	27731	28	56	84	112	139
74	.27564	27396	27228	27060	26892	26724	26556	26387	26219	26050	28	56	84	112	140
75	.25882	25713	25545	25376	25207	25038	24869	24700	24531	24362	28	56	85	113	141
76	.24192	24023	23853	23684	23514	23345	23175	23005	22835	22665	28	57	85	113	141
77	.22495	22325	22155	21985	21814	21644	21474	21303	21132	20962	28	57	85	114	142
78	.20791	20620	20450	20279	20108	19937	19766	19595	19423	19252	29	57	86	114	143
79	.19081	18910	18738	18567	18395	18224	18052	17880	17708	17537	29	57	86	114	143
80	.17365	17193	17021	16849	16677	16505	16333	16160	15988	15816	29	57	86	115	144
81	.15643	15471	15299	15126	14954	14781	14608	14436	14263	14090	29	58	86	115	144
82	.13917	13744	13572	13399	13226	13053	12880	12706	12533	12360	29	58	87	115	144
83	.12187	12014	11840	11667	11494	11320	11147	10973	10800	10626	29	58	87	116	145
84	.10453	10279	10106	09932	09758	09585	09411	09237	09063	08889	29	58	87	116	145
85	.08716	08542	08368	08194	08020	07846	07672	07498	07324	07150	29	58	87	116	145
86	.06976	06802	06627	06453	06279	06105	05931	05756	05582	05408	29	58	87	116	145
87	.05234	05059	04885	04711	04536	04362	04188	04013	03839	03664	29	58	87	116	145
88	.03490	03316	03141	02967	02792	02618	02443	02269	02094	01920	29	58	87	117	145
89	.01745	01571	01396	01222	01047	00873	00698	00524	00349	00175	29	58	87	117	145
90	.00000														

TABLE 3   NATURAL TANGENTS

Deg	0'	6'	12'	18'	24'	30'	36'	42'	48'	54'	Mean Difference 1	2	3	4	5
0	.00000	00175	00349	00524	00698	00873	01047	01222	01396	01571	29	58	87	116	146
1	.01746	01920	02095	02269	02444	02619	02793	02968	03143	03317	29	58	87	116	146
2	.03492	03667	03842	04016	04191	04366	04541	04716	04891	05066	29	58	87	117	146
3	.05241	05416	05591	05766	05941	06116	06291	06467	06642	06817	29	58	88	117	146
4	.06993	07168	07344	07519	07695	07870	08046	08221	08397	08573	29	59	88	117	146
5	.08749	08925	09101	09277	09453	09629	09805	09981	10158	10334	29	59	88	117	147
6	.10510	10687	10863	11040	11217	11394	11570	11747	11924	12101	29	59	88	118	147
7	.12278	12456	12633	12810	12988	13165	13343	13521	13698	13876	30	59	89	118	148
8	.14054	14232	14410	14588	14767	14945	15124	15302	15481	15660	30	59	89	119	149
9	.15838	16017	16196	16376	16555	16734	16914	17093	17273	17453	30	60	90	120	150
10	.17633	17813	17993	18173	18353	18534	18714	18895	19076	19257	30	60	90	120	150
11	.19438	19619	19801	19982	20164	20345	20527	20709	20891	21073	30	60	91	121	152
12	.21256	21438	21621	21804	21986	22169	22353	22536	22719	22903	30	61	92	122	153
13	.23087	23271	23455	23639	23823	24008	24193	24377	24562	24747	31	61	93	124	155
14	.24933	25118	25304	25490	25676	25862	26048	26235	26421	26608	31	62	93	124	155
15	.26795	26982	27169	27357	27545	27732	27920	28109	28297	28486	31	63	94	125	157
16	.28675	28864	29053	29242	29432	29621	29811	30001	30192	30382	32	63	95	127	158
17	.30573	30764	30955	31147	31338	31530	31722	31914	32106	32299	32	64	96	128	160
18	.32492	32685	32878	33072	33266	33460	33654	33848	34043	34238	32	65	97	129	162
19	.34433	34628	34824	35019	35216	35412	35608	35805	36002	36199	33	66	98	131	164
20	.36397	36595	36793	36991	37190	37388	37588	37787	37986	38186	33	66	99	133	166
21	.38386	38587	38787	38988	39190	39391	39593	39795	39997	40200	34	67	101	134	168
22	.40403	40606	40809	41013	41217	41421	41626	41831	42036	42242	34	68	102	136	170
23	.42447	42654	42860	43067	43274	43481	43689	43897	44105	44314	34	69	104	138	173
24	.44523	44732	44942	45152	45362	45573	45784	45995	46206	46418	35	70	105	141	176
25	.46631	46843	47056	47270	47483	47698	47912	48127	48342	48557	36	71	107	143	179
26	.48773	48989	49206	49423	49640	49858	50076	50295	50514	50733	36	73	109	145	182
27	.50953	51173	51393	51614	51835	52057	52279	52501	52724	52947	37	74	111	148	185
28	.53171	53395	53620	53844	54070	54296	54522	54748	54975	55203	38	75	113	151	188
29	.55431	55659	55888	56117	56347	56577	56808	57039	57271	57503	38	77	115	154	192
30	.57735	57968	58201	58435	58670	58905	59140	59376	59612	59849	39	78	118	157	196
31	.60086	60324	60562	60801	61040	61280	61520	61761	62003	62245	40	79	120	160	200
32	.62487	62730	62973	63217	63462	63707	63953	64199	64446	64693	41	82	123	164	205
33	.64941	65189	65438	65688	65938	66189	66440	66692	66944	67197	42	84	126	167	209
34	.67451	67705	67960	68215	68471	68728	68985	69243	69502	69761	43	86	129	171	214
35	.70021	70281	70542	70804	71066	71329	71593	71857	72122	72388	44	88	132	176	219
36	.72654	72921	73189	73457	73726	73996	74267	74538	74810	75082	45	90	135	180	225
37	.75355	75629	75904	76180	76456	76733	77010	77289	77568	77848	46	92	139	185	231
38	.78129	78410	78692	78975	79259	79544	79829	80115	80402	80690	47	95	142	190	237
39	.80978	81268	81558	81849	82141	82434	82727	83022	83317	83613	49	98	147	195	244
40	.83910	84208	84507	84806	85107	85408	85710	86014	86318	86623	50	100	151	201	252
41	.86929	87236	87543	87852	88162	88473	88784	89097	89410	89725	52	103	155	207	259
42	.90040	90357	90674	90993	91313	91633	91955	92277	92601	92926	53	107	160	214	268
43	.93252	93578	93906	94235	94565	94896	95229	95562	95897	96232	55	111	165	221	276
44	.96569	96907	97246	97586	97927	98270	98613	98950	99304	99652	57	114	171	229	286
45	1.00000	00350	00701	01053	01406	01761	02117	02474	02832	03192	58	118	177	237	296
46	1.03553	03915	04279	04644	05010	05378	05747	06117	06489	06862	61	123	184	245	307
47	1.07237	07613	07990	08369	08749	09131	09514	09899	10285	10672	63	127	191	255	319
48	1.11061	11452	11844	12238	12633	13029	13428	13828	14229	14632	66	132	199	265	331
49	1.15037	15443	15851	16261	16672	17085	17500	17916	18334	18754	69	138	207	276	344
50	1.19175	19599	20024	20451	20879	21310	21742	22176	22612	23050	72	143	216	288	359
51	1.23490	23931	24375	24820	25268	25717	26169	26622	27077	27535	75	150	225	300	375
52	1.27994	28456	28919	29385	29853	30323	30795	31269	31745	32224	78	157	235	314	392
53	1.32704	33187	33673	34160	34650	35142	35637	36134	36633	37134	82	164	247	329	411
54	1.37638	38145	38653	39165	39679	40195	40714	41235	41759	42286	86	172	259	345	431
55	1.42815	43347	43881	44418	44958	45501	46046	46595	47146	47700	91	181	272	362	453
56	1.48256	48816	49378	49944	50512	51084	51658	52235	52816	53400	95	191	286	382	477
57	1.53987	54576	55170	55767	56366	56969	57575	58184	58797	59414	100	201	302	403	504
58	1.60033	60657	61283	61914	62548	63185	63826	64471	65120	65772	106	213	319	426	533
59	1.66428	67088	67752	68419	69091	69766	70446	71129	71817	72509	113	226	339	452	564
60	1.73205	73905	74610	75319	76032	76749	77471	78198	78929	79665	120	240	360	481	600
61	1.80405	81150	81900	82654	83413	84177	84946	85720	86500	87283	128	255	383	511	639
62	1.88073	88867	89667	90472	91282	92098	92920	93746	95379	94517	136	273	409	546	683
63	1.96261	97111	97967	98828	99695	2.00569	2.01449	2.02335	2.03227	2.04125	146	292	438	584	731
64	2.05030	05942	06860	07785	08716	09654	10600	11552	12511	13477	157	314	471	629	786
65	2.14451	15432	16420	17416	18419	19430	20449	21475	22510	23553	169	338	508	677	846
66	2.24604	25663	26730	27806	28891	29984	31086	32197	33317	34447	183	366	549	732	915
67	2.35585	36733	37891	39058	40235	41421	42618	43825	45043	46270	199	397	596	795	994
68	2.47509	48758	50018	51289	52571	53865	55170	56487	57815	59156					
69	2.60509	61874	63252	64642	66046	67462	68892	70335	71792	73263					
70	2.74748	76247	77761	79289	80833	82391	83965	85556	87161	88783					
71	2.90421	92076	93748	95437	97144	98868	3.00611	3.02372	3.04152	3.05950					
72	3.07768	09606	11464	13341	15240	17159	19100	21063	23048	25055					
73	3.27085	29139	31216	33317	35443	37594	39771	41973	44202	46458					
74	3.48741	51053	53393	55761	58160	60588	63048	65538	68061	70616					
75	3.73205	75828	78485	81177	83906	86671	89474	92316	95196	98117					
76	4.01078	04081	07127	10216	13350	16530	19756	23030	26352	29124					
77	4.33148	36623	40152	43735	47374	51071	54826	58641	62518	66458					
78	4.70463	74534	78673	82882	87162	91516	95945	5.00451	5.05037	5.09704					
79	5.14455	19293	24218	29235	34345	39552	44857	50264	55777	61397					
80	5.67128	72974	78938	85024	91236	97576	6.04051	6.10664	6.17419	6.24321					
81	6.31375	38587	45961	53503	61220	69116	77199	85475	93952	7.02736					
82	7.11537	20661	30018	39616	49465	59575	69957	80622	91582	8.02848					
83	8.14435	26356	38625	51259	64275	77689	91520	9.05789	9.20516	9.35724					
84	9.51436	9.6768	9.8448	10.019	10.199	10.385	10.579	10.780	10.988	11.205					
85	11.4301	11.664	11.909	12.163	12.429	12.706	12.996	13.300	13.617	13.951					
86	14.3007	14.669	15.056	15.464	15.895	16.350	16.832	17.343	17.886	18.464					
87	19.0811	19.740	20.446	21.205	22.022	22.904	23.859	24.898	26.031	27.271					
88	28.6363	30.145	31.821	33.694	35.801	38.188	40.917	44.066	47.740	52.081					
89	57.2900	63.657	71.615	81.847	95.489	114.589	143.237	190.984	286.48	572.96					
90	∞														

TABLE 4   METRIC FLOOR JOISTS — LIVING QUARTERS (live load 1.9 kN/m²)

Commercial Designation	Grade	Metric Size	Live Load 1.9 kN/m² All Ceilings Joist Spacing		
			300 mm	400 mm	600 mm
		mm	m	m	m
Spruce Pine Fir (includes Spruce – all species except Coast Sitka Spruce – Jack Pine, Lodgepole Pine, Balsam Fir and Alpine Fir)	Select structural	38 × 89	1.98	1.79	1.57
		38 × 140	3.11	2.82	2.46
		38 × 184	4.10	3.72	3.25
		38 × 235	5.23	4.75	4.15
		38 × 286	6.36	5.78	5.05
	No. 1	38 × 89	1.98	1.79	1.57
		38 × 140	3.11	2.82	2.41
		38 × 184	4.10	3.72	3.18
		38 × 235	5.23	4.75	4.06
		38 × 286	6.36	5.78	4.93
	No. 2	38 × 89	1.91	1.73	1.49
		38 × 140	3.00	2.65	2.16
		38 × 184	3.96	3.49	2.85
		38 × 235	5.05	4.46	3.64
		38 × 286	6.15	5.42	4.43
	No. 3	38 × 89	1.58	1.37	1.12
		38 × 140	2.33	2.02	1.65
		38 × 184	3.07	2.66	2.17
		38 × 235	3.92	3.40	2.77
		38 × 286	4.77	4.13	3.37
	Construction	38 × 89	1.80	1.56	1.27
	Standard	38 × 89	1.35	1.17	0.95
	Utility	38 × 89	0.92	0.80	0.65
Western Cedars (includes Western Red Cedar and Pacific Coast Yellow Cedar)	Select structural	38 × 89	1.90	1.73	1.51
		38 × 140	2.99	2.72	2.37
		38 × 184	3.94	3.58	3.13
		38 × 235	5.03	4.57	3.99
		38 × 286	6.12	5.56	4.86
	No. 1	38 × 89	1.90	1.73	1.51
		38 × 140	2.99	2.72	2.37
		38 × 184	3.94	3.58	3.13
		38 × 235	5.03	4.57	3.99
		38 × 286	6.12	5.56	4.86
	No. 2	38 × 89	1.84	1.67	1.46
		38 × 140	2.89	2.63	2.18
		38 × 184	3.81	3.46	2.87
		38 × 235	4.87	4.42	3.67
		38 × 286	5.92	5.38	4.46
	No. 3	38 × 89	1.58	1.37	1.12
		38 × 140	2.33	2.02	1.65
		38 × 184	3.07	2.66	2.17
		38 × 235	3.92	3.40	2.77
		38 × 286	4.77	4.13	3.37
	Construction	38 × 89	1.77	1.57	1.28
	Standard	38 × 89	1.35	1.17	0.95
	Utility	38 × 89	0.92	0.80	0.65

TABLE 5   METRIC MAXIMUM SPANS FOR STEEL BEAMS IN BASEMENTS, CELLARS AND CRAWL SPACES[1][3]

No. of Storeys	Minimum Depth mm*	Minimum Mass kg/m*	Width[2] of Floor to be Supported, m				
			2.4	3.0	3.6	4.2	4.8
1	101	11.46[4]	4.06	3.63	3.33	3.07	2.90
	127	14.88[4]	5.11	4.57	4.19	3.89	3.63
	152	18.60[4]	6.25	5.61	5.16	4.77	4.47
	152	23.07[5]	7.01	6.30	5.77	5.38	5.03
	203	25.30[5]	8.28	7.47	6.81	6.33	5.87
	203	27.38[4]	8.66	7.80	7.01	6.63	6.20
2	101	11.46[4]	3.08	2.74	2.52	2.34	2.18
	127	14.88[4]	3.89	3.48	3.18	2.94	2.74
	152	18.60[4]	4.77	4.27	3.91	3.61	3.38
	152	23.07[5]	5.38	4.80	4.39	4.06	3.81
	203	25.30[5]	6.33	5.66	5.18	4.80	4.50
	203	27.38[4]	6.63	5.96	5.44	5.03	4.72

Notes to Table 5

[1]   This table applies only to beams with laterally supported top flanges. A beam may be considered to be laterally supported if wood joists bear on its top flange at intervals of 600 mm or less over its entire length, and if all the load being applied to this beam is transmitted through the joists, and if 19 × 38 mm wood strips in contact with the top flange are nailed on both sides of the beam to the bottom of the joists supported. Other additional methods of positive lateral support are acceptable.

[2]   Supported joist length means 1/2 the sum of the joist spans on both sides of the beam.

[3]   For supported joist lengths intermediate between those shown in the table, straightline interpolation may be used in determining the maximum beam span.

[4]   Based on I-shaped sections.

[5]   Based on wide flange sections.

TABLE 6 METRIC FLOOR JOISTS — BEDROOMS AND ATTICS ACCESSIBLE BY A STAIRWAY (live load 1.4 kN/m²)

Commercial Designation	Grade	Metric Size	Gypsum Board or Plastered Ceiling Joist Spacing 300 mm	400 mm	600 mm	Other Ceilings Joist Spacing 300 mm	400 mm	600 mm
		mm	m	m	m	m	m	m
Spruce Pine Fir (includes Spruce – all species except Coast Sitka Spruce – Jack Pine, Lodgepole Pine, Balsam Fir and Alpine Fir)	Select structural	38 × 89	2.19	1.99	1.74	2.50	2.28	1.99
		38 × 140	3.44	3.13	2.73	3.94	3.58	2.95
		38 × 184	4.54	4.12	3.60	5.19	4.72	3.89
		38 × 235	5.79	5.26	4.59	6.63	6.02	4.97
		38 × 286	7.04	6.40	5.59	8.06	7.32	6.04
	No. 1	38 × 89	2.19	1.99	1.74	2.50	2.28	1.88
		38 × 140	3.44	3.13	2.73	3.88	3.36	2.75
		38 × 184	4.54	4.12	3.60	5.12	4.44	3.62
		38 × 235	5.79	5.26	4.59	6.54	5.66	4.62
		38 × 286	7.04	6.40	5.59	7.95	6.89	5.62
	No. 2	38 × 89	2.11	1.92	1.68	2.41	2.08	1.70
		38 × 140	3.33	3.02	2.46	3.49	3.02	2.46
		38 × 184	4.38	3.98	3.25	4.60	3.98	4.35
		38 × 235	5.60	5.08	4.15	5.87	5.08	4.15
		38 × 286	6.81	6.18	5.04	7.13	6.18	5.04
	No. 3	38 × 89	1.80	1.56	1.27	1.80	1.56	1.27
		38 × 140	2.65	2.30	1.88	2.65	2.30	1.88
		38 × 184	3.50	3.03	2.47	3.50	3.03	2.47
		38 × 235	4.47	3.87	3.16	4.47	3.87	3.16
		38 × 286	5.44	4.71	3.84	5.44	4.71	3.84
	Construction	38 × 89	2.04	1.77	1.45	2.05	1.77	1.45
	Standard	38 × 89	1.54	1.33	1.09	1.54	1.33	1.09
	Utility	38 × 89	1.05	0.91	0.74	1.05	0.91	0.74
Western Cedars (includes Western Red Cedar and Pacific Coast Yellow Cedar)	Select structural	38 × 89	2.11	1.91	1.67	2.41	2.19	1.91
		38 × 140	3.31	3.01	2.63	3.79	3.44	2.99
		38 × 184	4.37	3.97	3.47	5.00	4.54	3.94
		38 × 235	5.57	5.06	4.42	6.38	5.80	5.02
		38 × 286	6.78	6.16	5.38	7.76	7.05	6.11
	No. 1	38 × 89	2.11	1.91	1.67	2.41	2.19	1.90
		38 × 140	3.31	3.01	2.63	3.79	3.41	2.78
		38 × 184	4.37	3.97	3.47	5.00	4.49	3.67
		38 × 235	5.57	5.06	4.42	6.38	5.73	4.68
		38 × 286	6.78	6.16	5.38	7.76	6.97	5.69
	No. 2	38 × 89	2.04	1.85	1.61	2.33	2.11	1.72
		38 × 140	3.20	2.91	2.48	3.51	3.04	2.48
		38 × 184	4.22	3.84	3.27	4.63	4.01	3.27
		38 × 235	5.39	4.90	4.18	5.91	5.12	4.18
		38 × 286	6.55	5.95	5.08	7.19	6.23	5.08
	No. 3	38 × 89	1.80	1.56	1.27	1.80	1.56	1.27
		38 × 140	2.65	2.30	1.88	2.65	2.30	1.88
		38 × 184	3.50	3.03	2.47	3.50	3.03	2.47
		38 × 235	4.47	3.87	3.16	4.47	3.87	3.16
		38 × 286	5.44	4.71	3.84	5.44	4.71	3.84
	Construction	38 × 89	1.96	1.78	1.46	2.07	1.79	1.46
	Standard	38 × 89	1.54	1.33	1.09	1.54	1.33	1.09
	Utility	38 × 89	1.05	0.91	0.74	1.05	0.91	0.74

Commercial Designation	Grade	Metric Size	Live Load 0.5 kN/m²					
			Gypsum Board or Plastered Ceiling			Other Ceilings		
			Joist Spacing			Joist Spacing		
			300 mm	400 mm	600 mm	300 mm	400 mm	600 mm
		mm	m	m	m	m	m	m
Spruce Pine Fir (includes Spruce – all species except Coast Sitka Spruce – Jack Pine, Lodgepole Pine, Balsam Fir and Alpine Fir)	Select structural	38 × 89	3.09	2.80	2.45	3.53	3.21	2.80
		38 × 140	4.85	4.41	3.85	5.55	5.05	4.41
		38 × 184	6.40	5.81	5.08	7.32	6.65	5.81
		38 × 235	8.16	7.41	6.48	9.34	8.49	7.41
		38 × 286	9.93	9.02	7.88	11.36	10.33	9.02
	No. 1	38 × 89	3.09	2.80	2.45	3.53	3.21	2.80
		38 × 140	4.85	4.41	3.85	5.55	5.05	4.18
		38 × 184	6.40	5.81	5.08	7.32	6.65	5.51
		38 × 235	8.16	7.41	6.48	9.34	8.49	7.03
		38 × 286	9.93	9.02	7.88	11.36	10.33	8.55
	No. 2	38 × 89	2.98	2.71	2.37	3.41	3.10	2.59
		38 × 140	4.69	4.26	3.72	5.30	4.59	3.75
		38 × 184	6.18	5.62	4.91	6.99	6.05	4.94
		38 × 235	7.89	7.17	6.26	8.92	7.73	6.31
		38 × 286	9.60	8.72	7.62	10.85	9.40	7.67
	No. 3	38 × 89	2.74	2.37	1.94	2.74	2.37	1.94
		38 × 140	4.04	3.50	2.85	4.04	3.50	2.85
		38 × 184	5.33	4.61	3.76	5.33	4.61	3.76
		38 × 235	6.80	5.89	4.80	6.80	5.89	4.80
		38 × 286	8.27	7.16	5.84	8.27	7.16	5.84
	Construction	38 × 89	2.87	2.61	2.20	3.12	2.70	2.20
	Standard	38 × 89	2.34	2.03	1.66	2.34	2.03	1.66
	Utility	38 × 89	1.60	1.39	1.13	1.60	1.39	1.13
Western Cedars (includes Western Red Cedar and Pacific Coast Yellow Cedar)	Select structural	38 × 89	2.97	2.70	2.36	3.40	3.09	2.70
		38 × 140	4.67	4.24	3.71	5.35	4.86	4.24
		38 × 184	6.16	5.59	4.89	7.05	6.40	5.59
		38 × 235	7.86	7.14	6.24	9.00	8.17	7.14
		38 × 286	9.56	8.68	7.58	10.94	9.94	8.68
	No. 1	38 × 89	2.97	2.70	2.36	3.40	3.09	2.70
		38 × 140	4.67	4.24	3.71	5.35	4.86	4.23
		38 × 184	6.16	5.59	4.89	7.05	6.40	5.58
		38 × 235	7.86	7.14	6.24	9.00	8.17	7.12
		38 × 286	9.56	8.68	7.58	10.94	9.94	8.66
	No. 2	38 × 89	2.87	2.61	2.28	3.29	2.99	2.61
		38 × 140	4.51	4.10	3.58	5.17	4.63	3.73
		38 × 184	5.95	5.41	4.72	6.82	6.10	4.98
		38 × 235	7.60	6.90	6.03	8.70	7.79	6.36
		38 × 286	9.24	8.39	7.33	10.58	9.47	7.73
	No. 3	38 × 89	2.74	2.37	1.94	2.74	2.37	1.94
		38 × 140	4.04	3.50	2.85	4.04	3.50	2.85
		38 × 184	5.33	4.61	3.76	5.33	4.61	3.76
		38 × 235	6.80	5.89	4.80	6.80	5.89	4.80
		38 × 286	8.27	7.16	5.84	8.27	7.16	5.84
	Construction	38 × 89	2.77	2.51	2.19	3.15	2.72	2.22
	Standard	38 × 89	2.34	2.03	1.66	2.34	2.03	1.66
	Utility	38 × 89	1.60	1.39	1.13	1.60	1.39	1.13

TABLE 8 — IMPERIAL FLOOR JOISTS — LIVING QUARTERS (live load 40 lb per sq ft) (CSA-0141 – 1970 Softwood Lumber Sizes)

Commercial Designation	Grade	Nominal Size (inches)	12" ft	12" in.	16" ft	16" in.	20" ft	20" in.	24" ft	24" in.
Spruce Pine Fir (includes Spruce – all species except Coast Sitka Spruce – Jack Pine, Lodgepole Pine, Balsam Fir and Alpine Fir)	Select structural	2 × 4	6	5	5	10	5	5	5	1
		2 × 6	10	1	9	2	8	6	8	0
		2 × 8	13	4	12	1	11	3	10	7
		2 × 10	17	0	15	5	14	4	13	6
		2 × 12	20	8	18	9	17	5	16	5
	No. 1	2 × 4	6	5	5	10	5	5	5	1
		2 × 6	10	1	9	2	8	6	7	9
		2 × 8	13	4	12	1	11	3	10	3
		2 × 10	17	0	15	5	14	4	13	1
		2 × 12	20	8	18	9	17	5	15	11
	No. 2	2 × 4	6	2	5	7	5	3	4	10
		2 × 6	9	9	8	7	7	8	7	0
		2 × 8	12	10	11	4	10	2	9	3
		2 × 10	16	5	14	6	13	0	11	10
		2 × 12	20	0	17	8	15	9	14	5
	No. 3	2 × 4	5	2	4	5	4	0	3	8
		2 × 6	7	5	6	5	5	9	5	3
		2 × 8	9	9	8	6	7	7	6	11
		2 × 10	12	6	10	10	9	8	8	10
		2 × 12	15	2	13	2	11	9	10	9
	Construction	2 × 4	5	9	5	0	4	5	4	1
	Standard	2 × 4	4	5	3	10	3	5	3	2
	Utility	2 × 4	2	11	2	7	2	3	2	1
Western Cedars (includes Western Red Cedar and Pacific Coast Yellow Cedar)	Select structural	2 × 4	6	2	5	7	5	2	4	11
		2 × 6	9	9	8	10	8	2	7	9
		2 × 8	12	10	11	8	10	10	10	2
		2 × 10	16	5	14	11	13	10	13	0
		2 × 12	19	11	18	1	16	10	15	10
	No. 1	2 × 4	6	2	5	7	5	2	4	11
		2 × 6	9	9	8	10	8	2	7	7
		2 × 8	12	10	11	8	10	10	10	0
		2 × 10	16	5	14	11	13	10	12	10
		2 × 12	19	11	18	1	16	10	15	7
	No. 2	2 × 4	5	11	5	5	5	0	4	8
		2 × 6	9	4	8	4	7	6	6	10
		2 × 8	12	4	11	1	9	10	9	0
		2 × 10	15	9	14	1	12	7	11	6
		2 × 12	19	2	17	2	15	4	14	0
	No. 3	2 × 4	4	11	4	3	3	10	3	6
		2 × 6	7	5	6	5	5	9	5	3
		2 × 8	9	9	8	6	7	7	6	11
		2 × 10	12	6	10	10	9	8	8	10
		2 × 12	15	2	13	2	11	9	10	9
	Construction	2 × 4	5	7	4	10	4	4	3	11
	Standard	2 × 4	4	2	3	8	3	3	2	11
	Utility	2 × 4	2	11	2	7	2	3	2	1

No. of Storeys	Minimum Depth (in.)	Minimum Mass (lb.)	Width[2] of Floor to be Supported				
			8 ft.	10 ft.	12 ft.	14 ft.	16 ft.
1	4	7.7	10	9	8.5	8	7.5
	5	10.0	12.5	11.5	11	10.5	10
	6	12.6	15	14	13	12.5	12
	7	16.3	18	17	16	15	14.5
	8	18.4	21	19.5	18.5	17.5	16.5
1 1/2 or 2	4	7.7	8	7.5	7	6.5	6
	5	10.0	10.5	9.5	8.5	8	7.5
	6	12.5	12.5	11.5	10.5	9.5	9
	7	15.3	15	14	13	12	11
	8	18.4	17.5	16	15	14	13

TABLE 9   IMPERIAL MAXIMUM SPANS FOR STEEL BEAMS IN BASEMENTS, CELLARS AND CRAWL SPACES[1][3][4]

Notes to Table 9

[1]   A beam may be considered to be laterally supported if wood joists bear on its top flange at intervals of 24 in. or less over its entire length, and if all the load being applied to this beam is transmitted through the joists, and if 1-in. by 2-in. wood strips in contact with the top flange are nailed on both sides of the beam to the bottom of the joists supported. Other additional methods of positive lateral support are acceptable.

[3]   Supported joist length means 1/2 the sum of the joist spans on both sides of the beam.

[4]   For supported joist lengths intermediate between those shown in the table, straightline interpolation may be used in determining the maximum beam span.

TABLE 10   IMPERIAL FLOOR JOISTS – BEDROOMS, AND IN ATTICS ACCESSIBLE BY A STAIRWAY (live load 30 lb per sq ft)

Live Load 30 lb per sq ft

Commercial Designation	Grade	Nominal Size	Gypsum Board or Plastered Ceiling Joist Spacing								Other Ceilings Joist Spacing							
			12 in.		16 in.		20 in.		24 in.		12 in.		16 in.		20 in.		24 in.	
		inches	ft.	in.	ft.	in.	ft.	in.	ft.	in.	ft.	in.	ft.	in.	ft.	in.	ft.	in.
Spruce Pine Fir (includes Spruce – all species except Coast Sitka Spruce – Jack Pine, Lodgepole Pine, Balsam Fir and Alpine Fir)	Select Structural	2 × 4	7	1	6	5	5	11	5	7	8	1	7	4	6	10	6	5
		2 × 6	11	1	10	1	9	4	8	10	12	9	11	7	10	6	9	7
		2 × 8	14	8	13	4	12	4	11	7	16	9	15	3	13	10	12	8
		2 × 10	18	9	17	0	15	9	14	10	21	5	19	6	17	8	16	2
		2 × 12	22	9	20	8	19	2	18	1	26	1	23	8	21	6	19	7
	No. 1	2 × 4	7	1	6	5	5	11	5	7	8	1	7	4	6	8	6	1
		2 × 6	11	1	10	1	9	4	8	10	12	6	10	9	9	8	8	10
		2 × 8	14	8	13	4	12	4	11	7	16	5	14	3	12	9	11	7
		2 × 10	18	9	17	0	15	9	14	10	21	0	18	2	16	3	14	10
		2 × 12	22	9	20	8	19	2	18	1	25	6	22	1	19	9	18	1
	No. 2	2 × 4	6	10	6	2	5	9	5	5	7	9	6	8	6	0	5	5
		2 × 6	10	9	9	9	8	9	7	11	11	3	9	9	8	9	7	11
		2 × 8	14	2	12	10	11	6	10	6	14	10	12	10	11	6	10	6
		2 × 10	18	1	16	5	14	8	13	5	19	0	16	5	14	8	13	5
		2 × 12	22	0	20	0	15	16	4	23	1	20	0	17	11	16	4
	No. 3	2 × 4	5	10	5	1	4	6	4	1	5	10	5	1	4	6	4	1
		2 × 6	8	5	7	3	6	6	5	11	8	5	7	3	6	6	5	11
		2 × 8	11	1	9	7	8	7	7	10	11	1	9	7	8	7	7	10
		2 × 10	14	2	12	3	10	11	10	0	14	2	12	3	10	11	10	0
		2 × 12	17	2	14	11	13	4	12	2	17	2	14	11	13	4	12	2
	Construction	2 × 4	6	6	5	8	5	1	4	7	6	6	5	8	5	1	4	7
	Standard	2 × 4	5	1	4	4	3	11	3	7	5	1	4	4	3	11	3	7
	Utility	2 × 4	3	4	2	11	2	7	2	4	3	4	2	11	2	7	2	4
Western Cedars (includes Western Red Cedar and Pacific Coast Yellow Cedar)	Select Structural	2 × 4	6	10	6	2	5	9	5	5	7	9	7	1	6	7	6	2
		2 × 6	10	9	9	9	9	0	8	6	12	3	11	2	10	3	9	5
		2 × 8	14	2	12	10	11	11	11	2	16	2	14	8	13	7	12	5
		2 × 10	18	0	16	5	15	3	14	4	20	8	18	9	17	4	15	10
		2 × 12	21	11	19	11	18	6	17	5	25	2	22	10	21	1	19	3
	No. 1	2 × 4	6	10	6	2	5	9	5	5	7	9	7	1	6	5	5	10
		2 × 6	10	9	9	9	9	0	8	6	12	2	10	6	9	5	8	7
		2 × 8	14	2	12	10	11	11	11	2	16	1	13	11	12	5	11	4
		2 × 10	18	0	16	5	15	3	14	4	20	6	17	9	15	11	14	6
		2 × 12	21	11	19	11	18	6	17	5	24	11	21	7	19	4	17	8
	No. 2	2 × 4	6	7	5	11	5	6	5	2	7	6	6	6	5	10	5	4
		2 × 6	10	4	9	4	8	6	7	9	10	11	9	6	8	6	7	9
		2 × 8	13	7	12	4	11	2	10	2	14	5	12	6	11	2	10	2
		2 × 10	17	4	15	9	14	3	13	0	18	5	16	0	14	3	13	0
		2 × 12	21	2	19	2	17	5	15	10	22	5	19	5	17	5	15	10
	No. 3	2 × 4	5	7	4	10	4	4	3	11	5	7	4	10	4	4	3	11
		2 × 6	8	5	7	3	6	6	5	11	8	5	7	3	6	6	5	11
		2 × 8	11	1	9	7	8	7	7	10	11	1	9	7	8	7	7	10
		2 × 10	14	2	12	3	10	11	10	0	14	2	12	3	10	11	10	0
		2 × 12	17	2	14	11	13	4	12	2	17	2	14	11	13	4	12	2
	Construction	2 × 4	6	4	5	5	4	11	4	5	6	4	5	5	4	11	4	5
	Standard	2 × 4	4	9	4	1	3	8	3	4	4	9	4	1	3	8	3	4
	Utility	2 × 4	3	4	2	11	2	7	2	4	3	4	2	11	2	7	2	4

TABLE 11 IMPERIAL CEILING JOISTS – ATTIC NOT ACCESSIBLE BY A STAIRWAY (live load 10 lb per sq ft)

Commercial Designation	Grade	Nominal Size	Live Load 10 lb per sq ft							
			Gypsum Board or Plastered Ceiling				Other Ceilings			
			Joist Spacing				Joist Spacing			
			12 in.	16 in.	20 in.	24 in.	12 in.	16 in.	20 in.	24 in.
		inches	ft. in.	ft. in.	ft. in.	ft. in.	ft. in.	ft. in.	ft. in.	ft. in.
Spruce Pine Fir (includes Spruce – all species except Coast Sitka Spruce – Jack Pine, Lodgepole Pine, Balsam Fir and Alpine Fir)	Select Structural	2 × 4	10 2	9 3	8 7	8 1	11 8	10 7	9 10	9 3
		2 × 6	16 0	14 7	13 6	12 9	18 4	16 8	15 6	14 7
		2 × 8	21 2	19 3	17 10	16 9	24 3	22 0	20 5	19 3
		2 × 10	27 0	24 6	22 9	21 5	30 11	28 1	26 1	24 6
		2 × 12	32 10	29 10	27 8	26 1	37 7	34 2	31 9	29 10
	No. 1	2 × 4	10 2	9 3	8 7	8 1	11 8	10 7	9 10	9 3
		2 × 6	16 0	14 7	13 6	12 9	18 4	16 8	15 1	13 9
		2 × 8	21 2	19 3	17 10	16 9	24 3	22 0	19 11	18 2
		2 × 10	27 0	24 6	22 9	21 5	30 11	28 1	25 5	23 2
		2 × 12	32 10	29 10	27 8	26 1	37 7	34 2	30 11	28 2
	No. 2	2 × 4	9 10	8 11	8 4	7 10	11 3	10 3	9 4	8 7
		2 × 6	15 6	14 1	13 1	12 4	17 7	15 3	13 8	12 5
		2 × 8	20 5	18 7	17 3	16 3	23 3	20 1	18 0	16 5
		2 × 10	26 1	23 9	22 0	20 9	29 8	25 8	23 0	21 0
		2 × 12	31 9	28 10	26 9	25 2	36 1	31 3	27 11	25 6
	No. 3	2 × 4	9 2	7 11	7 1	6 5	9 2	7 11	7 1	6 5
		2 × 6	13 1	11 4	10 2	9 3	13 1	11 4	10 2	9 3
		2 × 8	17 4	15 0	13 5	12 3	17 4	15 0	13 5	12 3
		2 × 10	22 1	19 2	17 1	15 7	22 1	19 2	17 1	15 7
		2 × 12	26 11	23 3	20 10	19 0	26 11	23 3	20 10	19 0
	Construction	2 × 4	9 6	8 7	7 11	7 3	10 3	8 10	7 11	7 3
	Standard	2 × 4	7 11	6 10	6 1	5 7	7 11	6 10	6 1	5 7
	Utility	2 × 4	5 3	4 7	4 1	3 8	5 3	4 7	4 1	3 8
Western Cedars (includes Western Red Cedar and Pacific Coast Yellow Cedar)	Select Structural	2 × 4	9 10	8 11	8 3	7 9	11 3	10 3	9 6	8 11
		2 × 6	15 6	14 1	13 0	12 3	17 8	16 1	14 11	14 1
		2 × 8	20 5	18 6	17 2	16 2	23 4	21 3	19 8	18 6
		2 × 10	26 0	23 8	21 11	20 8	29 10	27 1	25 2	23 8
		2 × 12	31 8	28 9	26 9	25 2	36 3	32 11	30 7	28 9
	No. 1	2 × 4	9 10	8 11	8 3	7 9	11 3	10 3	9 6	8 11
		2 × 6	15 6	14 1	13 0	12 3	17 8	16 1	14 9	13 5
		2 × 8	20 5	18 6	17 2	16 2	23 4	21 3	19 5	17 9
		2 × 10	26 0	23 8	21 11	20 8	29 10	27 1	24 10	22 8
		2 × 12	31 8	28 9	26 9	25 2	36 3	32 11	30 2	27 7
	No. 2	2 × 4	9 6	8 7	8 0	7 6	10 10	9 10	9 2	8 4
		2 × 6	14 11	13 6	12 7	11 10	17 1	14 10	13 3	12 1
		2 × 8	19 8	17 10	16 7	15 7	22 6	19 7	17 6	15 11
		2 × 10	25 1	22 9	21 2	19 11	28 8	25 0	22 4	20 4
		2 × 12	30 6	27 8	25 9	24 2	34 11	30 4	27 2	24 9
	No. 3	2 × 4	8 9	7 7	6 9	6 2	8 9	7 7	6 9	6 2
		2 × 6	13 1	11 4	10 2	9 3	13 1	11 4	10 2	9 3
		2 × 8	17 4	15 0	13 5	12 3	17 4	15 0	13 5	12 3
		2 × 10	22 1	19 2	17 1	15 7	22 1	19 2	17 1	15 7
		2 × 12	26 11	23 3	20 10	19 0	26 11	23 3	20 10	19 0
	Construction	2 × 4	9 1	8 3	7 8	7 0	9 10	8 7	7 8	7 0
	Standard	2 × 4	7 5	6 5	5 9	5 3	7 5	6 5	5 9	5 3
	Utility	2 × 4	5 3	4 7	4 1	3 8	5 3	4 7	4 1	3 8

TABLE 12 AMORTIZATION CHART

Monthly Payment per $1 000.00 of Mortgage

Rate of Interest	Length of Mortgage						
	1 Year	3 Years	5 Years	10 Years	15 Years	20 Years	25 Years
8.00%	$86.93	$31.28	$20.22	$12.07	$ 9.49	$ 8.29	$ 7.64
8.25%	87.05	31.39	20.33	12.20	9.63	8.44	7.80
8.50%	87.16	31.50	20.45	12.33	9.77	8.59	7.96
8.75%	87.27	31.62	20.57	12.45	9.91	8.74	8.12
9.00%	87.38	31.73	20.68	12.58	10.05	8.90	8.28
9.25%	87.49	31.84	20.80	12.71	10.19	9.05	8.45
9.50%	87.60	31.95	20.92	12.84	10.34	9.21	8.62
9.75%	87.72	32.06	21.04	12.98	10.48	9.36	8.78
10.00%	87.83	32.18	21.15	13.11	10.63	9.52	8.95
10.25%	87.94	32.29	21.27	13.24	10.77	9.68	9.12
10.50%	88.05	32.40	21.39	13.37	10.92	9.84	9.29
10.75%	88.16	32.52	21.51	13.51	11.07	10.00	9.46
11.00%	88.27	32.63	21.63	13.64	11.22	10.16	9.63
11.25%	88.38	32.74	21.74	13.78	11.37	10.32	9.80
11.50%	88.50	32.85	21.86	13.91	11.52	10.49	9.98
11.75%	88.61	32.97	21.98	14.05	11.67	10.65	10.15
12.00%	88.72	33.08	22.10	14.19	11.82	10.81	10.32
12.25%	88.83	33.19	22.22	14.32	11.97	10.98	10.50
12.50%	88.94	33.31	22.34	14.46	12.13	11.15	10.68
12.75%	89.05	33.42	22.46	14.60	12.28	11.31	10.85
13.00%	89.16	33.54	22.59	14.74	12.44	11.48	11.03
13.25%	89.27	33.65	22.71	14.88	12.59	11.65	11.21
13.50%	89.39	33.76	22.83	15.02	12.75	11.82	11.39
13.75%	89.50	33.88	22.95	15.16	12.90	11.99	11.56
14.00%	89.61	33.99	23.07	15.30	13.06	12.16	11.74
14.25%	89.72	34.11	23.19	15.44	13.22	12.33	11.92
14.50%	89.83	34.22	23.31	15.58	13.38	12.50	12.10
14.75%	89.94	34.34	23.44	15.72	13.54	12.67	12.29
15.00%	90.05	34.45	23.56	15.87	13.70	12.84	12.47
15.25%	90.16	34.57	23.68	16.01	13.86	13.02	12.65
15.50%	90.27	34.68	23.81	16.15	14.02	13.19	12.83
15.75%	90.38	34.80	23.93	16.30	14.18	13.36	13.01
16.00%	90.50	34.91	24.05	16.44	14.34	13.54	13.20
16.25%	90.61	35.03	24.18	16.59	14.50	13.71	13.38
16.50%	90.72	35.14	24.30	16.73	14.66	13.89	13.56
16.75%	90.83	35.26	24.43	16.88	14.83	14.06	13.75
17.00%	90.94	35.37	24.55	17.02	14.99	14.24	13.93
17.25%	91.05	35.49	24.68	17.17	15.16	14.42	14.11
17.50%	91.16	35.61	24.80	17.32	15.32	14.59	14.30
17.75%	91.27	35.72	24.93	17.47	15.49	14.77	14.48
18.00%	91.38	35.84	25.05	17.61	15.65	14.95	14.67
18.25%	91.49	35.95	25.18	17.76	15.82	15.13	14.85
18.50%	91.60	36.07	25.30	17.92	15.98	15.30	15.04
19.00%	91.82	36.30	25.56	18.21	16.32	15.66	15.41
20.00%	92.26	36.77	26.06	18.81	16.99	16.38	16.51
21.00%	92.70	37.24	26.57	19.42	17.67	17.10	16.90
22.00%	93.14	37.71	27.09	20.03	18.35	17.82	17.65
23.00%	93.58	38.18	27.61	20.65	19.04	18.55	18.39

ESTIMATING your monthly payment, find the figure under the mortgage interest rate (%) that corresponds to the number of years you want to pay off the loan.
FOR EXAMPLE: If your interest rate is 10% and the term of the mortgage is 25 years, then you need to pay $8.95 per month for each $1000.00 of mortgage.
Your monthly payment: $8.95 × (MORTGAGE AMOUNT) = MONTHLY PAYMENT
$\hspace{4cm}$ 1000
CALCULATING: If your mortgaged amount is $30 000 your monthly payment = $8.95 × $30 000 = $268.50
$\hspace{9cm}$ 1000

Monthly Salary Requirement Chart (Based on GDS ratio of 30% including taxes)

Monthly Payment	Monthly Salary	Monthly Payment	Monthly Salary	Monthly Payment	Monthly Salary
$350	$1167	$500	$1667	$750	$2500
375	1250	525	1750	800	2666
400	1333	550	1833	850	2833
425	1417	575	1917	900	3000
450	1500	600	2000	950	3166
475	1583	700	2333	1000	3333

Glossary

ACTIVE SOLAR HEATING   A method of using panels to collect heat from the sun's rays and transferring the heat to storage tanks to be used on demand.

AESTHETICS   The beauty or look of a design.

ALIGNED DIMENSIONING   A system of placing dimensions on a drawing so that they can all be read from the right-hand side of the sheet.

ALLOWABLE STRESS   The amount of stress to which a member of a structure should be subjected for safety. Allowable stress is determined by the ultimate stress of the material divided by the factor of safety appropriate for the task.

AMORTIZE   To arrange mortgage payments over a period of time so that the debt may be discharged by a given date.

AMPERE   Unit of electrical current denoting amount of pressure.

ANCHOR BOLT   A steel bolt used to secure a structural member to a foundation. It is usually deformed at one end to ensure a grip in the concrete or masonry in which it is embedded.

ANGLE IRON   An L-shaped steel section frequently used as a lintel to support masonry work over a window or door opening.

APPLIANCE CIRCUITS   Wiring with a rating of 120 V and 15 A.

APPRAISAL   The process whereby the lending value of the property is determined. This is not always the same as the purchase price.

ARC   A portion of the circumference of a circle.

ARCADE   An open passageway usually surrounded by a series of arches.

ARCH   Arrangement of building materials over an opening to support load.
Types
   Corbell: blocks of stone overlapping — Minoan style
   Voussoirs: wedge-shaped blocks forming Roman style arches.
   Ogee: double curvature — Byzantine style

ASSYMMETRICAL BALANCE   Visually, but not equally, balanced. The balancing items are of differing sizes, numbers, and values.

ATRIUM   A room lighted by an opening in the roof.

ATTACHED GARAGE   A garage that adjoins one side of the main building and has a separate roof structure.

ATTIC   The space between the roof and ceiling under a gable roof.

AWNING WINDOW   An outswinging window hinged at the top of the sash.

AZIMUTH   An angle measured in a clockwise direction from the north meridian. It is written as a number of degrees with N preceding it. Example: N 156°. Azimuths can be used to calculate bearings.

BACK FILL   To re-fill an excavation around the outside of a foundation wall or trench.

BANDSAW ARCHITECTURE   Ornate woodwork popular in the Victorian era.

BALCONY   A deck projecting from the wall of a building above ground level.

BALLOON FRAME   A type of wood framing in which the studs extend from sill to eaves for more than one storey without interruption.

BALUSTER   Vertical supports for a handrail or a guardrail that hold the rails parallel to the floor or stair slope and form a barrier on the open side of the stairs or stairwell; often ornamental.

BARGEBOARD   The finishing board covering the projecting portion of a gable roof.

BARREL VAULT   A ceiling formed by placing arches one behind the other.

BASEBOARD   The finishing trim board where the base of an interior wall and floor meet.

BASE LINE   A line drawn from the line of sight to the left vanishing point and to the right vanishing point.

BATT   A type of insulation of a width to fit between framing members.

BATTEN   The narrow strips of wood nailed vertically over the joints of boards to form board-and-batten siding.

BATTER BOARD   Horizontal boards at exact elevations nailed to posts outside the corners of a proposed building. Strings are stretched across the boards to locate the outline of the foundation for workers.

BAY WINDOW   A combination of sashes that project out from the wall of a building. The centre sash is parallel to the wall, and the sides are angular.

BEAM   A horizontal structural member used to support vertical loads. This can be steel, built up wood beams, or concrete.

BEAM POCKET   A notch formed at the top of a foundation wall to support the end of a beam.

BEARING

1. The portion of a structural member; for example, a beam, column, joist, or girder, that rests upon a support.
2. An angular direction taken from the meridian. A bearing is a direction, and a bearing line of N46°E is the same as the bearing line of S46°W, which indicates that the angular deviation is 46° to the east or west of the meridian depending on whether one is facing north or south. On survey drawings, it is common practice to give bearings from a northern aspect. A bearing cannot be greater than 90°.

BEARING WALL   A wall that supports a weight above in addition to its own weight and carries this load to its own footings.

BENCH MARK   The mark on a permanent monument related to a fixed datum level to which other land elevations are related.

BERMS (OR EARTH BERMS)   Mounds of earth built to alter the land contours for functional or aesthetic reasons.

BITUMINOUS   A coating substance of hydrocarbons that is used for waterproofing cement.

BLUEPRINTS   Technical drawings copied so that a white line on a dark blue background is produced. This process is no longer used but the name has now become generic for all copies of technical plans.

BOND   In masonry, the pattern in which bricks are laid to tie the individual units together so that the entire wall will act as a complete unit.

BOTTOM PLATE   The lower horizontal member of a wood-frame wall nailed to the base of the wall studs.

BRICK VENEER   A facing of brick on the outer side of wood frame or masonry. Not part of the structural support.

BRIDGING   Thin wood or metal pieces fastened diagonally between floor joists to act as both tension and compression members for the purposes of stiffening and spreading concentrated loads.

BRITISH THERMAL UNIT (B.T.U.)   The amount of heat required to raise one pound of water one degree Fahrenheit.

BROKEN PEDIMENT   A pediment that has an incomplete apex. The apex is formed into angled or curved shapes.

BRUNELLESCHI   Renaissance architect who was one of the first to demonstrate a system of making perspective drawings. He designed many outstanding structures such as the Cupola of Florence Cathedral.

BUILDING LINE   An imaginary line on a plot beyond which the building may not extend.

BUILDING PERMIT   A certificate obtained from the municipality before a building can be erected or repaired extensively.

BUILT-IN GARAGE   A garage that adjoins the house; may have a room above it and its roof usually forms part of the main roof system.

BUILT-UP ROOF   A roofing composed of layers of felt impregnated with pitch, coal tar, or asphalt. The top is finished with crushed stone or gravel. It is used on flat or low-pitched roofs.

BUTTRESS   The pilaster that gives a masonry wall or an arch additional support. An exterior half arch leaning against a point in a wall to counteract the weight of an interior arch or vault. Example: flying buttress used in Gothic churches.

CAD (COMPUTER-AIDED DRAFTING)   Software programs that will enable an operator to draft on a computer. A modern drafting tool.

CANTILEVER   A beam unsupported at one end, which projects out from a structure, so that the upper part is in tension and the lower part is in compression.

CAPITAL   The upper part of a column, usually decorated.

CASEMENT WINDOW   A type of window where the sash units are hinged vertically so that they swing similarly to a door. They can be made to open either in or out.

CASING   Trim around a window or door opening.

CAULKING   A compound used to fill cracks around door or window frames to prevent air leakage.

CAVITY WALL   A masonry wall having a 38 mm (2") air space between brick wythes.

CEMENT   A fine, grey powder made from lime, silica, iron oxide, and alumina that when mixed with water and aggregate produces concrete.

CENTRING   The temporary wooden support used for building an arch or vault.

CERAMIC   Term supplied to vitreous clay products. Floor and wall tiles for kitchens or bathrooms are often made of ceramic.

CHIMNEY FLUE   A passageway housed in a chimney through which smoke and gases are carried from a fuel-burning appliance, fireplace, or incinerator to the exterior.

CHISEL POINT   Flattened sharp point used for drawing long lines and bricks, boards, and shading.

CHORD   The top and bottom members of a truss spanning the distance between supports.

CHROMA   Refers to the intensity — the brightness or dullness — of a colour.

CIRCUITS WITH HIGH RATINGS   Circuits wired for 220 V for appliances such as stoves, dishwashers, and air conditioners.

CLAPBOARD   A house covering made of overlapping boards.

CLEAT   A small board fastened to another member to serve as a brace support.

CLOSURE   The result of subtracting southerly latitudes from northerly latitudes, and westerly departures from easterly departures. To obtain a closure, the answers must be zero.

CIRCUIT   A path over which electrical current flows. In house wiring, a circuit will service several outlets.

CIRCUIT BREAKER   A switch that automatically opens or interrupts an electric current when the current becomes too strong.

CLASSIC   Term applied to monumental architectural style of early periods such as Greek and Roman.

CLERESTORY   Windows that form the upper part of the wall and that are above the lower part of the roof.

COLLAR TIE BEAM   The horizontal member connecting roof rafters on either side of the ridge.

COLLATERAL   Items that have a marketable value equal to the amount of a loan.

COLLECTOR/STORAGE LOOP   Used in solar heating; made up of flat-plate collectors directly connected to the storage tanks.

COLONIAL   Term applied to architecture that is representative of the building styles of the early years of colonization in North America.

COLONNADE   A row of columns supporting a row of arches across an entrance to a building.

COLOUR WHEEL   A chart that has the three primary, three secondary, and six tertiary colours arranged equally around a circle.

COLUMN   A cylindrical, vertical support or freestanding monument.

COMMON RAFTER   The most common of a series of rafters extending from the top of an exterior wall to the ridge of a roof.

COMPOSITE COLUMN   Tall column combining use of acanthus leaves (Corinthian) and volutes (Ionic); developed by the Romans.

COMPOSITION   The arrangement of the items in a drawing in such a way that the picture is balanced.

COMPRESSIVE STRESS   Stress set up when particles of a material are being forced together or squeezed. If the load becomes excessive, the material will eventually collapse.

CONCENTRATED LOAD   A vertical load that exerts pressure in a specific location.

CONDENSATION   The drops of water that form when warm air comes in contact with a cold surface.

CONDOMINIUM   Dwelling units that are individually owned but that are grouped collectively and have group management in some degree.

CONDUIT   A pipe that serves as a sleeve for electrical wires.

CONICAL POINT   Rounded sharp point; suitable for most linework and letter.

CONIFEROUS   Trees of the evergreen variety.

CONTEMPORARY   A term applied to present-day architectural styles or items belonging to the same time frame.

CONTOUR   The curved lines that represent the relative levels or elevations of a property.

CONTOUR INTERVAL   The vertical distance between any two adjacent contour lines.

CONTRAST OF TONES   The use of light, medium, and dark tones in a picture.

CONVERGING LINES   Lines that appear to move together as they race into the distance and that will eventually meet at one point, the vanishing point, if taken to infinity.

COPING   A cap or top course of masonry on a wall to prevent moisture penetration.

CORBELLING   The laying of masonry units, in such a manner that each course projects slightly beyond the one below. Used in fireplace and chimney construction.

CORINTHIAN COLUMN   Column with a high base or pedestal, slender shaft with flutes, and a capital of acanthus leaves; a late ancient Greek design.

CORNICE   The horizontal projection of the roof overhang at the top of a wall.

COURSE   A continuous layer of bricks or masonry units in buildings; the term can be also used for shingles.

COVE   A concave moulding usually used on horizontal inside corners.

CRAWL SPACE   The shallow space below the floor of a house that goes down only to the frost line. Generally it is surrounded by the foundation wall.

CROSS-HATCHING   Ink lines drawn at angles to each other.

CUL-DE-SAC   A court or street with no outlet. Usually, a turnaround for vehicles is provided.

CUPOLA   A small, decorative structure placed on a roof, which can be used as a ventilator or lantern.

CURING   The period between the time concrete is poured and the time it has reached its final set.

CURTAIN WALL
1. An exterior wall that is non-load-bearing and that is supported by other structural members.
2. A non-bearing wall built between columns or piers for the enclosure of a space.

CURVED-LINE DESIGN   A somewhat ornate design, using lines like the sinuous, vine-like curves found in nature.

DAMPER   A metal door at the base of a chimney that regulates the draft in a fireplace. Also used in heating ducts as a means of varying the amount of heat that passes.

DAMP-PROOFING   The process of coating the outside of a foundation wall with a special preparation to resist passage of moisture.

DATUM   A reference point or plane used as a basis for computing land levels, elevations, or dimensions of a drawing.

DEAD LOAD   Load resulting from the weight of the materials that make up a structure.

DECIDUOUS   Trees that shed their leaves in winter.

DEED   A legal document that transfers the title of a property from one person to another.

DEFORMATION   The change that takes place in the size of structural members as a result of strain created by imposed loads.

DEFAULT   Failure to abide by the terms of a loan agreement.

DETACHED GARAGE   A garage that is entirely separate and is usually behind the main house.

DETAIL DRAWING   Drawings at larger scales than the rest of the drawing, giving information needed to construct specific parts of a building; e.g., stairs, fireplaces, cupboards.

DIAZO   A method of printing using paper treated with a diazo compound that disintegrates in the light and is developed with the use of dyes.

DIMENSION LINE   Lines that show the distance between two points.

DOME   A semi-spherical roof over a circular or square building.

DOMUS   A single-family Roman house.

DORIC COLUMN   Simplest of classical orders — no base, short fluted shafts, undecorated capital, used in early ancient Greek architecture.

DORMER   Vertical window framed by a small roof section that protrudes from a sloping roof.

DOUBLE GLAZING   Two thicknesses of glass in a door or window, with an air space between the panes and sealed as a single unit.

DOUBLE HUNG   A type of window having two sashes that will slide up or down.

DRY BRUSH   An illustrating technique for creating textures; the brush, which has only a little ink on it, is pushed down on the medium so that the bristles are fanned out.

DRYWALL FINISH   Interior wall and ceiling finish other than plaster, such as gypsum board, plywood, fibreboard panels, etc.

DUCT   Sheet-metal conductors for air distribution throughout a building.

DUPLEX OUTLET   Electrical wall outlet having two plug receptacles.

EASEMENT   A right held by a company to make use of the land of another for a limited purpose. Example: The hydro company may have a right to service or repair their lines on certain property providing the condition of the property is restored to its original state.

EAVE   The lower portion of the roof that overhangs the wall.

EAVESTROUGH   A trough fixed to an eave to collect and carry the run-off of water from a roof. Also called a gutter.

ECLECTIC (TRANSITIONAL) DESIGN   Mixing and blending of features taken from other styles and periods.

ELEVATION
1. On survey or site plan drawings, the land levels and heights in relation to some stated datum.
2. Drawings of the exterior sides of a building.

ELL   An extension of a building usually at right angles to it.

EMPIRICAL FORMULA   A formula that does not depend on a provable theory but has been arrived at by trial and error over an extended period of time.

ENSUITE   Part of a set of rooms. Example: a bedroom with a bathroom and a dressing room as part of the unit.

ENTASIS   Slight bulge given to columns to correct optical illusion; used in ancient Greek architecture.

ENVIRONS   Surrounding conditions or influences such as the effect of a nearby community or landscape on a structure.

ERGONOMICS   The study of the mechanical ability of the human frame.

EXPANDED METAL   A metal network formed by stamping sheet metal and stretching it to form open meshes. It is used as reinforcing for concrete construction and as lathe for plastering and stucco.

EXPANSION JOINT   A flexible joint used around concrete floors to prevent cracking or breaking because of expansion and contraction due to temperature changes.

EXTENSION LINES   Lines that extend beyond the lines that represent the outline of an object.

EXTERIOR PERSPECTIVE   A three-dimensional drawing of the outside of a building where the horizontal lines recede towards vanishing points.

FAÇADE   The exterior or the front view of a building.

FACTOR OF SAFETY   In structural design, the relationship between the allowable stress and the ultimate strength of a material.

FANLIGHT   Fan-shaped window over a door; Georgian style architecture. Recent manufacturers refer to similar sashes as round tops.

FASCIA BOARD   A horizontal member on the edge of the roof overhang that provides a finish around the face of eaves and to which the eavestrough is fastened.

FAX OR FACSIMILE MACHINE   A method of sending drawings by phone lines.

FENESTRATION   The arrangement and size of windows and doors in an elevation.

FIELD NOTES   A surveyor's notes that are recorded after traversing a lot.

FINIALS   An ornament on the top of a roof, the corner of a tower, etc.

FIREBRICK   A clay of high heat-resisting qualities used in fireplaces.

FIRECUT   The angular cut on the ends of floor joists where they enter a masonry wall.

FIREPLACE   A recessed opening in a wall that provides for the burning of fossil fuel or wood. Surrounded by masonry and located at the base of a chimney.

FIREPROOFING   Any material or combination of materials used to enclose structural members to make them more fire resistant.

FIRE WALL   A wall that subdivides a building to resist the spread of fire, starting at the foundation and extending continuously through all storeys to the roof.

FLAGSTONES   Thin, flat stones used for floors, steps, walks, etc.

FLANGE   A projecting edge, rib or rim, or the top and bottom of I-beams.

FLARE   The point where the hard top of a road meets the driveway.

FLASHING   Sheet metal or other material used in roof and wall construction to prevent leakage between wood and masonry portions.

FLAT-PLATE COLLECTOR   A solar energy collector made from metal piping with a glass cover.

FLOOR JOIST   Horizontal structural member of a floor.

FLOOR PLAN   A section taken looking down on the house which shows the layout of each room in relation to other areas, at each floor level.

FLUE   The passage in a chimney through which smoke, gases, and fumes escape to the outer air.

FLUE LINING   Ceramic tiles glazed on the interior in 610 mm (2'- 0") lengths that line the flue to protect the chimney walls from hot gases.

FOAM-CORE OR ALLIGATOR BOARDS   Boards with a styrofoam core; they are strong and light-weight.

FOCAL POINT   The most important part of the picture; one's eye should be led there naturally.

FOOTING   A wide section of poured concrete, at the base of a foundation wall, pier, or column. It is broader than the foundation to distribute weight over a large surface.

FOOTING SECTION   Part of a drawing showing how the foundation wall is keyed to the footings.

FORESHORTENING   The apparent reduction in distances and heights as large objects recede from the viewer.

FORM FOLLOWS FUNCTION (OR FUNCTIONALISM)   A concept in which the form is established by the use to which the object will be put. Simplicity of shape is the hallmark of this type of architecture.

FORMWORK   Temporary wooden boards carefully fixed and braced to form required profile into which concrete is poured, e.g., for a concrete foundation wall. Removed when concrete is properly set.

FOUNDATION   The portion of a substructure that supports the superstructure by carrying the load of the building. Applies to walls, columns, and footings.

FOUNDATION PLANTING   Shrubs, often evergreen, planted around the foundations of a house.

FOUNDATION WALL   The portion of a load-bearing wall below the level of the first-floor beams or joists.

FRAME
1. That part of the structure that serves as the skeleton and about which the building is enclosed.
2. The framing around windows and doors, into which these units are secured.

FRIEZE   Portion of building above architrave and below cornice often used for a continuous band of carving; seen in ancient Greek and Roman architecture.

FROST LINE   The deepest level of frost penetration in soil. This depth varies in different climates. Footings must be placed below the frost line to prevent rupturing the foundation.

FULCRUM   The centre about which something is balanced.

FURRING STRIP   Thin strips of wood fastened to walls or ceilings for levelling and for receiving the finishing surface material.

FUSE   An electrical device that acts as a safety valve, breaking the circuit when it becomes overloaded.

GABLE ROOF   A roof with two sides that slope in two opposite directions from a central ridge.

GAMBREL ROOF   A roof with two pitches, the lower slope is steeper than the upper.

GENERAL PURPOSE RESIDENTIAL CIRCUITS   Wiring designed for household lighting fixtures and outlets.

GEODETIC SURVEYING   A branch of surveying that deals with large land masses and the inherent spherical shape of the earth.

GEORGIAN COLONIAL   A popular style of architecture in the southern United States, using porticoes and columns. Also called Neo-Classic.

GINGERBREAD ARCHITECTURE   Ornate woodworking used on houses built in the eighteen hundreds, made possible by the development of machinery after the Industrial Revolution.

GLAZING   The installation of glass in a window sash.

GOTHIC   Architectural style having narrow pointed arches, high steep roofs, and flying buttresses; developed in Europe during the Middle Ages.

GOUACHE WATERCOLOUR   Opaque watercolours that can be used as washes.

GRADE
1. Method of separating lumber into different classifications depending upon its suitability for different uses.
2. The level of the ground surface around the foundation wall.

GRADIENT   The rate of ascent or descent of an inclined surface.

GREENHOUSE EFFECT   Occurs when light rays pass through glass and are transformed into heat rays that cannot pass back through the glass.

GRID   The square pattern used as a basis for locating measurements (a) when using CAD and (b) for measuring elevations in surveying.

GROIN VAULT   Formed by placing two barrel vaults at right angles to each other.

GROPIUS, WALTER   An inventive architect and educator who was the head of the Bauhaus school of design in Germany. He eventually had to flee to England and the United States to carry on his unique style of architecture.

GROSS INCOME   The total of all income before taxes; it includes pensions, family allowances, and investment income.

GROUND FAULT INTERRUPTER   Devices that react to electrical leaks to prevent shocks that could cause injury or death.

GROUND LINE   In a perspective drawing, the plane on which the object is sitting.

GUARDRAIL   A protective barrier around a stairwell opening or a balcony. Guardrails are required on all openings that are 600 mm (2'-0") or more above adjacent levels. The minimum height of a guardrail is 1070 mm (3'-7").

GUSSET   A plywood or metal plate used to strengthen the joins in a truss.

GUTTER   A metal or wood trough for carrying water from a roof.

GYPSUM   Hydrous sulphate of calcium used in the manufacture of plaster and plaster products.

HANDRAIL   A support for persons using a stairway that runs parallel to the stair slope and is usually on the open side. There must be a handrail on a stairway of more than three risers.

HEADER (FRAMING)   A wood member at right angles to a series of joists or rafters at which the joists or rafters terminate.

HEADROOM   The vertical distance from the underside of the ceiling to the stair nosing. The minimum allowable headroom is 1950 mm (6'- 4").

HEARTH   The portion of the floor in front of the fireplace. Built of some incombustible material, it may be flush with or raised above the floor level.

HEAT RECOVERY VENTILATION SYSTEM (HRV)   A heating system that controls the flow of air within the house as well as the amount of air entering or leaving the house.

HIP ROOF   A type of roof that slopes from four sides; often referred to as a cottage roof.

HORIZON LINE   A horizontal line is at eye level, which is usually taken to be 1600 mm (5'-4") for the average person in a standing position. However, if the eye level is lower because the person is seated, or higher because he or she is standing on a platform, the level of the horizon line will change accordingly.

HUE   The name given to a colour (red, brown, green, etc.).

HUMAN SCALE   How the proportions of buildings, for example, relate to human proportions.

I BEAM   Steel member whose cross section resembles the letter I.

IMBALANCED   Things that do not look perpendicular, level, or secure.

INCOMBUSTIBLE   Any material that is not subject to rapid oxidation within the temperature limits of a standard fire test of not less than 2 1/2 hours' duration. Materials that burn during this time period are termed combustible.

INDUSTRIAL REVOLUTION   Changes in economic and social organization that began in 1760 in England when blast furnaces were able to produce metal speedily and power-driven machines replaced hand tools.

INFILTRATION   Leakage of air through cracks around windows and doors.

INK AND WASH   An ink technique in which ink, which can be diluted, is applied with a brush.

INSULA   A Roman city block.

INSULATION   Material used to resist heat transmission through walls, floors, and roofs. The resistance of insulation is given an 'R' or 'R.S.I.' rating.

INTERIOR PERSPECTIVE   A drawing of the inside of a building where horizontal parallel lines recede towards vanishing points on the horizon to create a three-dimensional drawing.

INTERIOR TRIM   General term for all the finishing moulding, casing, baseboard, etc., applied within the building by finishing carpenters.

INTERPOLATION   The act of introducing new points in a mathematical progression; used to determine contours from an elevation grid.

IONIC COLUMN   A Greek column design from Asiatic Greece of the 5th century B.C. A fluted column with the capital formed of spiral volutes.

ISOMETRIC DRAWING   An object drawn as if tilted towards the viewer so that all horizontal lines are at an angle of 30°.

JACK RAFTER   A rafter that is shorter than common rafters. Its span reaches from the wallplate to a hip rafter or from a valley rafter to the roof ridge.

JALOUSIE   A type of window having a number of small, unframed yet movable pieces of glass used for ventilation.

JAMB   The side post or lining of a doorway, window, or other opening.

JOIST   One of a series of horizontal wood members, usually of 38 mm (2") thickness, used to support a floor, ceiling, or roof.

JOIST HANGER   A steel section shaped like a stirrup, bent so it can be fastened to a beam to provide end support for joists.

JURISDICTION   The extent of judicial or legal authority. The territory over which authority is exercised.

KEYSTONE   The wedged centre stone at the crown of an arch.

KILN-DRIED LUMBER   Lumber that has been properly dried and cured to produce a higher grade of lumber than that which has been air dried.

LALLY COLUMN   A steel column used to support a beam in the foundations of a building.

LAMINATED BEAM   A beam made of superimposed layers of similar materials by uniting them with glue and pressure.

LANDING   A square platform at the top and bottom of stairs to provide access to the stairs or an insert in a run of stairs to facilitate a change of direction. Minimal allowable size 860 mm × 860 mm (2'- 10" × 2'- 10").

LANDLORD (LESSOR)   The person who leases accommodation to a tenant.

LANDSCAPE FORMAT   Drawn in such proportions that the width is greater than the height.

LANDSCAPING   The treatment given to the land involving grading and plantings around a building.

LAND SURVEYING   A branch of surveying that deals with relatively small areas of land and does not take the curvature of the earth into account.

LAYOUT   An accurate drawing that will determine for the designer an unknown dimension that is difficult to establish by the calculation process.

LEASE   A signed agreement to rent accommodation for a set period of time for an established price.

LE CORBUSIER   The architect who inspired the modern movement. He also developed a system of proportions based on mathematical progressions.

LEONARDO DA VNCI   The greatest of the Renaissance inventors, he was an architect, scientist and artist and one of the first to appreciate the value of drafting for planning, recording, and transmitting ideas to others.

LIEN   A claim on property as security, arising out of indebtedness.

LINE   Straight and curved lines are the two basic kinds of lines.

LINEAL MEASUREMENT   Measurement along a straight line.

LINTEL   A horizontal structural member (beam) that supports the weight of the structure over an opening such as a door or window.

LIVE LOAD   In structural design, these loads comprise people and furnishings or changeable items. Also includes wind and snow loads.

LOAD-BEARING WALL   A wall designed to support the weight imposed upon it from above.

LOCATION POINT   In two-point perspective, location points are at either end of the picture plane line. Angular lines from these points are drawn parallel to the sides of the structure in order to determine the station point. Perpendicular lines from the location points are used to locate the vanishing points on the horizon line.

LOGGIA   A gallery or arcade open to the outdoors on at least one side.

LONGITUDINAL SECTION   A section drawn lengthwise through a building parallel to the front. Usually used for split level or split entry houses.

LOT LINE   The line forming the legal boundary of a piece of property.

LOUVRE   An opening or slatted grill allowing ventilation while providing protection from rain.

MANSARD ROOF   A hip-type roof having two slopes on each of the four sides.

MASONRY   A general term for construction of brick, stone, concrete block, or similar materials.

MASS   Created by form. Mass is considered in design for volume, weight, colour, texture, and substance compared to linear forms.

MATT   The cardboard frame that is placed around a pictorial drawing.

MEASURING LINE   A vertical line projected from where the floor plan touches the picture plane line to the ground line. This is the only line along which true heights can be measured in perspective drawing.

MEETING RAILS   On a single or double hung window, the horizontal frame members that meet.

MERIDIAN   An imaginary line from north to south celestial poles. The angle of the meridian is shown on all survey plans by an arrow that points in the direction of north. All bearings are measured from the meridian.

METAL WALL TIES   Corrugated metal strips used to tie masonry veneer to frame walls.

MEZZANINE   A storey placed between two other floor levels.

MICRO-CLIMATE   The localized climate of a given site that is different from surrounding general climatic conditions because of topography, vegetation, and orientation to the sun.

MILLWORK   Building materials made of finished wood, including such items as doors, windows and door frames, panel work, mouldings, and interior trim.

MITRE
1. A joint formed by cutting and butting two pieces of board on a line bisecting the angle of their junction.
2. A line at 45° in orthographic drawing allowing projection from the top view to the side view.

MIXED MEDIA   The use of more than one type of material in a drawing or presentation.

MODULAR CONSTRUCTION   Term applied to construction in which material sizes are based upon the 100 mm (4") module.

MOISTURE BARRIER   A sheet material that retards moisture penetration into walls, floors, ceilings, etc.

MONOLITHIC   Term applied to concrete poured as one unit.

MORTAR   A substance produced from prescribed proportions of cement aggregate and water and which sets hard after mixing.

MORTGAGE   Money provided on a loan basis for the purchase of property.

MORTGAGEE   The person who, having loaned money, holds a mortgage on property.

MORTGAGOR   The borrower of a mortgage on a property.

MORTICE   A hole, slot, or recess cut into a piece of wood to receive a projecting part (tenon) made to fit.

MOSAIC   Designs produced when small pieces of glass or tile are set in grouting.

MULLION   The vertical dividing member separating window units in a wall.

MULTIMODULES   A basic module of 100 mm used in multiples to establish a horizontal and verical modular grid.

MUNTIN   The vertical and horizontal members that separate individual lights or panes of glass in a window sash.

NEO-CLASSIC   A term used to describe the period of Georgian architecture.

NEWEL POST   An enlarged post that, with the balusters, is part of the handrail support system. Newel posts are used at the top and at the bottom of stairways.

NON-STATIC LINE   Diagonal lines suggesting movement.

NON-WINDER STAIR   Stairs that have a landing before a change of direction.

NOSING   The rounded and projecting edge of a stair tread, window sill, etc.

OBLIQUE DRAWING   A drawing which shows the front view parallel to the plane of paper and the side view at a receding angle of 30°, 45°, or 60°.

ON CENTRE (O.C.)   A method of indicating the spacing between framing members by stating the measurement from the centre of one member to the centre of the succeeding one.

ONE-POINT PERSPECTIVE   Shows a structure that has one side parallel to the picture plane and the other side receding to a vanishing point on the horizon.

OPAQUE   A material through which light will not pass.

OPEN STRING   A type of stair where the ends of the treads and risers are exposed to view and not concealed behind a wall.

ORDERS   The designs of columns, which were the most important element in classical architecture (Greek and Roman).

ORGANIC ARCHITECTURE   Type of design where the house should appear to be part of the landscape; philosophy adhered to by Frank Lloyd Wright.

ORIENTATION   The location of a building on a piece of property in relation to the points of a compass or the physical layout of property.

ORTHOGRAPHIC   The correct use of symbols and views to produce two-dimensional drawings that can be interpreted in only one way.

OVERHANG   The projecting area of a roof or upper storey beyond the wall of the lower part.

PANE   The light or glass portion of a window sash.

PANEL   A flat, rectangular surface framed with a thicker material.

PARGE COAT   A coat of plaster or cement mortar applied to masonry or concrete walls in order to make them damp proof.

PARQUET FLOORING   An inlaid wood floor using small blocks of wood.

PARTITION   An interior wall one storey or less in height.

PARTY-WALL   A wall that divides two houses and forms a common boundary.

PASSIVE SOLAR HEATING   An integral energy system using only natural and architectural components to utilize solar energy.

PATIO   A courtyard, or terrace open to the sky.

PEDIMENT   The triangular shape at the end of a gabled roof, over an entrance or window.

PERIOD-STYLE DESIGN   The historic styles of architecture since the Renaissance.

PERMANENT FIXATIVE   A spray used on a drawing to prevent it from smearing when the work is complete.

PERMAFROST   Soil that is at or below freezing point all year round and remains stable.

PERSPECTIVE   A view that is drawn to show how the eye sees large objects. The relative dimensions will be similar to those of a photograph taken from the same viewpoint.

PICTURE PLANE LINE   The line that represents the foremost level of the picture. Measurements can be made only in the elevation view for items that touch this line in the plan view.

PICTORIAL DRAWING   A drawing that shows a three-dimensional view of how an object looks.

PIER   A column of masonry, usually rectangular, used to support structural members.

PILASTER   A pier forming an integral part of a wall and partially projecting from the wall face.

PITCH   A relationship between the height of the roof and the span that determines the slope.

PLAN VIEW   A view looking down on an item, such as a floor plan.

PLATE   The horizontal member on top of the studs, upon which joists or rafters rest.

PLOT PLAN   A drawing showing the location of the building on a specific lot.

PLUMB   Said of an object when it is in true vertical position as determined by a plumb bob or vertical level.

PLUMBING   The pipes, fixtures, and other apparatus for the water supply and the removal of water-borne wastes.

POLYETHYLENE   Strong, lightweight synthetic polymers of ethylene resistant to chemicals and moisture used in sheet form. Used as vapour barrier.

POLYGON   A closed figure that can have any number of sides.

PORTICO   A porch or covered walk with a roof supported by columns.

PORTRAIT FORMAT   Drawn in such proportions that the height is greater than the width.

POST-AND-LINTEL (OR BEAM)   A form of construction where a horizontal member or lintel is supported at its ends by vertical posts.

PRECAST   Concrete units that are cast and finished at the plant rather than at the site of the construction.

PREFABRICATION   The construction of buildings through the use of items assembled in a plant or designed to eliminate cutting on the job.

PRESENTATION DRAWINGS   Drawings that provide a client with an understanding of what the building will look like and its approximate size.

PRESSURE-TREATMENT   Impregnation of wood or plywood with chemicals under pressure to prevent decay and insect (termite) attack.

PRIMARY COLOURS   Three colours, red, yellow, and blue, that cannot be made by mixing any other colours together.

PRINCIPLES OF DESIGN   Using the elements of design correctly: balance, repetition, rhythm, variety, emphasis, unity.

PROFILE   A section made by taking an imaginary cut through a piece of property, to show the variation in land levels.

PROPERTY LINES   The boundaries of a lot that are shown on a drawing by using a line composed of one long dash and two small dashes. The corners of the lot are further emphasized by small circles. Each property line is described by a bearing and a distance.

PROTECTIVE SERVICES   Services such as a police force and firefighting unit.

PUBLIC SERVICES   Services such as water mains, sewage lines, hydro, natural gas, and telephone connections supplied by a municipality.

PYRAMID   Solid with square base and triangular sides sloping upward to make a point – constructed by Egyptians from 6000 B.C. onward.

PURLINS   Horizontal roof members laid over trusses to support rafters.

QUADRANTS   Four quadrants make up the compass. The northeast quadrant measures from 0° - 90° on the compass. The southeast quadrant measures from 90° - 180° on the compass. The southwest quadrant measures from 180° - 270° on the compass. The northwest quadrant measures from 270° - 360° on the compass.

QUARTER ROUND   Small moulding presenting the profile of a quarter circle.

QUICKSAND   A type of sandy soil through which water passes, rendering it unstable for the support of any loads.

QUOINS   Large squared stones set in the corners of a masonry building for appearance's sake.

R-2000   The R-2000 is a low-energy house; that is, it is constructed to control air leakage, provided with high insulation, efficient heating systems, and continuous mechanical ventilation.

RADIANT HEATING   A method of heating with the use of radiating heat rays.

RADIATING LINES   Lines drawn in a spiral or like rays from the sun.

RAFTER   A roof's structural member running from the wall plate to the ridge. There are jack, hip, valley, and common rafters. The structural members of a flat roof are usually called roof joists.

RAIL   A horizontal piece of wood extending from one vertical member to another in the construction of doors, fences, balustrades. In panelling, the horizontal pieces are rails and the perpendicular are stiles.

RECEPTACLE (ELECTRICAL)   A wall-mounted electrical outlet, often called convenience outlets, into which appliances may be plugged.

REINFORCED CONCRETE   Concrete containing steel bars or wire mesh to increase its load-bearing qualities.

RENAISSANCE   The transition between the medieval and the modern world. Caused by an increase in trading and exploration, producing a great burst of knowledge and art between the 14th and 16th centuries.

RENDERING   Treatment given a perspective drawing to provide a realistic impression of a building's exterior materials; e.g., shades, shadows.

REPETITION   Repeating the same forms.

RETAINING WALL   A heavy wall that supports an earth embankment.

RETROFIT   To go back over the structure in order to adapt it for a more modern heating system.

RHYTHMIC LINES   Straight or curved lines that are repeated in a pattern.

RISE
1. The vertical height between floors.
2. The distance of the ridge of a sloping roof above the horizontal run of the eaves.
3. The vertical distance between two treads.

RISER   A vertical board of a stair that supports and encloses the rise. Open stairs can be constructed without risers, but safety is a concern.

ROCOCO   An assymetrical curved design that uses informal balance.

ROUGHING-IN   The act of providing services for later installation of plumbing fixtures.

ROUGH OPENING   An unfinished opening in the framing into which doors, windows, and other units are placed.

ROUNDED POINT   Point used for rendering heavy textures.

ROW HOUSING   A number of single dwellings that are separated from one another by common walls.

RUN   The horizontal distance of a flight of stairs, or the horizontal distance from the outer wall to the ridge of a roof.

R (RSI) VALUE   Unit of thermal resistance in rating insulating materials; higher values are better insulators.

SADDLE ROOF   A small gable roof placed at the back of a chimney on a sloping roof to shed water and debris.

SASH   The opening portion of a window unit, or the glass part of a window that fits into the frame.

SCALES   Measuring devices marked with several systems of gradations.

SCHEDULE   A list of similar items and information about them, such as a window or door schedule.

SEARCH THE TITLE   To search records to ensure that the new owner of a property will have clear title to the land as described on the deed.

SECONDARY COLOURS   Three colours, green, orange, and violet, that are made by mixing two of the primary colours together.

SEMI-DETACHED HOUSE   A house that is part of a building containing living accommodation for two families; there is a common central wall.

SEPTIC TANK   A unit that receives sewage, decomposes the solid matter through bacterial action, and dissolves these into liquids.

SETBACKS   The distances that the house, garage, storage buildings, fences, hedges, and septic tank beds must be set back from the lot boundary lines.

SEWER   Pipe that carries away either storm water or waste from fixtures to community services.

SHADE   A darkened colour.

SHAKE   A shingle split from a block of wood and used for roofing and siding.

SHAPE   Shape has two dimensions, width and height; shown in illustrations by outlining the edges.

SHARP POINT   Point used for rendering small details and fine natural textures.

SHEAR   Term applied to stresses that pull against each other in opposite directions, setting up a slicing or shearing action in a member.

SHEATHING   The rough boarding or covering over the framing of a house.

SHEATHING PAPER   Paper treated with tar or asphalt used under exterior wall cladding as protection against the passage of water or air.

SHED DORMER   A full-width dormer with a single roof sloping in one direction.

SHED ROOF   A sloping roof having its surface in one plane.

SHIM   A thin piece of material used to fill a space between two members.

SIDING   In wood-frame construction, material other than masonry or stucco used as an exterior wall covering.

SILL   The lower exterior portion of a doorway frame or window frame that extends beyond the face of the wall.

SILL PLATE   A structural member anchored to the top of a foundation wall, upon which the floor joists rest.

SILL SECTION   Part of a drawing that shows how the foundation wall supports and intersects the floor system.

SINGLE-FAMILY DETACHED DWELLING   A dwelling that stands on its own lot and usually has a private driveway.

SITE PLAN   A drawing made from a survey of the property, to which has been added the location of the building and driveway.

SKYLIGHT   A flat window in a roof.

SMOKE CHAMBER   The enlarged portion of a chimney immediately above a fireplace opening.

SOFFIT   The underside of a beam, lintel of stairway, or overhang of a roof.

SOIL BORINGS   Samples taken from the earth for testing by soil specialists to determine the bearing qualities of the soil, done before plans for construction of a building are prepared.

SOIL STACK   The vertical pipe in a plumbing system that carries the sewage.

SPAN   The horizontal distance between supports for beams, joists, rafters, etc.

SPECIFICATION   A written document that forms part of a legal building contract. It specifies the type, kind, quality, etc. of materials and workmanship to be used.

SPLIT RECEPTACLE   A receptacle with separate circuits running to each of the dual sockets in each outlet so that the sockets are isolated from each other electrically. Used for high-energy consuming appliances.

SQUARE   A unit of measure – 100 sq. ft. Commonly used in reference to the amount of roofing material to cover 100 sq. ft.

SQUARE FORMAT   Drawn in such proportions that the width is approximately the same as the height.

STAIR LANDING   A square platform between flights of stairs.

STAIRWELL OPENING   The amount of space required as an opening in an upper floor level to provide head room for someone mounting the stairs.

STATIC LINE   Lines that suggest the least amount of movement; usually vertical and horizontal lines.

STATION POINT   The position of the viewer. In one-point perspective, the vanishing point is perpendicular to the station point. In two-point perspective, the station point is usually perpendicular to the front corner of the building.

STIPPLE TECHNIQUE   A slow but effective technique of using dots to indicate shading.

STORM SEWER   Sewer that handles surface or storm water rather than sanitary sewage.

STRATA TITLES   A term used in British Columbia for condominium ownership.

STRENGTH OF MATERIALS   The study of the loads that various materials can carry when forces creating stresses (compression, tension, shear) are applied.

STRINGER   The inclined structural member supporting the treads and risers of a stairs.

STUCCO   A cement plaster finish applied to exterior walls.

STUD   One of a series of wooden vertical structural members usually 38 mm (2") thick used as supporting elements in walls and partitions.

SUBFLOORING   Boards or sheet material laid on joists over which a finished floor is constructed.

SUBLET   Getting someone to assume the remaining portion of a lease.

SUBORDINATION   Ranking parts of a building in importance from a visual viewpoint.

SUPERSTRUCTURE   The portion of the building that is above the ground.

SURVEY   A drawing that shows land levels and defines property boundaries.

SURVEY IRON BARS (S.I.B.)   Semi-permanent markers, which are numbered and recorded stakes placed in the ground so that the top protrudes. A surveyor has to find and identify a marker's location so that he or she can take measurements from a known point. They are indicated on a survey plan by a small square or circle and the letters S.I.B.

SYMMETRICAL BALANCE   Something that is balanced evenly by items that are the same in size, number, and weight.

TANGENT   A line that touches a circle at one point only

TANGENT ARC   An arc on an object that has rounded corners.

TANGENT POINT   The point where a tangent touches the circle.

TENANT (LESSEE)   The person who leases accommodation from a landlord.

TENDER The form on which the contractor submits the cost and profit estimate for a building project. The submitted tender is also referred to as the contractor's bid.

TENSILE STRENGTH The greatest longitudinal stress a structural member can bear without adverse effects (breaking or cracking).

TENSION The stress that is created by a stretching action.

TERTIARY COLOURS Six colours that are made by mixing a primary colour with a secondary colour.

TEXTURE A term that refers to the surface of materials, brick being a good example.

THERMOSTAT An automatic temperature recording device that controls heating and cooling devices.

THRESHOLD A strip of wood, metal, or other material bevelled on each edge and used at the junction of two different floor finishes.

THROAT The opening portion where the flue meets the fireplace and into which the damper is installed.

THUMBNAIL SKETCHES Small freehand sketches to initiate the design process.

TINT A lightened colour.

TITLE A legal right to the possession of property.

TONGUE-AND GROOVE LUMBER Lumber machined so that there is a groove on one edge and a corresponding tongue on the other.

TOOTH (OF PAPER) A rough surface on paper in order that the medium being used, i.e., pencil or ink, will adhere more readily.

TOP PLATE In building, the horizontal member nailed to the top of the partition or wall studs.

TOP SOIL The top layer of fertile soil that is replaced around a building after construction has been completed.

TOPOGRAPHY A detailed description of the physical features of land.

TRANSFER LOOP Used in solar heating; consists of a heat exchanger, thermostat, and fans that move heat to various areas of the house.

TRANSIT An instrument set on a tripod used by a surveyor to determine the levels or elevations of a parcel of property and angles.

TRANSLUCENT Material that is partially transparent.

TRANSPARENT Material that clearly transmits the passage of light.

TRANSVERSE SECTION A section through a structure with the cutting plane line going from the front to the back of the building.

TRAP In plumbing, the U-shaped pipe adjacent to the fixtures; it receives the waste and prevents the return of undesirable odours.

TRAVERSE Another name for a survey plan. The traverse is made from field notes that are the results of readings taken as the surveyor walks around or "traverses" a lot.

TREAD The horizontal surface of a step. The depth of a tread should never be less than 230 mm (9") at any point except in the case of winders.

TRIM A general term given to the mouldings and finishing members on a building.

TRIMMER Double joists running parallel with the regular joists and used in framing around floor openings.

TRUSS A wood or steel framework composed of members joined together in a series of triangles used for roofs or floors to support load.

TUSCAN COLUMN Developed from Etruscan architecture by the ancient Romans. Similar in form to the Doric capital but with the column left smooth rather than fluted.

UNDERLAY The treatment applied to rough flooring to receive the finished flooring.

UNIDIRECTIONAL DIMENSIONING A system of placing dimensions on a drawing so that all numbers can be read from the bottom of the sheet.

URBAN Pertaining to a city or town.

VALANCE Box-like enclosure extending over the head of a window inside a room, and behind which is concealed drapery track, the top of draperies, and sometimes lighting.

VALLEY ROOF The angle formed by the junction of two sloping sides of a roof.

VALLEY RAFTERS Rafters that are located at the centre of roof valleys to support the jack rafters.

VALUE When describing a colour, refers to its lightness or darkness.

VANISHING POINT A point, in perspective drawing, where all the parallel lines of a structure would converge if taken to infinity.

VAPOUR BARRIER Film used to retard the passage of water vapour or moisture.

VAULT An arched masonry or concrete structure built so that the parts support each other and serve as a roof over a space. Developed by the Romans.

VAULTED CEILING   A ceiling formed by placing arches one behind the other.

VELLUM   Parchment-like paper used for drafting.

VENEERED CONSTRUCTION   Type of wall construction in which frame or masonry walls are faced with other exterior surfacing materials such as brick veneer.

VENT STACK   A vertical soil pipe connected to the drainage system to allow ventilation and pressure equalization.

VESTIBULE   A small entrance room.

VINYL   A synthetic resin used in the manufacture of floor tile.

VISUAL RAY   The imaginary line that goes from the observer's eye to the object in perspective drawing.

VITRUVIUS   An architect of 3rd century B.C. in ancient Rome whose book on architecture was rediscovered in the Renaissance period and used as a standard for column design at that time.

VOLTAGE   Electrical force or pressure related to flow.

WAINSCOT   The surfacing on the lower part of an interior wall when finished differently from the remainder of the wall.

WALLBOARD   Large sheets of gypsum or fibreboard that are usually nailed to framing to form interior walls.

WALL PLATES   The horizontal members attached to the ends of the studs. Also called top or bottom plates, depending on their location.

WATER TABLE   The level below which the ground is saturated with water.

WATT   Unit of electrical power.

WEATHER STRIPPING   A strip of fabric or metal fastened around the edges of windows and doors to prevent air infiltration.

WEB   In steel beams, that portion between the two flanges.

WET ON WET   An illustrating technique in which the medium is dampened with water and the wash is applied with a brush to the dampened board.

WHITEPRINTS   Copies of original drawings; made with a dark line on a white background. Often referred to by the generic term "blueprints."

WINDER   A radiating, wedge-shaped tread of a stair, which forms an angle of 30° so that three winders make a 90° turn. Only one such set of winders is permitted between each floor level.

WORKABLE FIXATIVE   A spray used on a drawing to stop it from smearing, but one that allows work to be continued on the drawing.

WORKING DRAWINGS
1. Drawings that, with the specification, are used by a contractor in estimating the cost of construction.
2. Drawings that a builder or contractor uses during construction.

WORK TRIANGLE   An imaginary triangle joining the centre front of the sink, refrigerator, and cooking unit. This area is the basis for all kitchen design.

WROUGHT IRON (ROLLED IRON)   An improved type of iron formed as curved designs for decoration on iron fences, gates, railings, posts, etc.

ZERO-LOT-LINE PLANNING   A method of planning that allows houses to be built on the lot line, giving greater density of single-family houses.

Index